CONTACT PHOTOGRAPHERS

9TH EDITION

★ ELFANDE

PUBLISHERS STILL
NICHOLAS GOULD
BARRY O'DWYER

PUBLISHED IN
THE UK BY
ELFANDE ART
PUBLISHING LTD
UNIT 39
BOOKHAM IND PARK
CHURCH ROAD
BOOKHAM
SURREY
KT23 3EU

PHONE US ALL ON
0372 459559
OR EVEN BY FAX
0372 459699

PRODUCED UNDER
GREAT STRESS IN
HONG KONG BY
WORLD PRINT CO

TYPESETTING ON
AN APPLE MAC
(WHAT ELSE) BY
TYPESTYLE

PRODUCTION
DIRECTOR
'NO DOT WHITE'
NICHOLAS GOULD
ASSISTED BY
MR MAGOO

SALES – UK
ANNE GOULD

SPECIAL THANKS
TO JOHN BRAID
(CUSTOMER CARE
DEPT) FOR HIS
SPARKLING REPARTEE
TO CATHAY PACIFIC
FOR NUMEROUS
SHOWINGS OF
'THREE MEN & A BABY'

ADMIN/COFFEE
RUM BABA ETC
ANNABELLE GARDNER

FRONT & BACK
COVER PHOTOGRAPHY
BY BARBARA &
ZAFER BARAN

PHOTOGRAPHY
THIS PAGE
GEORGE KAVANAGH

DESIGN & ART DIRECTION
BY (NO SMOKING PLEASE)
BARRY O'DWYER

COPYRIGHT

All copy and transparencies in this book have been supplied by those appearing in Contact and have been reproduced on the condition that they are reproduced with the knowledge and prior consent of the client company, illustrator, photographer and other interested parties concerned. No responsibility is accepted by the publisher for any infringement of copyright or otherwise arising out of the publication thereof. Work in this publication is the choice of the advertiser and/or their representatives, not of the publisher.

Whilst every effort has been made to ensure accuracy, the publisher does not, under any circumstances, accept responsibility for errors or omissions.

ISBN NO 1 870458 35 4

CONTENTS

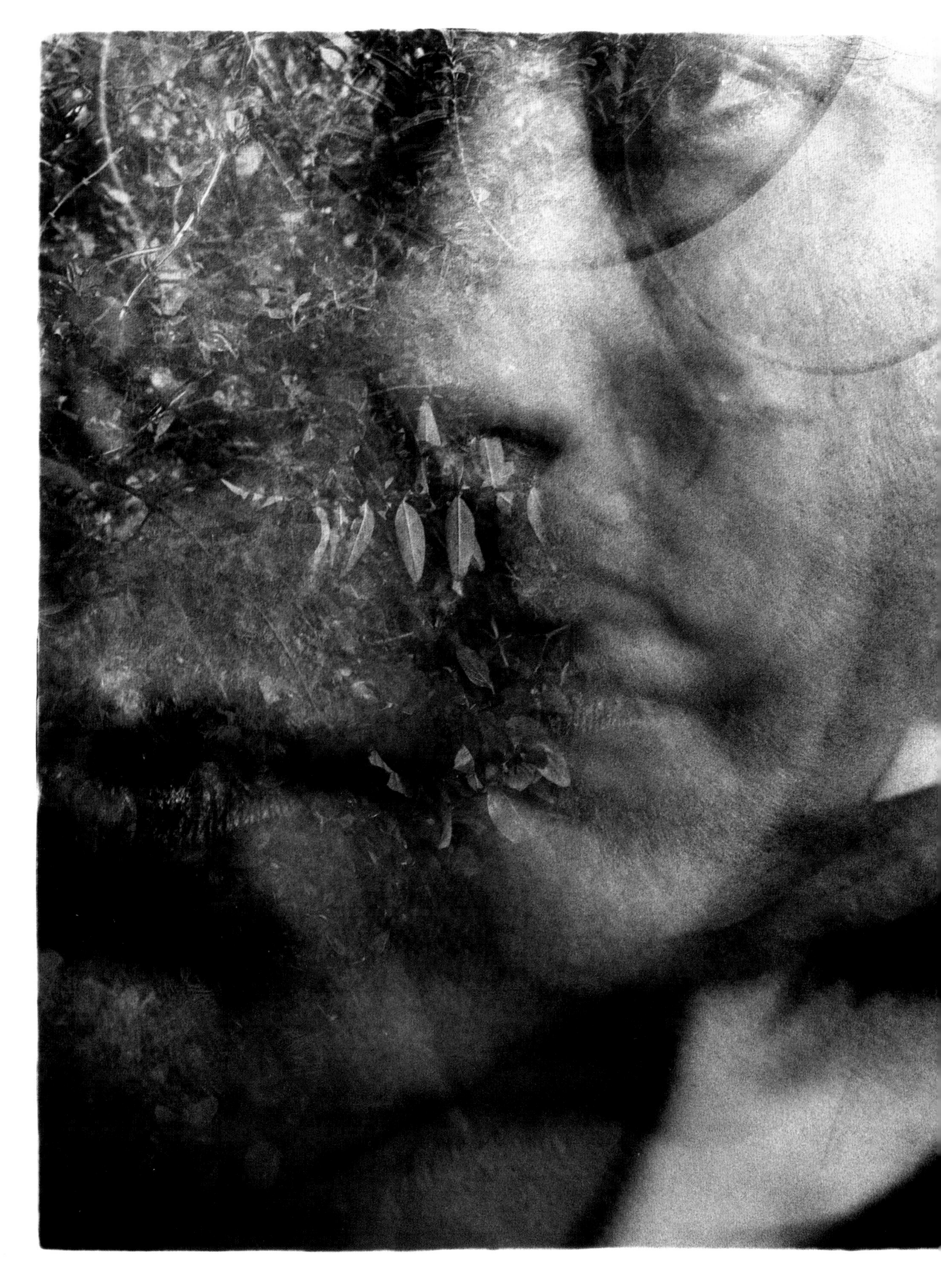

COVER STORY

Zafer and Barbara Baran have been working together since 1981, when they met studying photography at Goldsmiths' college. Although from different backgrounds (one in graphic design and fine arts, the other in linguistics) they found common ground in photography, and were soon exhibiting, both individually and as a partnership, in venues such as Impressions Gallery of Photography, York, the Royal Festival Hall and Photographers' Gallery, London.

It was only in 1988 that they ventured into commissioned work and new experiments, stemming from their original interests in documentary, conceptual and abstract photography. Since then, their range of commercial work has steadily broadened to include portraiture, architectural subjects, still lifes, typographical imagery and pure abstractions.

Whilst a certain proportion of their commissioned work involves complex briefs, with a good deal of problem-solving attached, for the most part they are left to their own devices, to interpret the commission more or less freely. This mode of working enables them to pursue their own ideas and to experiment as far as each brief will allow. A case in point is their recent work for the English National Opera, including posters, brochures and seasonal identities, all produced to a fairly open brief.

Working in partnership allows them a free and continuous exchange of ideas, each contributing from a different perspective. This enables them to progress in new directions, and stimulates both their personal and commissioned work.

Self-portrait, 1993

Film strip (detail), 1992

'BEST OF THE BOOK' PHOTOGRAPHY AWARDS

JUDGING PANEL

JANE LANGLEY

GROUP DESIGN CO-ORDINATOR
W H SMITH GROUP PLC

ULI WEBER

PHOTOGRAPHER

FIANNA PURCELL

ART BUYER
STILL PRICE:
LINTAS ADVERTISING AGENCY

The W H Smith Group has a design management strategy which promotes and instigates the effective use of design as a core business resource.
Her role is to act as a coach and advisor to individual businesses, helping them to achieve design excellence with reference, to their commercial aims and marketing strategies. She is also involved in the design development of our corporate communications.
Working with the most talented illustrators and their photographers is one of the keys to maintaining high design standards. In supporting today's artists, through project commissions and through the W H Smith Illustration Awards, they are continuing a long-established corporate practice.

Uli Weber was born in Germany and educated at the University of Rome. He came to England seven years ago and spent the first three years as a freelance assistant to such photographers as Clive Arrowsmith, Stevie Hughes, and Terry O'Neil. In 1988 he set up as a full time photographer and is now shooting both fashion and portraiture for, amongst others: Arena, L'Uomo Vogue, The Sunday Times, and Interview magazines. Advertising campaigns to his credit include: Alvin Ailey for the ENO with Carroll, Dempsey and Thirkell and Round the Clock Hosiery in the USA with Peter Roger Agency.
Uli works regularly in London (represented by Terri Manduca) – Milan (represented by Studio Imagine) – and in New York (represented by Majka).

Fianna commissions photography (and to a lesser extent illustration) on behalf of their wide ranging list of clients.
Fianna's background comprises photography production with Nadav Kander and then representing fine art photographers on behalf of the Special Photographers company.
She sits on the IPA (Institute of Practitioners in Advertising) Creative Services Committee and chairs the new IPA Art buying Committee.

MARION DEUCHARS

ILLUSTRATOR

WAYNE FORD

ART EDITOR
XYZ MAGAZINE

JENNIE BURNS

JENNIE BURNS DESIGN

BA Hons illustration/Printmaking 1987 Duncan of Jordanstone College of Art, Dundee
MA with distinction (Illustration) 1989 Royal College of Art, London. Marion currently works from a studio based in East London.
Recent commissions and work include: an exhibition of paintings and prints at the Roupell Gallery, London; A series of 12 paintings commissioned by Moss Bros Group; 'Chargeurs' Annual Report for Wolff Olins Design Group; Silkscreen image for Trickett & Webb/Augustus Martin Annual Calendar and other clients in the field of Advertising/Design & Publishing.

Wayne Ford is Art Editor of XYZ, the highly acclaimed, state-of-the-art design technology magazine.
Wayne 27, studied graphics at the Swindon School of Art and Design. He joined Haymarket Publications in 1987 as assistant to the Group Art Director. A short time later he became art editor on one of Haymarket's most prestigious titles, *What Car?* In his four years on the title, Wayne firmly established excellent design and production values which have made *What Car?* one of the UK's premier motoring titles.
In February '92 Wayne left cars behind him to steer the new look of XYZ which is also owned by Haymarket.

Jennie Burns Design is a small, highly professional and established design practice involved in all areas of graphic design. They have designed and produced a variety of successful packaging ranges, new product development and re-launches for a number of high profile clients – including Harrods, Fortnum and Mason, Gateway, Marks and Spencer, Grants of St. James's, Boots the Chemists, Thorntons, Safeway and Guinness.
They have also designed and produced a number of high quality brochures, and corporate identity programmes.

'BEST OF THE BOOK'

GOLD
AWARD WINNER
PHOTOGRAPHY

George Kavanagh

PUBLISHERS
ELFANDE ART PUBLISHING LTD

YH 308

'BEST OF THE BOOK'

★
ELFANDE

SILVER
AWARD WINNER
PHOTOGRAPHY

Sara Taylor

Nick Gould

Barry O'Connor

PUBLISHERS

ELFANDE ART PUBLISHING LTD

'BEST OF THE BOOK'

BRONZE
AWARD WINNER
PHOTOGRAPHY

Ron Bambridge

PUBLISHERS
ELFANDE ART PUBLISHING LTD

The judging panel requested that the work of Barbara & Zafer Baran together with Simon Wood be specially commended

PHOTOGRAPHER: IMAGE-MAKER OR IMAGE-TAKER?

Just as compact discs and digital cassettes have transformed sound quality, digital imaging is revolutionising photography with computer power.

While purists will close their eyes to this, believing that such techniques do not constitute 'real' photography, it's worth mentioning that Polaroids, as well as the use of 35mm cameras for professional work were once also regarded in the same light.

Collectively, photographers have been slow to adopt new technology, especially when you consider that the big electronic systems have been around since the early 80s. While graphics and image enhancement packages for desktop computers have existed seriously for the last four years or so.

There are a number of reasons why some photographers have remained untouched by the technological passover. For one, many feel that new technology just doesn't affect them, and as they've been doing fine with traditional methods, which get great results, why change?

Secondly, computers have got a bit of an image problem. When it comes to the non-techie person the very word computer can bring out a condition commonly known as technophobia. Computers are seen as frightening and impersonal grey boxes which make funny noises, are complicated to use, and by their very nature inhibit the flow of one's creative juices.

The integration of new technology into the photographer's tool kit has many implications for the photographer and the medium in general. For example what do computers mean to the historical nature of the image? Will the photographer, who has always in essence been an 'image-taker', become an 'image-maker', or even for that matter some kind of computer technician? Will computers mean a loss of control for photographers? For example, if images are available in a digital format it means they are very easy to reproduce and leaves them open to abuse in terms of copyright.

Well, let's go back to the beginning. In the good old bad old days, a photograph was an image that you captured on film, which was developed on paper using chemicals. If you wanted special effects, these were created conventionally in the dark room and, if any corrections or enhancements had to be made, the surface emulsion of the photograph was retouched by hand using special dyes and inks.

But now it's a different story. Instead of film, images can be recorded on computer disk and output on a high resolution colour printer eliminating any need for conventional processing.

Filmless cameras

A number of so-called filmless cameras have been developed by the big photographic companies such as Kodak, Canon and Nikon. While the quality is still not yet as good as traditional film, their very existence is significant. The advantages are that there is no processing required and consumables are drastically reduced. In the professional world, these cameras are ideal for deadline-critical situations such as news and sports reporting.

Due to the adoption of computers in the publishing world, images captured on such filmless cameras can be easily transferred to the pages of say a newspaper or other publication in seconds.

So let's take a closer look at what's available in the filmless camera market.

Still video cameras

Still video cameras record images onto reusable floppy disks which are loaded into the camera just like film. Discs hold either 25 full resolution images or 50 at half resolution. As you would expect, Sony, Nikon, Canon, Fuji and Kodak all have still video cameras in their product ranges. These include studio rostrum cameras as well as portable ones. A number of newspapers have had the Canon still video camera on trial and the *Evening Standard* bought two over two years ago. In 1990, photographer Ken Towner took a colour photo of the Derby winner which appeared in its final edition, only 45 minutes after the race finished. Using traditional film this would have been impossible. The Auto Trader series of titles, which formerly used Polaroid to capture its weekly crop of cars for sale has switched to still video, having purchased a number of Canon ION cameras. Here the volume of pictures is more important than quality because cars are shown no bigger than thumbnail sizes.

David Hockney employed the use of the Canon, along with the Canon CLC 500 copier to produce his series of now famous 'electronic snaps'. As a result, he pushed out the boundaries of photography, producing images more akin to paintings.

Digital cameras

Digital cameras record the image directly onto a portable hard disk drive. Kodak has come up with one of the market leaders with its DCS camera, designed with newspaper photographers in mind. It is basically a Nikon F3 SLR camera (the most popular news stills camera in the world) with a digital back developed by Kodak. It has one of the highest resolution of all the electronic cameras available, beaten only by digital-backed studio models like those from Rollei and Arca

Produced by Mike Laye for Telegraph Weekend Magazine using Crosfield's Mamba. The studio shot of Ramprakash was converted to a sepia-tone, then mixed 50/50 with the original colour transparency, and finally pasted onto a background taken from old cigarette cards.

Swiss which have exposure times of up to two minutes. The disk drive can hold up to 200 colour pictures and you can also plug in a computer keyboard which lets you write captions of up to 40 characters. A colour pic taken with the DCS can be modemed over standard phone lines to anywhere in the world in around seven minutes. Although it sounds like an indispensable piece of kit for the field, the hard disk drive is very heavy.

Photo CD

Somewhere in between traditional film photography and digital imaging falls the Kodak Photo CD system. Some say it is Kodak's insurance against an all-digital future, given that they are one of the world's biggest producers of film and photographic consumables. Whatever you think, it is a technological breakthrough. Basically, it takes images photographed on conventional film, and converts them to digital matter, via scanning, onto an optical disc. Kodak has initially aimed it directly at Joe Public, who can in future look at their holiday snaps on a TV screen rather than in an album. The service is available through high street photo labs as a standard option to customers who take film in for processing. While, Photo CD may not have a direct significance for the professional photographer, nevertheless, the implications to the photographic medium, are immense.

The camera never lies

Since the earliest days of photography, images have always been retouched. Remember Stalin's infamous removal of Trotsky from official photos. But despite this widespread tampering, it has always been held that the photograph is an absolute truth and that the camera never lies. Now however, with the increasing use of computers in the photographic arena, retouching has become a far more serious, and altogether different ball game. With the use of electronic retouching and image manipulation systems, it is possible to penetrate into the very fabric of the photograph and make changes which are totally undetectable. Once an image is brought into a computer environment it is translated into a digital code which on screen is represented by thousands of pixels or dots. These pixels can be moved, duplicated, or deleted, and in doing so affect the image.
Not surprisingly, the advertising industry has taken to electronic retouching systems in a big way. Products are often 'retouched' or 'cleaned-up' to give them

Produced by Mike Laye for Telegraph Weekend Magazine using Tapestry's Crosfield Mamba. Animator Dave Edwards was photographed at a desk, then cut and pasted into his own illustrated background. His shirt was 'cartoonized' and his body compressed to help him 'sit' into the final image.

optimum consumer appeal. Creative concepts on which ads are hinged can become more inventive. The undetectable nature of electronic manipulation allows the impossible to become possible and the unbelievable believable, giving the hidden persuaders more power with which to persuade.

On the other hand

Undetectable manipulation is fabulous, especially when you're involved in a creative concept,, but like most things there is a downside.

The idea that news photographs can be seamlessly tampered with causes outright furore. Images which appear in newspapers are commonly regarded as the printed representation of an historical event. However, changes are made to newspaper pictures frequently. Telegraph wires can be painted out, outlines defined and images cropped for a picture editor's convenience. The use of electronic camera and picture desks blur the distinction between original and retouched pictures. In the case of electronic cameras, images can be sent down modern lines to electronic newspaper picture desks. In such cases no actual hard copy of the image exists, and therefore there is a potential danger of images being abused.

Systems are doing it for themselves.

To date electronic manipulation has been the sexy frontline issue when it comes to new technology and photography. While some photographers have embraced electronic systems with gusto, others have reservations, seeing them as short cuts to make not-so-good-pictures better. Hand in hand with this, is the concern that computers will bring about a decline in photographic standards.

On the other hand however, users will testify how the computers can act as effective quick fixers, removing aggravations which were unavoidable during the shoot. Stray hairs, mosquito bites, changes in the lighting conditions are all things which can and do happen any time, any place, anywhere.

Apart from retouching, electronic manipulation allows the photographer to experiment and create new types of images which conventionally would have been exceptionally difficult to create. This pushes the boundary of photographic opportunities. Now, rather than a photographer representing a personal vision of the world, technology can help the photographer to construct a personal universe.

Electronic manipulation systems aren't great levellers. While they can improve images they can't turn mediocre photographers into great ones. Naturally, as with any developing discipline, there are bound to be bad examples of work, but the important thing to remember is that photography is all about having an 'eye' and seizing opportunities. No matter how impressive the system – this principle will not change.

The power and the glory

There are a number of retouching systems which are available to the photographer. These range from the affordable retouching and paint packages that run on Macintoshes and PCs, like Adobe Photoshop and Letraset ColorStudio, to the bigger more expensive pieces of kit like the Quantel Graphic Paintbox and the Crosfield Mamba, installed in photolabs and facilities houses. The big difference between the two, apart from cost, is that while the desktop systems let the photographer get 'hands on', the more expensive high-end systems like the Paintbox and Mamba

utilise the services of highly skilled, highly trained operators. In the early days because of the prohibitive expense of the high-end systems, electronic retouching was very much the domain of the advertising agency art director. However, this is rapidly changing. In much the same way that photographers took control of their own hand retouching and comping, many of them are now extending their toolkits to the big electronic systems and include this service as part of their fee.
The Graphic Paintbox was the first such retouching system to appear on the scene and is a print resolution version of the Video Paintbox used to create special effects on television. Other dedicated retouching systems include the Barco Creator, Dalim Litho, Kodak Premier, Crosfield Mamba, Scitex Imager. In addition, other pre-press manufacturers like Agfa and Scangraphic have retouching systems in their product ranges.
Increasingly, more photographers are using the combination of a personal computer and desktop retouching software like Adobe Photoshop or ColorStudio to achieve the effects they want. Training courses aimed specifically at photographers who want to learn about electronic retouching are being set up and bureaux offer the use of desktop workstations running retouching software packages as a service.
Photoshop has earned much support from the photographic community, particularly because of its ease of use. Veteran photographer Frank Horvat created the first digital fairytale, a version of Puss in Boots, using Photoshop. Here he was able to construct the tale using his own archive images along with new shots, courtesy of Photoshop. The real value of using a desktop package on your own personal workstation is that you have the freedom to experiment, says Horvat.

Somewhere between the big high-end systems and desktop packages like Photoshop, are lower cost second generation retouching systems from big manufacturers. Quantel has produced a Desktop Paintbox which runs on a Macintosh, and Barco has recently introduced a range of high-power low-cost Creator systems running on Silicon Graphics platforms. In short, to the photographer such developments mean more power for less bucks.

Whose copyright is it anyway?

Copyright is a subject close to every photographer's heart and there can be no doubt that electronic imaging throws up a number of grey areas in the law. It once again comes back to the pliability of the digital image. There is a growing fear amongst photographers for instance, that electronic retouching systems will promote unlicensed use of their work. Say a retouching house needed a piece of perfect blue sky to complete a job for one of its clients. They remember that a previous job has exactly what they want. There is little apart from conscience to stop them electronically comping it in to the new image. To avoid detection they could easily move the pixels about to change the cloud formation. Although in one way this seems fairly practical it constitutes an abuse of the copyright laws. (As you will know the 1988 Copyright Designs & Patents Act gave copyright on all artistic works to the author i.e. the photographer). There are currently moves afoot to produce a code of conduct which would prevent this from happening.

And so to bed.....

New technology offers photography new possibilities and directions. While the latest developments point to a filmless world, so far this is limited to areas where quality is not the most important issue. For example electronic cameras have raised the eyebrows of the newspaper industry both for editorial use and classified ads, but as yet the use is still very limited.
The translation of photos into digital formats either from electronic cameras, or scanned film makes the photo pliable – not only in the way it can be processed but in the way it can be viewed and transferred from A to B. After a slow start, ad agencies are finally kitting out with Macintoshes. So now photographers could, if they wished, transmit photos to art directors for approval down a telephone line or, even make corrections to images on screen, while the self same image is being viewed on screen by an art director X number of miles away. The way too, that photographers will show their books will change. Rather than cumbersome portfolios, images will be loaded onto compact disk which can be read through a monitor or conventional TV screen.
But perhaps the most important thing to photography is the new breadth of vision new technology affords it. Photography is no longer only about what's in your eye vision, but also what's in your mind's eye. And the only limitation is really your imagination.

MELONY ROCQUE
Assistant Editor
XYZ Magazine

PHOTOGRAPHER BARRY MEEKUMS COMMENTS...

Technology during the past few years has overcome both prohibitive price and the need for lengthy training in the use of computers to manipulate the conventional photographic image.
Initial fears of the image being taken away from the hands of the originator and being changed into something unrecognisable or disagreeable from the original are, to a large extent, unfounded.
Unfounded, because in my own experience nearly always my client has made sure that I am at the last stages during which any alteration to my work takes place. Now it is at last possible to have at a realistic price similar computers in one's own studio to be sure that the final image for production goes to the client as intended.
It may still be true that images can be taken away and used in breach of copyright with this new medium, but has this not always been the case simply by copying an image with another camera?
After the early stages of distorted bendy mirror type images, and the other gimmicky looks, I think photographers will settle down and use this new tool to accomplish what conventional techniques cannot do; namely easy photocomping, easy retouching and even putting light where mirrors and tiny spots cannot. Most of all, this will be accomplished with enormous savings in both time spent trying to achieve the impossible, in and out of the studio.
Apart from the above practical reasons I can only see that this new technology

will both enhance and open up new creative ideas.
The main picture of the cat peering into the mouse hole was taken with flash using a Fuji GX680 camera. At the time we shot the cat we knew the final composition relative to where the cat would actually be placed and how we could relate the mouse to look as if the cat was ignoring it. With the chosen cat transparency we were able to shoot the toy mouse separately and comp this into the main picture, (also overcoming depth of field problems on the overall picture). The computer was able to add multiple images of the mouse in a chosen arc to look as though is was avoiding the cat.

Agency: Reay Keating Hamer. Client: Scrumpy Jack Cider. Retouching: Tapestry, Mamba system.

Tobi Corney BECTU

2nd Floor
Lymehouse Studios
38B Georgiana Street
London NW1 0EB

Tel: 071 284 2148
Fax: 071 284 0437
Radio pager: 081 884 3344
ID Code: Toby 1

Advertising, Music Business, Editorial, Film and TV
Specialist areas: People, Portraiture, and Artist Promotion

Pictures clockwise:
Smashie and Nicey – Quick on the draw
Sir Anthony Caro – Personal work
Alfred Schnittke – Sony Hamburg
Q The Blues – Quick on the draw

Berry H. G. Bingel ARPS, LBIPP, AFAEP

1 Keith Avenue
Balmedie
Aberdeen AB23 8ZR
Scotland

Tel: (0358) 42571

Stock photos
Archive bildr
Phototheque
Archivo fotografia

Contact:
John Panton
Ace Photo Agency
Tel: +44 (0) 71 629 0303
Fax: +44 (0) 71 495 6100

Gus York

Tel: 0628 75242
Fax: 0628 773257
Car: 0836 226750

Food
Still Life
Location
Special Effects

Desmond Burdon

Studio 4
38 St. Oswalds Place
Vauxhall
London SE11 5JE

Tel: +44 71 582 0559
Fax: +44 71 582 4528

Represented: BARCELONA:
Fotograficas – Price – 323 3288
Fax: 323 3074
DUSSELDORF:
Milena Najdanovic – 890 3444
Fax: 890 3999
MILAN:
Photogroup – 498 0426
Fax: 481 93788

NEW YORK:
Susan Miller – 905 8400
Fax: 427 7777
LOS ANGELES:
Keswick Hamilton – 931 2474
Fax: 938 6574

Pedestrian
Subway

John Mason

Studio: 23/25 Great Sutton Street
London EC1V 0DN

Tel: 071 251 4402
Fax: 071 608 2782

London Agent: Europe Unlimited
Tel: 071 267 6862
Fax: 071 485 9423

Paris Agent: Maureen Sale
Tel: 1 42 24 09 67
Fax: 1 42 24 19 65

Harley Davidson U.S.A.

Honda Japan

Peter Hince

Shaftesbury House
13/14 Hoxton Market
Coronet Street
London N1 6HG
Tel: 071 729 6727
Fax: 071 739 2321

Paris
Represented by Cosmos
Tel: 33 (1) 45 06 18 80

Recent Clients include: Abbey National, Alliance & Leicester, Bayer, Boots, Braun, British Airways, Britax, BUPA, C & A, Canon, Citroën, Coca Cola, Dolcis, Fuji, Gillette, Halifax, Head, Jockey, Lilt, Mars, Molson Lager, Nationwide, Natwest, Nescafé, Norwich Union, Prudential, Ravel, Rover, Renault, Sunworld, Telecom, Texaco, Wella, Wolsey, Whiskas and Yamaha.

Client – Fuji professional

Head/M.S.A.

Lilt/Harrison Agency

Bon Appétit/USA

Kabi Pharmacia

C & A/Direct

peter
HINCE

telephone

071 729 6727

facsimile

071 739 2321

Michael Banks

London

Tel: 071 831 2547
Fax: 071 405 3922

Abstraction. Stills and Film.

Recent commissions for: British Rail, Courtaulds, Ford, Highland Distilleries, Grosvenor Estates, Kuwait Oil Co., London Electricity, McNaughton Paper, Northumbrian Water, Olympia and York, RIBA, Secker and Warburg, Shellys, Sheraton Hotels, Shimizu Corp, Siebe, Victoria and Albert Museum, Virgin, Woodhouse.

Tim Hill AFAEP

59 Rosebery Road
Muswell Hill
London N10 2LE

Tel: 081 444 0609

Area of endeavour:
Large format, still life and food photography for editorial and design clients.

Art direction Tim and Zoë Hill
All photography by Tim Hill
All styling by Zoë Hill Tel: 0831 881122
Assistant Adrian Swift.

By courtesy of Pan MacMillan – Yan Kit So Classic Food of China

By courtesy of Taste Mag

George Wright

Mountover Farm
Rampisham
Dorchester
Dorset DT2 0PL

Tel: 0935 83333
Fax: 0935 83326

Clients include: Independent, Observer & Telegraph magazines, Country Living, The National Trust, BBC Publications, Country Life, Channel Four, Conran Octopus, Weidenfeld & Nicolson, The Edward James Foundation, KLM, Vogue Decoration, Istituto Geografico de Agostini.

Geoff Langan

3 Pavement Studios
40-48 Bromells Road
Clapham
London SW4 0BG

Tel: 071 720 3371
Mobile: 0850 754471

People
Still Life
Studio
Location
Corporate
Editorial
Advertising

Ian Hooton

Southern Light Studios
35A Britannia Row
London N1 8QH
Tel: 071 226 4441
Mobile: 0860 666774

Clients include: Oil of Ulay, Alberto V05, L'Oreal, T.S.B. Littlewoods, Wella, Essentials, Schwarzkopf, C&As, Optrex, Clairol, Farah Clothing, American Vogue, Virgin, Ilford Films, Boots, Gillette, Silverkrin, Clynol, Eylure, Saatchi & Saatchi, Coppertone, Nestles Milky Bar Kid, Highland Spring Water, Harmony Hairspray, Paton Knitwear, Yardley, Womans Own, Bella, Prima, Me, Womans Own, Best, Woman & Home.

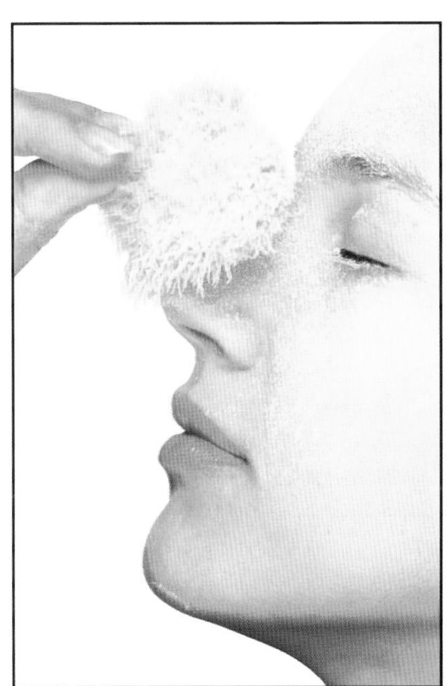

Peter Barry

The Studio
4 Grafton Mews
London W1P 5LF

Tel: 071 388 1933
Fax: 071 388 0472

Food Photographer

Represented by Julian Cotton
12 Thornton Place
Off York Street
London W1H 1FG

Tel: 071 486 3307
Fax: 071 486 6565

Paul Rees

Flashpoint Studios
8 Fitzroy Road
Primrose Hill
London NW1 8TX

Tel: 071 586 2935
Fax: 071 483 1292

42 Malkolm Warrington

14 Emerald Street
London WC1N 3QA

Tel: 071 242 4966
Fax: 071 831 1619

"Specialist in large format still life".

MALKOLM WARRINGTON
TEL: 071 242 4966
FAX: 071 831 1619

44 Jean-Louis Batt

24 Stonor Road
London W14 8RZ

Tel: 071 603 2401
Fax: 071 603 2401

Speciality: Colour Montage, Business, People.

Clients include: Unilever plc, British Telecom, Reckitt & Colman, Unitech plc, Bank of Scotland, NFC plc.

NFC plc/Holmes & Marchant Enskat

Butler's Wharf/HHL Publishing

Cambridge Cables/DCM Design

Anthony Holmes ABIPP

Contact: Sarah
404 Tower Street
Century Building
Brunswick Business Park
Liverpool
Merseyside L3 4BJ

Tel: 051 709 7281
Fax: 051 709 7281

Let your light

So shine before men

...That they may see your good works.

George Kavanagh

28 Britton Street
London EC1M 5NQ

Tel: 071 278 6829
Fax: 071 336 7043
Mobile Tel: 0831 316368

Personal work

Agency: Burson Marsteller
Client: Arthur Andersen

George Kavanagh

Agency: BMP DDB Needham
Client: Euro-Tunnel

Agency: Burson Marsteller
Client: Arthur Andersen

Michael St Maur Sheil

Tel: 036787 276
Fax: 036787 641

Corporate: Industrial: Travel: Aerial.
During my career shooting corporate reports in over 40 countries I have become familiar with environments from arctic to equatorial, I have worked in every conceivable industrial plant and research establishment and I understand scientific and industrial processes.
My current clients include Costains, The European Commission, McAlpines, Merck Sharpe & Dohm, Minorco, Mobil Corporation, The National Geographic, RTZ, Readers Digest, The Partners, Shell & Texaco.
So if you need a photographer who is able to work anywhere, organize long, complex shoots, work fast with minimum call on client resources and return with powerful exciting images which communicate exactly what you want, please ask for my portfolio.

Global Finance

Merck Sharpe & Dohm

Mobil Corporation

The Partners/Costain

Kim Taylor

Warren House
Albury Heath
Guildford GU5 9DB

Tel: 048 641 3354
Fax: 048 641 3783

Animals in action.

Mel Allen

101 Salmon Street
London NW9 8NG
Tel: 081 205 1721
Mobile: 0860 429414

Andrew Hall

142 Mildmay Road
London N1 4NE

Tel: 071 241 6899
Fax: 071 275 7040
Mobile: 0860 426531

Agent: Peter Bailey
Tel: 071 935 2626
Fax: 071 935 7557

Credits: Top left: TCI Communications. A.D. Phil Gamble. Client: Bausch & Lomb.
Top right: PDI Group. A.D. James Clancy. Client: B.T.
Bottom left: BMP. Countrywide. A.D. Chris Pearson. Client: ICI.
Bottom right: Folio.

Garry Hunter

21 Little Portland Street
Oxford Circus
London W1N 5AF

Studio Tel: 081 671 1243
Mobile Tel: 0860 435693

Recent commissions include:
G.Q., Sony, Columbia Tri-Star, Phillips, Bull, Sunday Times, Apple Computers, Ecover, BBC TV, Microsoft, Reuters, Monotype, Letraset, Sol beer, United Distillers, Methuen, Haymarket Publishing, MacUser UK and Dennis Publishing.

Also work with architects, graphic and product designers.

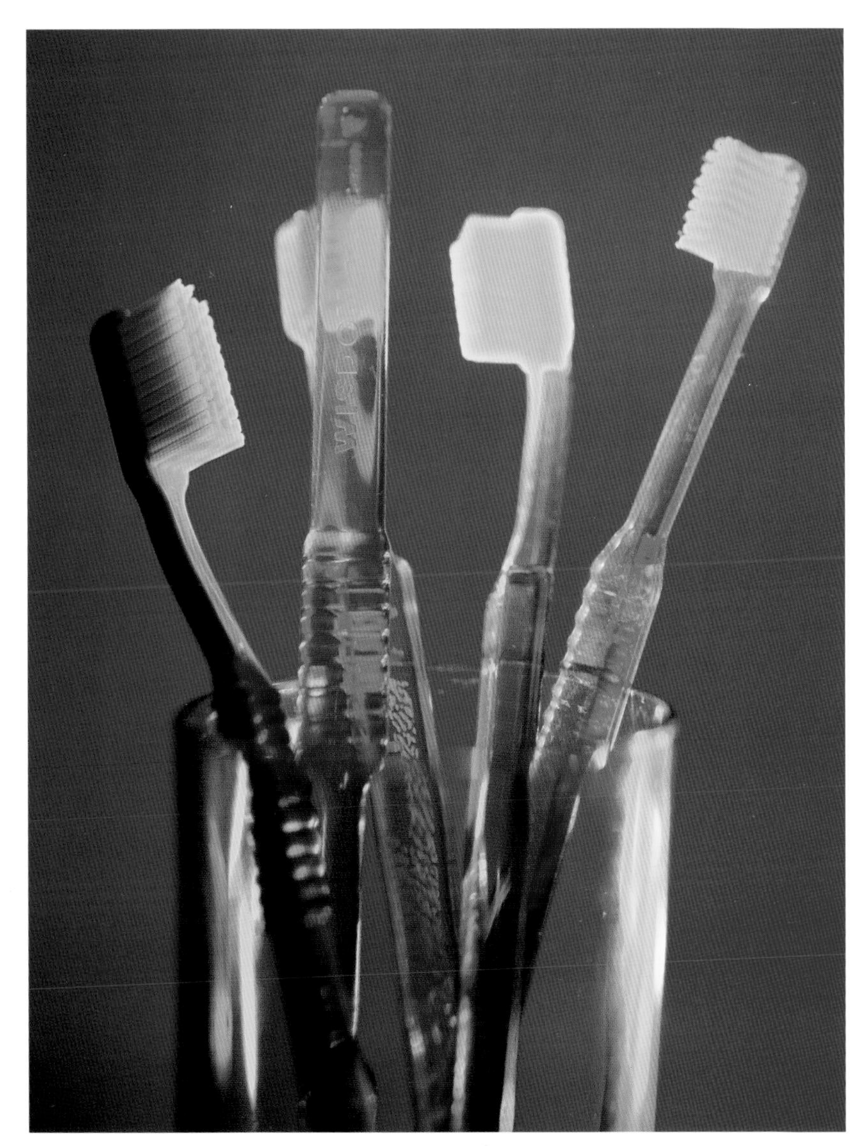

56 **Greg Bartley**

3b Healey Street
London NW1

Tel: 071 482 4346

Roger Payling

27 Heddon Street
London W1R 7LG

Tel: 071 734 3277
Fax: 071 439 4891

Represented by: Schelley Kiah
Tel: 071 351 0371
Fax: 071 352 6124

Roger Payling

27 Heddon Street
London W1R 7LG

Tel: 071 734 3277
Fax: 071 439 4891

Represented by: Schelley Kiah
Tel: 071 351 0371
Fax: 071 352 6124

Retouching by T&S Lightbox Ltd.

Derek Richards

1 Alma Studios
32 Stratford Road
London W8 6QF

Tel: 071 937 7533
Fax: 071 937 8285

Agent: Noelle Pickford
Tel: 071 584 0908

Specialising in: people, travel, locations, corporate reports for Ad. Agencies and Design Groups.

ROLLS
ROYCE
HOIST POINT

Richard Surman

12 Thornton Place
London W1H 1FL

Represented by Julian Cotton
Tel: 071 486 3307
Fax: 071 486 6565

Location photography worldwide, for editorial, advertising, travel, architectural and corporate clients.

Essential Guide to Greece

Development Board of Rural Wales

British Rail Regional Railways

British Tourist Authority

Nigel James

Tel: 081 566 9034
Pager: 0426 934 772

Area of expertise:
All aspects of still-life.

James Bareham

Tel: 071 384 2903

Represented by: Julian Cotton
12 Thornton Place
off York Street
London W1H 1FL

Tel: 071 486 3307
Fax: 071 486 6565

Recent Clients Include: Aramis Int., Associated Newspapers, Canon Cameras, De Beers, Dentsu Inc, G.Q. Magazine, Hugo Boss, IMG, Mumm Champagne, PBA International, Raleigh Bikes, Rothmans Subaru, Rover Cars.

P.B.A. International

K2 Snowboards

Own Portfolio

Harrods

Associated Newspapers

Molyneux Associates

Contact: Helen or Stephanie

Tel: 0291 625013
Fax: 0291 627215
Mobile: 0836 216909

Colin and Andrew Molyneux shoot places, people and objects world wide for a long list of international clients.
For stock photography contact The Image Bank offices or call Helen on 0291 625013.

Derek Lomas

69 Lambeth Walk
London SE11 6DX

Tel: 071 735 0993
Fax: 071 582 2379

Clients include: Advertising Agencies, Design Groups, G.Q., Good Housekeeping, Gold Council, Marie Claire, Max Factor, Options, Tatler, Vogue, Womans Journal, "W".

Andy Whale

16-24 Underwood Street
London N1 7JQ

Tel: 071 608 3743

If a picture paints a thousand words.
I've had it!!!

Cheap beer shots a speciality.
Always up to standard.
Client incentive scheme in operation.
(Backhanders always discussed).
Phone now for a free trial.
All formats as long as it's 35mm.

Clients: Finnigans Fags Ltd. (A member of the Tabs for Toddlers Association),
Bubble Blowers of Brownsea Island.
(Suppliers of little plastic bubbles that go in those wine shots),
Fresh & Fruity plc.
(Phallic fruit & veg. grown to order).

Julian Deghy

No. 4 Carol Street Workshops
43 Carol Street
London NW1 0HT

Tel: 071 267 7635
Fax: 071 267 8706

Represented by
Anthea Bowen – 0860 389 352

Recent Clients Include:
Boots Cosmetics
BMW
Canon Photocopiers
Ceylon Tea
The Electricity Council
Fosters Lager
Fullers Beer
Norwich Union
Rank Xerox

David Steen

Represented by
Mary Mackillop
16 Norfolk Mansions
Prince of Wales Drive
London SW11 4HL

Tel: 071 622 4111

Clients
BUPA, British Rail, Beechams, Kodak, Royal Mail, Sky TV, Fred Olsen, Sectron, Gateway, L.E.B., Allied Breweries.

Barbara & Zafer Baran

Tel: 081 948 3050
071 627 4225

Abstract and experimental photography: still life, product, people, architectural, in colour and b/w.

Recent clients include: Andersen Consulting, British Telecom, Creative Circle, Decca, Dorling Kindersley, English National Opera, Forward Publishing, Gruppo Rinascente, Guinness, IBM, London Business School, Michael Conrad/Leo Burnett (Germany), Nationwide, Nat West, NEC, Our Price, Penguin, Redwood Publishing, Rutland Group, Scottish Television, Stanhope, 3i, United Airlines, United Distillers, Viking Books.

See also pp. 218/219

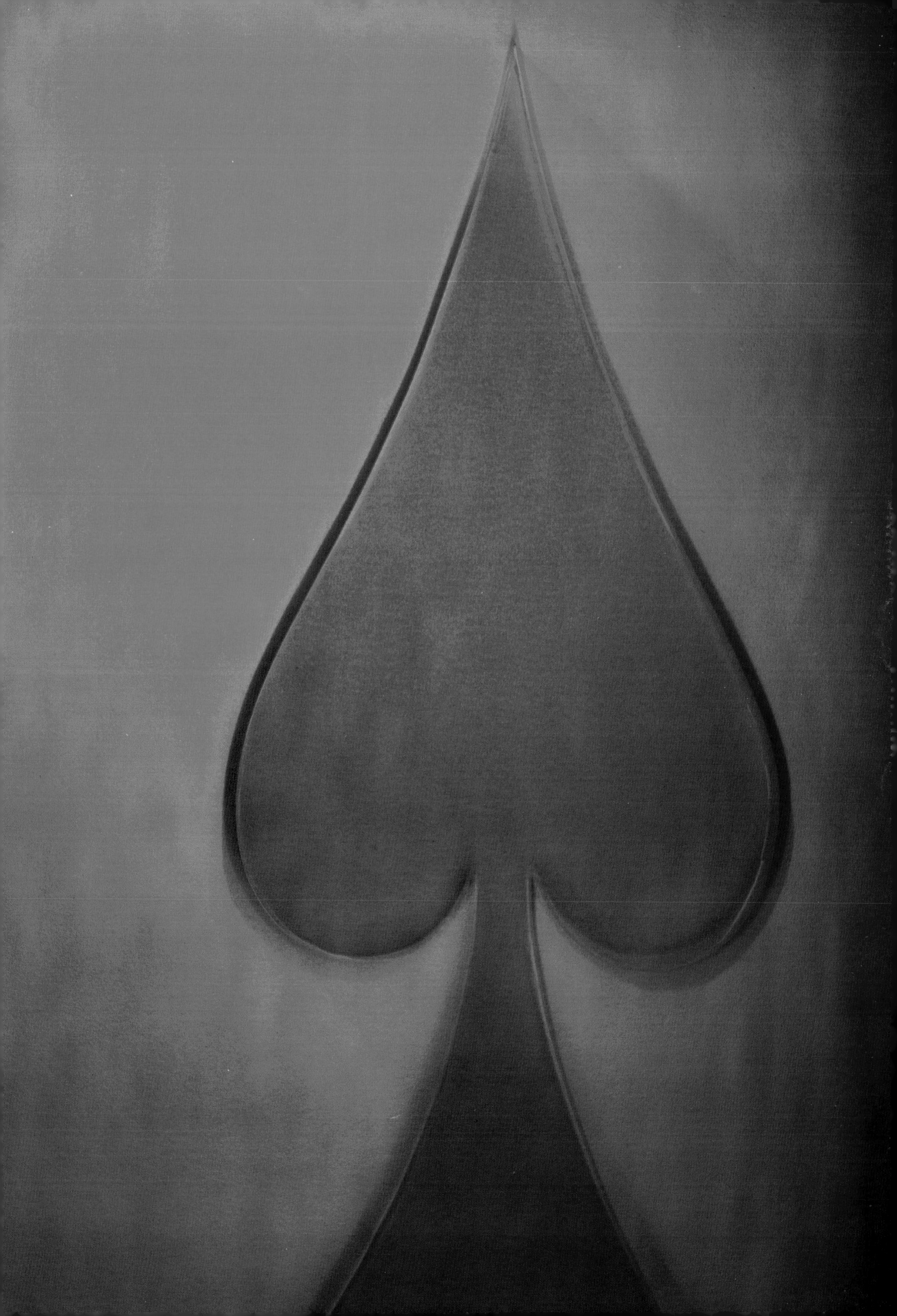

Jhon Kevern

16-17 Novello Street
London SW6 4JB

Tel: 071 731 7438
Mobile Tel: 0836 296694

Malcolm Russell

Duthy Hall
Great Guildford Street
London SE1 0ES

Tel: 071 261 0360
Fax: 071 620 0602

Sears Davies/Provident Mutual

Sears Davies/Provident Mutual

Ian O'Leary

70/71 Wells Street
London W1P 3RB

Tel: 071 580 3306
Fax: 071 580 4050

Agent: Julian Cotton
Tel: 071 486 3307

Specializes in food photography for packaging advertising and editorial. Clients, recent project's have included work for Birdseye, Colman's, Matteson's, Walker's Crisps and John West Food's.

Peter Dazeley

The Studios
5 Heathmans Road
Parsons Green
London SW6 4TJ

Tel: 071 736 3171
Fax: 071 371 8876

Represented by: Sarah Ryder Richardson
Tel: 071 736 2999

Peter Dazeley's work covers still-life, cars, fashion, food, people and corporate literature, both on location and in his large drive-in studio in Fulham.
Recent clients include: Civil Aviation Authority, Elonex Computers, Forte Hotels, Guinness, Hasbro Bradley Games, John Lelliot, Lever Brothers, M&S, Mario Barruti, Modern Security Systems, Multisoft, Nationwide, Office Angels, Suits You, Telstar Records and Yellow pages.

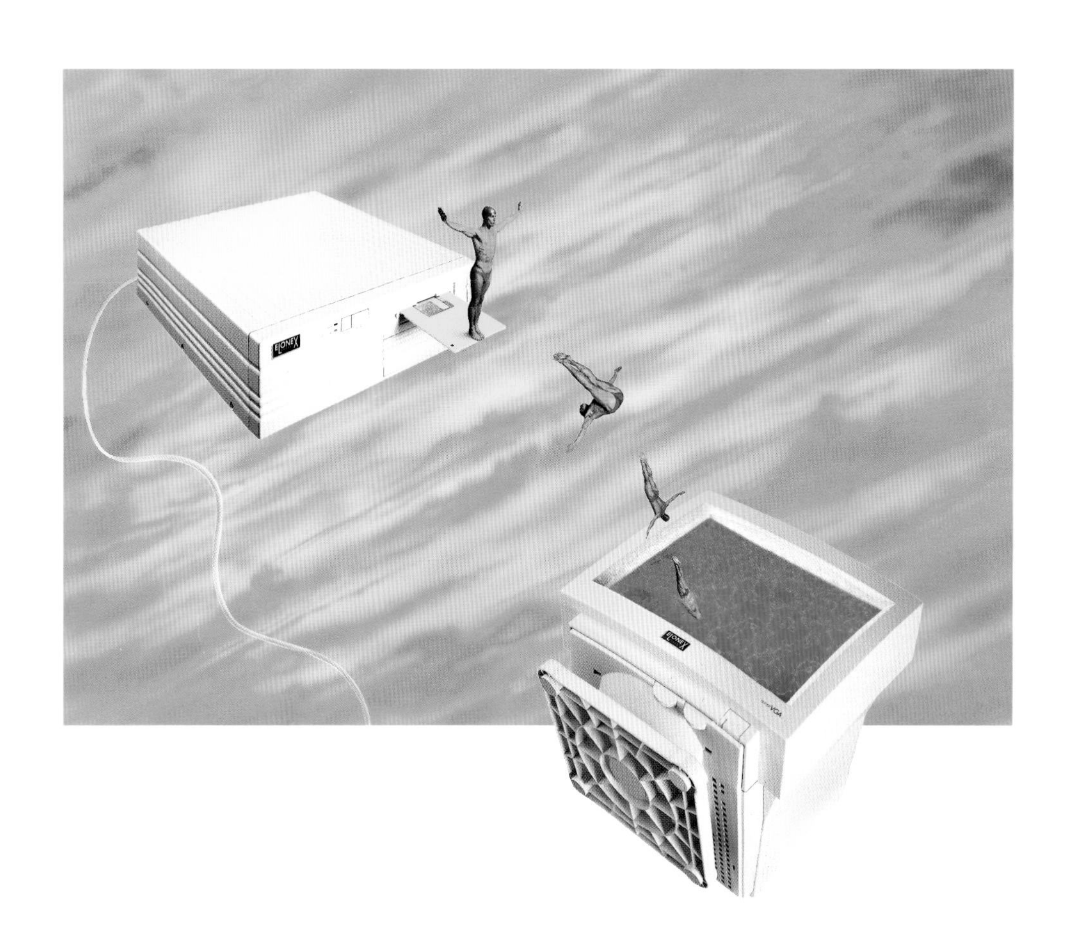

photo-composition using quantel paint box

a series for a new product launch advertising campaign

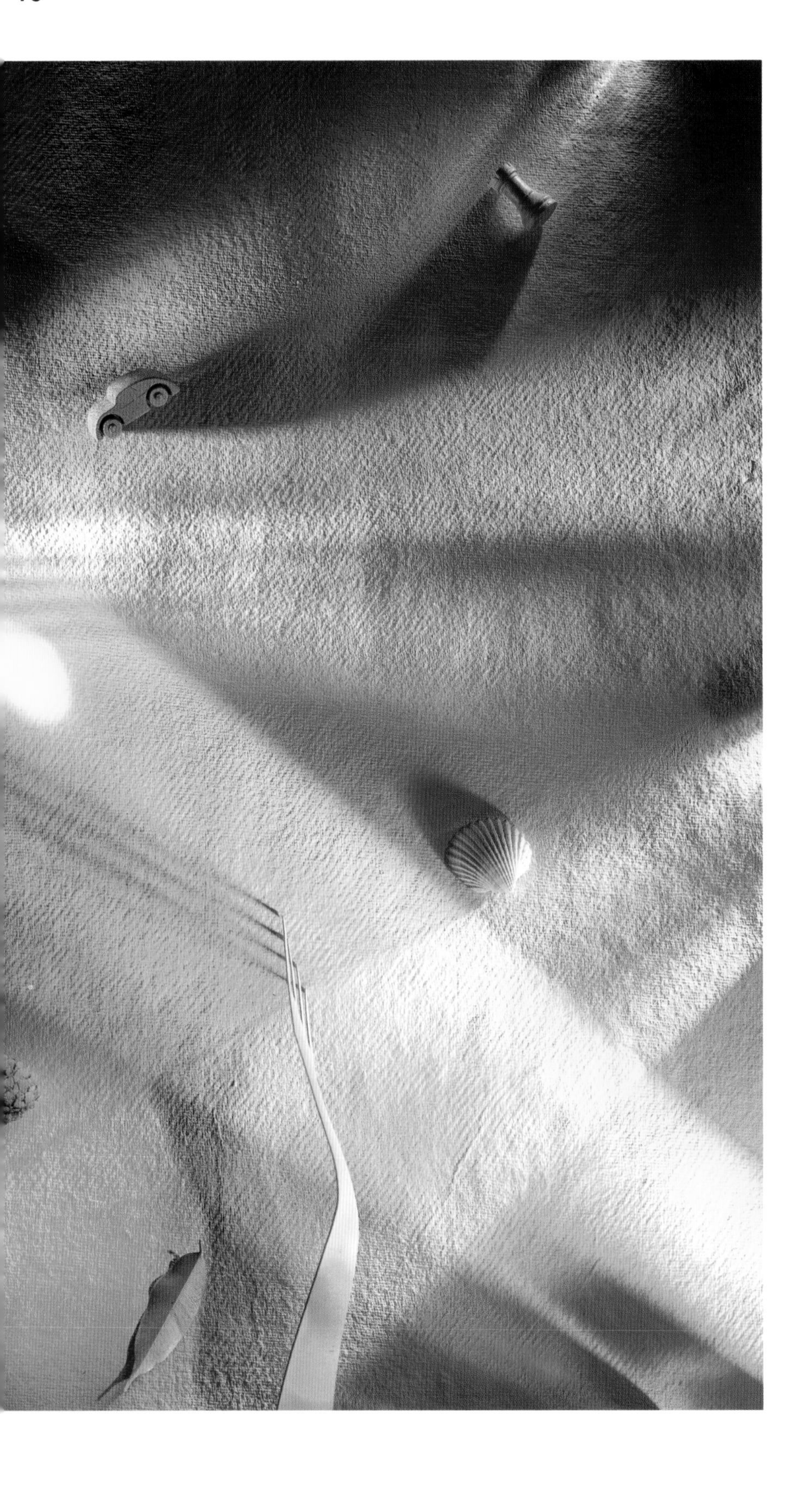

brand image
for product literature

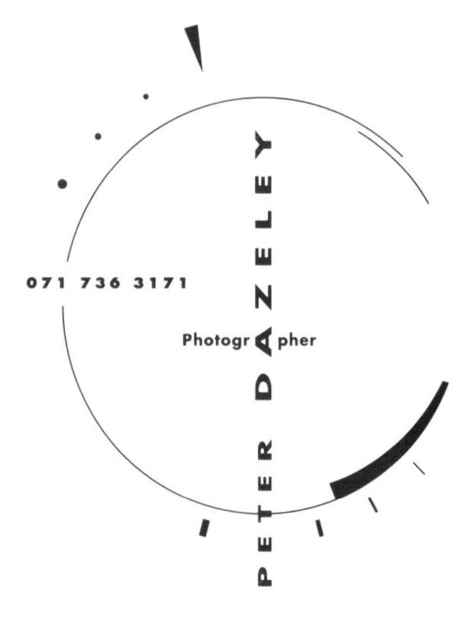

exhibition images for
'idols, icons and heroes'

hand colouring by
helen z

peter dazeley, photographer

location shots for
divisional corporate brochure

peter dazeley, photographer

071 736 3171

hand toning by gerry daniels

design consultancy christmas
card - 'pantomine horse'

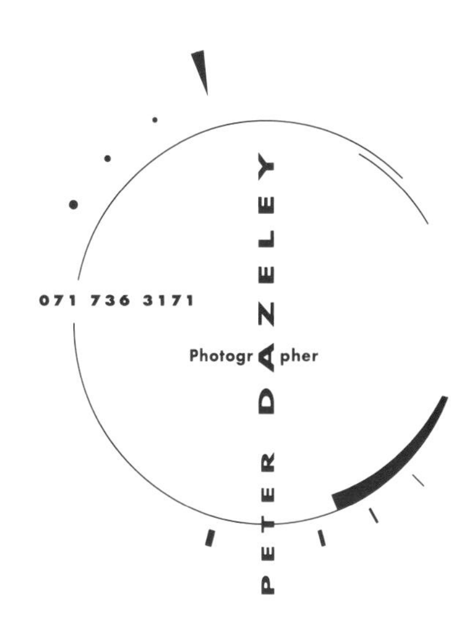

Colin Barker

6A Pratt Street
London NW1 0AB

Tel: 071 380 1056
Fax: 071 380 0829

Contact: Francoise Tison

Howard Grey

1 Studio Place
Kinnerton Street
London SW1X 8EW

Tel: 071 235 4001
Fax: 071 823 1490

Represented by Julian Cotton
Tel: 071 486 3307
Fax: 071 486 6565

Specialises in lifestyle photography in any format, from billboards to brochures, colour and black and white, and provides video casting and scouting. He shoots business people, crowds, celebrities, families, children and lovers and is about the best when it comes to lighting tricky indoor or outdoor locations. Howard Grey works all over the world and has access to all the right facilities.

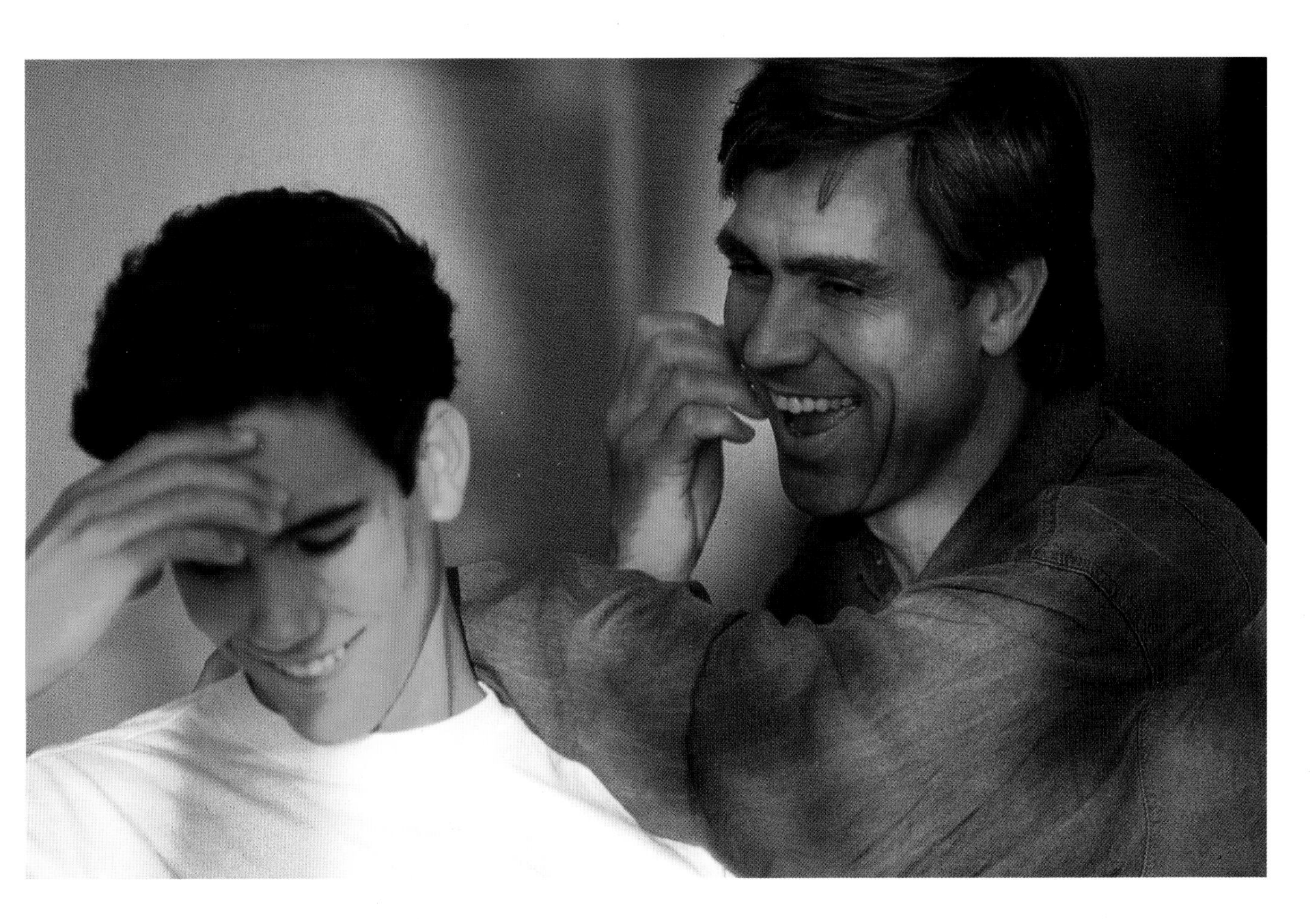

John Waterman

Fox-Waterman Photography Ltd
14-18 Ham Yard
Great Windmill Street
London W1V 7PD

Tel: 071 437 2288
Tel: 071 434 3834
Fax: 071 437 4222

John Waterman and his team operate out of Studios in Soho.

John Ferrara

Studio 28
Waterside
44-48 Wharf Road
London N1
Tel: 071 608 1115

Represented by
Sue Young
Tel: 071 262 0189
Mobile Tel: 0831 504094

Saatchi Saatchi/Direct

PML/Grey

Ranger Read SilBurn

Saatchi Saatchi/Direct

Jason Hawkes Aerial Photography

Represented by Julian Cotton
12 Thornton Place
London W1H 1FL

Tel: 071 486 3307
Fax: 071 486 6565

Shot on location in New York for JWT

Random Century Publishing

Random Century Publishing

Oli Tennent

12 Talina Centre
Bagleys Lane
London SW6 1XX

Tel: 071 371 0645
Fax: 071 731 7185

An experienced sports photographer turned to advertising and editorial. Clients include: The Colt Car Co, Sunseeker Powerboats, Uomo Mare Vogue, Xerox, British Airways, Shell Oils, Kleinwort Benson, For Him and more.

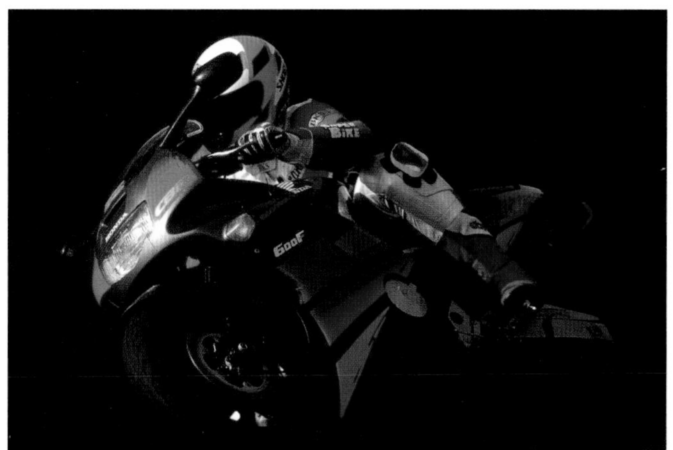

88 Antonia Deutsch

14a Hesper Mews
London SW5 0HH

Tel: 071 244 8772
Fax: 071 373 9313
Mobile Tel: 0836 344972

Areas of expertise:
People
Babies and Children
Landscapes

Norwich Union

Marcus Lyon

The Glassworks
1c Montford Place
Kennington Green
London SE11 5DE

Tel: 071 735 9933
Fax: 071 735 9273

Recent clients:
Amnesty International
Barclays
Bowater
Carlsberg
Emerson Electric
Levis Strauss
Minorco
Southern Electric
The Arts Council
Unilever

The Arts Council

Minorco

Martin Forrest

Duthy Hall
Great Guildford Street
London SE1 0ES

Tel: 071 537 2307
Fax: 071 620 0602

Ogilvy and Mather Direct A/D Andy Budd

Rohan Van Twest

Tel: 071 627 2868
Mobile Tel: 0831 340363

Location Photography.

Photographs reproduced with the kind permission of East Surrey Water (Holdings) plc and Citigate Design Limited.

Illustration by Weef.

John Timbers

61 St. James's Drive
London SW17 7RW
Tel: 081 767 8386

Photographs people

Rumpole of The Bailey

Quartet Camerata

Clive Streeter

3rd Floor
33 Great Sutton Street
London EC1V 0DX

Tel: 071 253 2101

Howard Allman

Studio 18
Aberdeen Studios
22 Highbury Grove
London N5 2EA

Tel: 071 704 1408
Fax: 071 359 1962

Food and Still Life

Patrick Gosling

11/12 Talina Centre
Bagleys Lane
London SW6 1XX
Tel: 071 371 0710
Fax: 071 731 7185
Mobile Tel: 0831 587350

Cars, Motorcycles, People and Movement.

Clients include:
Philip Morris
Duckhams
Goodyear
Gallaher
Suzuki
Honda
Yamaha

For Cycle Magazine Riverside California

Le Mans 24 hour for Gallaher

Chris Coles

Havelock Studios
2 Havelock Terrace
London SW8 4AR

Tel: 071 627 0463
Fax: 071 738 8443
Mobile Tel: 0831 687089

Chris shoots from his large drive-in studio or on location for a wide range of clients including: Royal Mail, Citroen, Mercedes-Benz, Hewlett Packard, British Telecom and Midland Bank.

Steve Shipman

12 Printing House Yard
15 Hackney Road
London E2 7PR

Tel: 071 739 5858
Fax: 071 739 1756

Steve Shipman is a people photographer specialising in corporate, advertising and design work. He works on location or in his studio, and is happy to coordinate casting, propping, styling and location-finding.

Represented by: Kathrine Maginnis
Tel: 081 946 8281
Fax: 081 944 7876

Jason Priestley – Sunday Magazine A.D. Simon Bridge

Egg Design/Hill Samuel A.D. Nicky French

Damien Hopley – For Him Magazine A.D. Francis Cottam

Brookes and Vernons A.D. Dino Maddalena

Carl Warner

25 Malvern Mews
London NW6 5PT

Tel: 071 328 6534
Fax: 071 625 0221

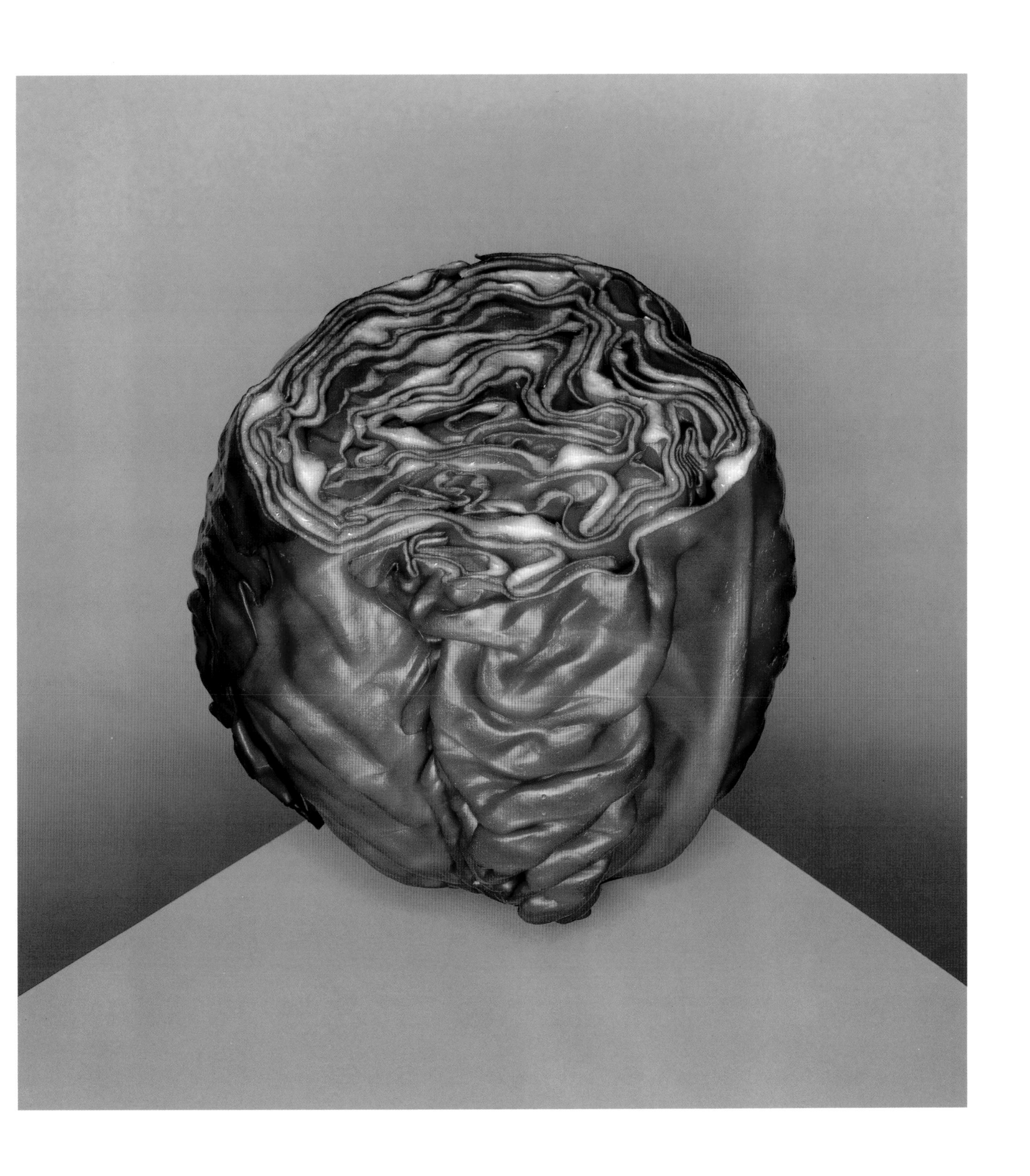

Martin Levenson

Canalside Studios
2a Orsman Road
London N1 5QJ

Tel: 071 613 2994
Fax: 071 729 1698
Mobile Tel: 0831 389235

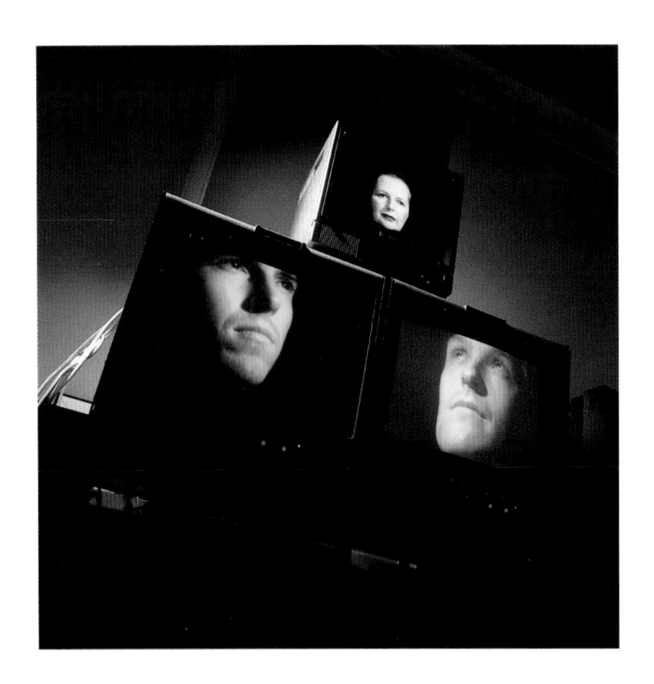

John David Begg

Tel: 071 354 2446
Mobile: 0836 353339

Architecture
Interiors
Industry
People
Landscape

Chris Honeywell

Oxford
Tel: 0865 793 278
Tel: 0831 843 338

Specialising in:
Corporate and Industrial Photography at home and abroad.

Trevor Beynon

221 Canalot Production Studios
222 Kensal Road
London W10 5BN

Tel: 081 960 1090

The Art Course

Design for Business

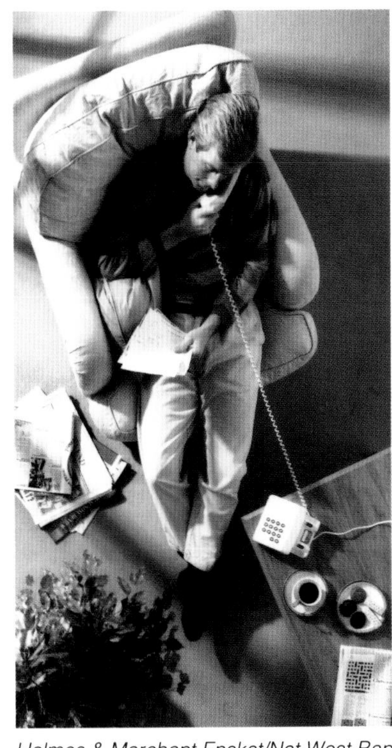

Holmes & Marchant Enskat/Nat West Bank

Michael Trevillion

68 Bickenhall Mansions
Bickenhall Street
London W1H 3LD

Tel: 0459 139301

People and places.

Tim Flach

Beechwood Studio
6-8 Vestery Street, London N1 7RE
Tel: 071 253 5261
Fax: 071 253 3923

Represented by Julian Cotton
12 Thornton Place, Off York Street
London W1H 1FG
Tel: 071 486 3307
Fax: 071 486 6565

Abstract and Conceptual Photography incorporating Still-Life, Architecture, People and Corporate Images.

Recent clients include: COI, General Accident, Glaxo, BP, Esso, Post Office, Guardian Royal Exchange, Conoco UK, Vauxhall, Courage and Whitbread Breweries.

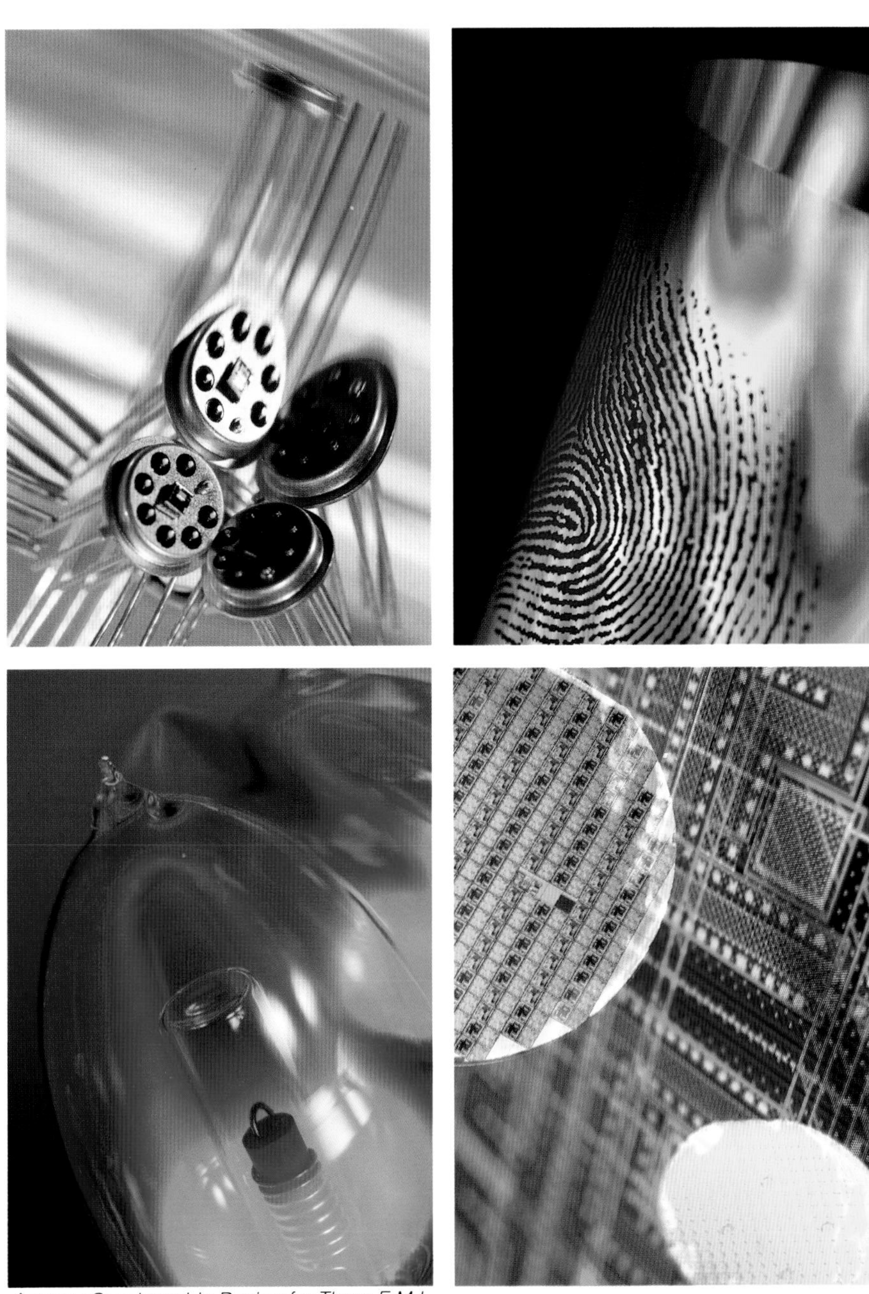

Agency Quadgraphic Design for Thorn E.M.I.

Julian Lee

23 Sussex Street
London SW1V 4RR

Tel:/Fax: 071 233 9489

I believe in creating original image, from portraiture, fashion , still life to book covers and illustration.
Clients include: Time-Out Magazine, Bloomsbury Book, Pentagram Design, Laura Ashley, Orion Publishing, Minerva and Vintage Paperbacks, Liberation Newspaper (Paris) and Phaidon Books etc.

1991 Eurocreation Young Artist Award

Mark Williams

The Soap Factory
9 Park Hill
London SW4 9NS

Tel: 071 622 2283
Fax: 071 498 6445
Mobile Tel: 0831 855797

Shoots: people, places, still life, architecture.
For: publishing, editorial, advertising and PR clients.
Including: Reed Books, New Cavendish Books, River Books (Thailand), World of Interiors, Elle, Reed Magazines, Identity, Outline, Blueberry, The Crown Estates, Nobilis Fontan Fabrics, Le Meridien Hotel.

Tim Imrie

24 Brook Mews North
Lancaster Gate
London W2 3BW

Tel: -44 (0) 71 402 7517
Fax: -44 (0) 71 723 0454

Contact Stills Producer: Anna Imrie-Tait

In his 2,000 sq. ft., high ceilinged studio very close to the West End, Tim Imrie photographs Still Life, Room Sets and Food for many and varied prestigious clients from advertising, design, book publishing and magazines.

His work also takes him out of the studio to locations throughout the UK, Europe and beyond.

New and potential clients are always made welcome and we are happy to look at budgets. Requests to see portfolios are always responded to quickly.

Laura Ashley

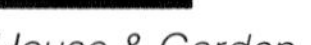

House & Garden

Conde Nast

Opposite page –
Random Century.
'Glorafilia: The Impressionist Collection'
Location: Château De Brecourt, France

Ron Bambridge

RONBAMBRIDGE
PHOTOGRAPHER

Tel: 0420 562818
Mobile Tel: 0831 803232

Represented by: Jenny Ungless
Tel: 081 870 7916
Mobile Tel: 0860 607394

Client list includes: Yamaha Cars, Powergen, Seacontainers, Renault, Travel & Leisure Magazine, Countrylife, Securicor, Anglian Water, British Rail, Coke Cola, Land Securities.

Iceland

Securicor

Laing Construction

Laurie Evans

Studio 11, James Cameron House
12 Castlehaven Road
Camden
London NW1 8QW
Tel: 071 284 2140
Fax: 071 284 2130

Agent: Jenny Ungless
Tel/Fax: 081 870 7916
Mobile Tel: 0860 607394

William Webster

7s Hewlett House
Havelock Terrace
Battersea
London SW8 4AS

Tel/Fax: 071 498 3707

Agent: Jenny Ungless
Tel/Fax: 081 870 7916
Mobile Tel: 0860 607394

Clients include:
BMW, Coca-Cola Schweppes, Forte, Gestetner, Hewlett Packard, Massey Ferguson, Nationwide, Olympus Sport, Polaroid, Psion, Red Star, Securicor, Thames Water, TNT,

Massey Ferguson
A. Schwartzman (Designer L.A. Olympics)

Unisys

Owen Smith

1 Alma Studios
32 Stratford Road
London W8 6QF

Tel: 071 937 7533
Fax: 071 937 8285

Dunhill

Des Montres, Paris

Paula Rosa Kitchens

Martin Vallis

Alexandra Studios
3 Jubilee Place
London SW3 3TD

Tel: 071 727 5983
Fax: 071 352 3669

Represented by: Julian Cotton
Tel: 071 486 3307
Fax: 071 486 6565

Specializing in clothing fabrics and abstract photography

Lee Higham

The Studio
46 Sherbrooke Road
London SW6 7QW

Tel: 071 381 2806
Mobile Tel: 0831 172 173

Specialist areas include all types of location photography, involving people, industrial settings and still-life.

Recent clients have included: Sony UK, United Distillers, Rothmans, Bass, Hambro, Argyll, Sedgwick.

Rothmans
50·3 TONNES
Rothmans
KING SIZE
SEDDON
ATKINSON
DPC 698
B315 XTW
G532 CDC

Carl Lyttle

Dufours Place Studios
London W1

Represented by Lisa Ellis

Tel: 071 431 6911
Mobile Tel: 0836 311339
Studio Tel: 071 287 0884

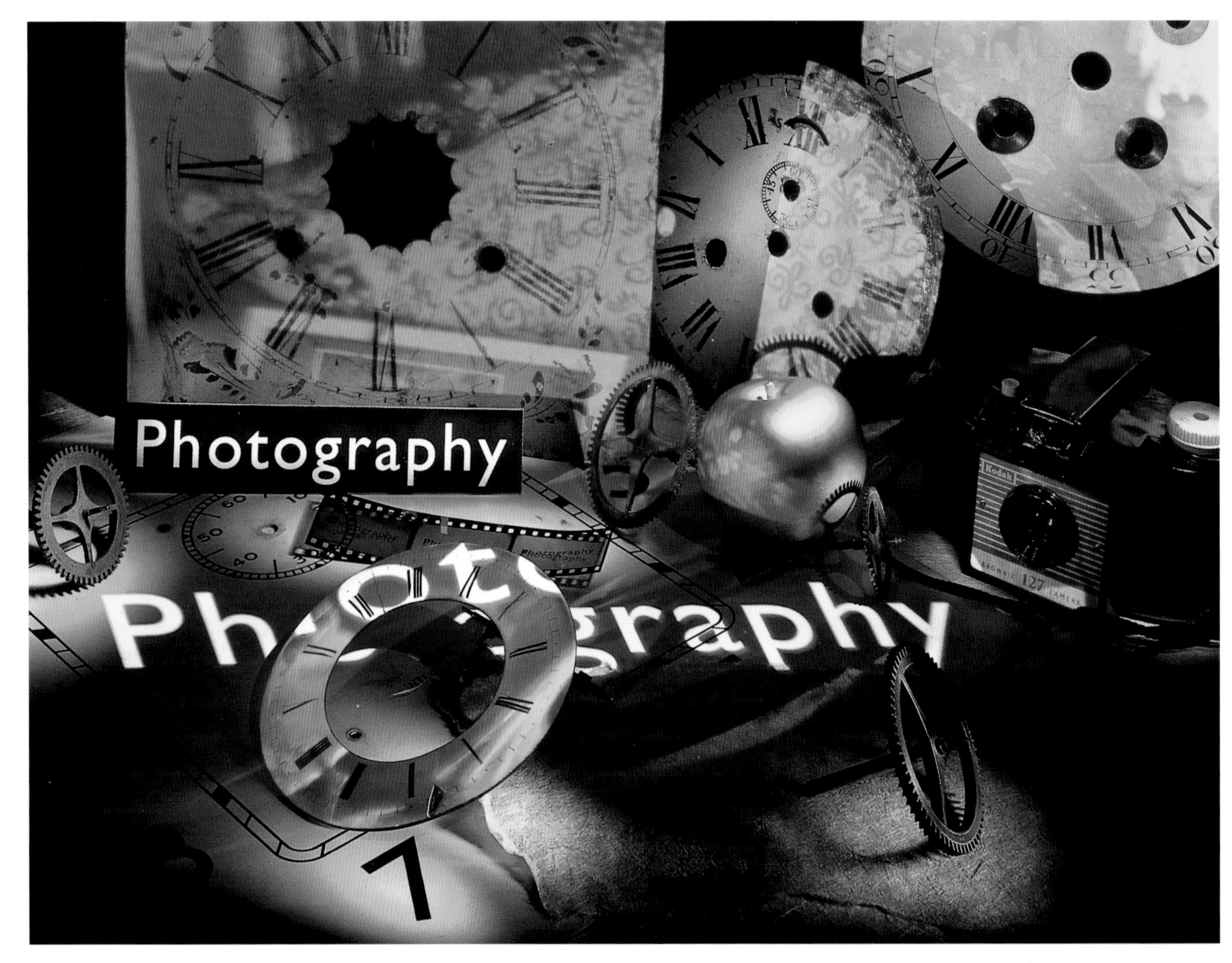

Mike Galletly

Studio 3
The People's Hall
Olaf Street
London W11 4BE

Tel: 071 221 0925
Fax: 071 229 1136

Barry Marsden

218 Boundaries Road
London SW12 8HF

Tel: 081 767 6430

126 Tony Hutchings

44 Earlham Street
Covent Garden
London WC2H 9LA

Tel: 071 379 6397

Represented by Julian Cotton
Tel: 071 486 3307

Still life, concepts and experimental

Martin Haswell

Arch Four
Berkeley Court
Earl Russell Way
Lawrence Hill
Bristol BS5 0BX

Tel: 0272 411040
Fax: 0272 411039
Mobile Tel: 0831 243719

People and places,
Corporate and editorial,
On location and in the studio.

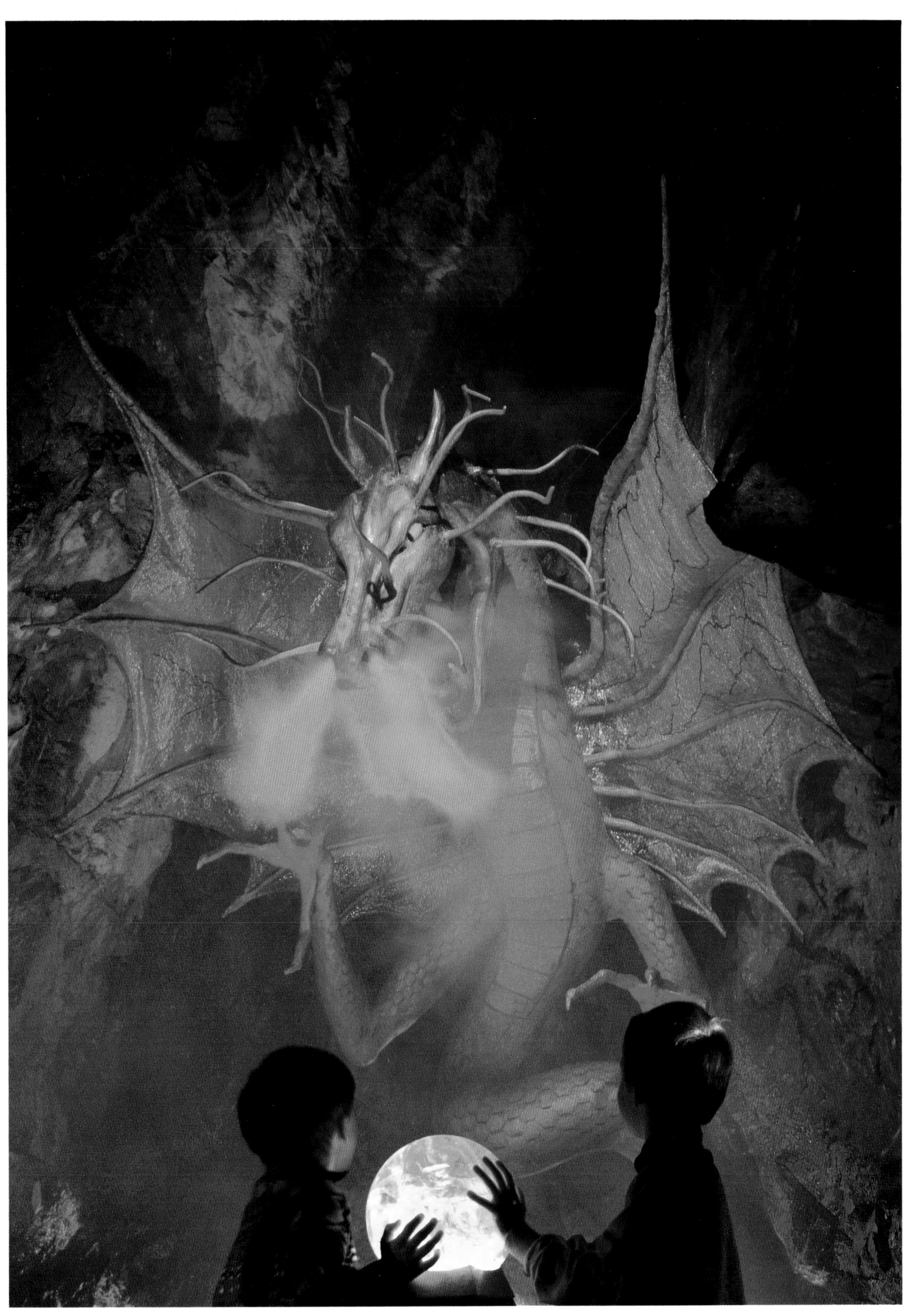

Theo Bergström

Studio 6
5 Old Nichol Street
London E2 7HR

Tel: 071 613 0996
Fax: 071 613 0944

Food and Still Life

Mark Hamilton

071 609 6922

Specialist in black and white photography, hand colouring and creative printing.

Cover for the Independent on Sunday (Sunday Review)

David Partner

Tel: 071 603 1240

Agent: Julian Cotton
Tel: 071 486 3307
Fax: 071 486 6565

Corporate and industrial photographer.

Clients in 1992 include: British Aerospace, Unigate, Electra Trust, Sampson Tyrell.

Tracey Rowe

Represented by: Mary Mackillop
16 Norfolk Mansions
Prince of Wales Drive
London SW11 4HL

Tel: 071 622 4111

Graham Lowe

36A Marlborough Road
Skelton
Saltburn By Sea
Cleveland TS12 2JH

Tel: 0287 651836

"I Can Do That!"
Specialising in black & white, tinting,
hand colouring etc.,
Refer to Contact 8 for further work.

Stunning Corporate Photography

273 Chiswick Village
London W4 3DF

Tel: 081 995 2259
Fax: 081 995 2259

Contact: Steve Dunning

We question first and shoot later.

We tackle usually dreadful locations for company advertising, reports and brochures, and come back with something great. From a new PC system in a peat-briquette factory to an article on barcoding, from engineering to holograms, from high-colour to hardly any.

To get great pictures we ask questions. Lots of them.

Once we know as much as we can about where the picture is going to be used, what it's really trying to say, the product or company, it's USPs, market position and customer profile, *then* we can go out and get something that's really usable. We never forget that the aim is to sell: companies to shareholders, products to customers. So that's what we do.

Call us now and we'll send more samples (and a long client list in case you're impressed by such things). Alternatively we'll come and show you some more great pictures. And ask lots of questions.

CORPORATE

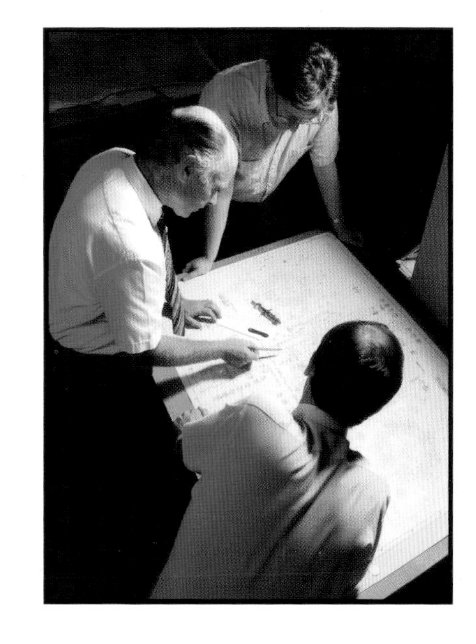

Paul Campbell

14a Hesper Mews
London SW5 0HH

Tel: 071 244 7724
Fax: 071 373 9313

Justin Pumfrey

148 Stephendale Road
London SW6 2PJ

Tel: 071 731 5859
Mobile Tel: 0850 315427

People and places.
Clients: The Arts Council, Britax, Boots, The British Post Graduate Medical Federation, Courtaulds, J.P. Morgan & Co., Northumbrian Water Group, Talkland Mobile Phones, Utell, Yamaha Kemble, BBC, Channel 4, English National Opera, Good Housekeeping, Management Today, The Observer Magazine, Redwood Publishing, The Sunday Times Magazine.

Jimmy Saville

Angela Rippon

Richard O'Brien

Jonathan Dimbleby

The Northumbrian Water Group plc

Bullock Partners

Contact: Jacqui

17 Southfield Road
Southam
Leamington Spa
Warwickshire CV33 0FB

Tel: 0926 815154
Fax: 0926 815079

Bullock Partners are a team committed to creative image making. We are totally geared to serve the design and advertising industry and are experienced in all aspects of studio and location photography.

Please telephone or fax for more examples from our book.

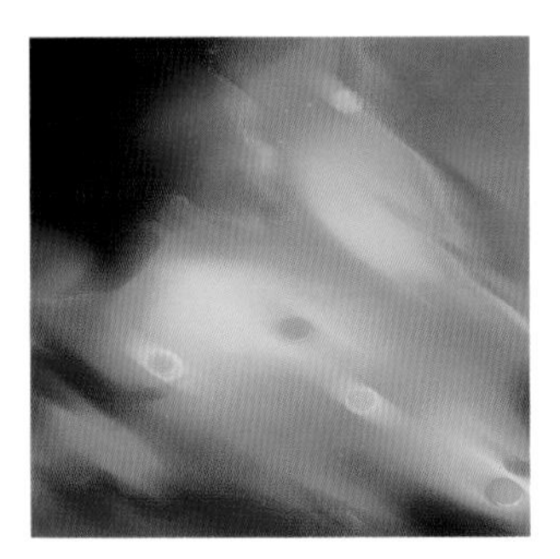

LAND
ROVER

144 Chris Timotheou

44 Earlham Street
Covent Garden
London WC2H 9LA

Tel: 071 379 6397

John Knill

6 Hesper Mews
London SW5 0HH

Tel: 071 373 4896
Fax: 071 244 6091

Still Life & People

Clients include:
Ballantines Whisky, British Gas, Budweiser, British Telecom, Gordons Gin, JVC, Knorr, Winston cigarettes.

146 Jonathan Slatter

Tel: 071 603 6616

Bruce C. Smith

198 Maypole Road
Taplow
Berkshire SL6 0NF

London Tel: 071 793 8177
Mobile Tel: 0860 527486

Fashion
Beauty
People

Scott Morrison

Unit 3b
The Old Malthouse
Little Ann Street
Bristol BS2 9EB

Tel: 0272 540360
Fax: 0272 559025

Commissioned by Simply Creative for Brand Paper

Gavin Cottrell

16 Elizabeth Mews
London NW3 4UH

Tel: 071 586 8625
Fax: 071 586 8978

Agent: Julian Cotton
Tel: 071 486 3307
Fax: 071 486 6565

Area of expertise:
Drinks, Still life
Clients include:
United Distillers
Bulmers
Revlon
Hennessy
Courage
Courvoisier
Schweppes

Geoff Brightling

33 Great Sutton Street
London EC1V 0DX

Tel: 071 253 7504
Fax: 071 490 2558

Clients include: Athena, American Express, Sainsburys, Mercury, Shell, Prudential, Toshiba, BUPA, Longmans, Girobank, BP, British Airways, Lowenbrau, Microsoft, Dorling Kindersley, Redwood Publishing.

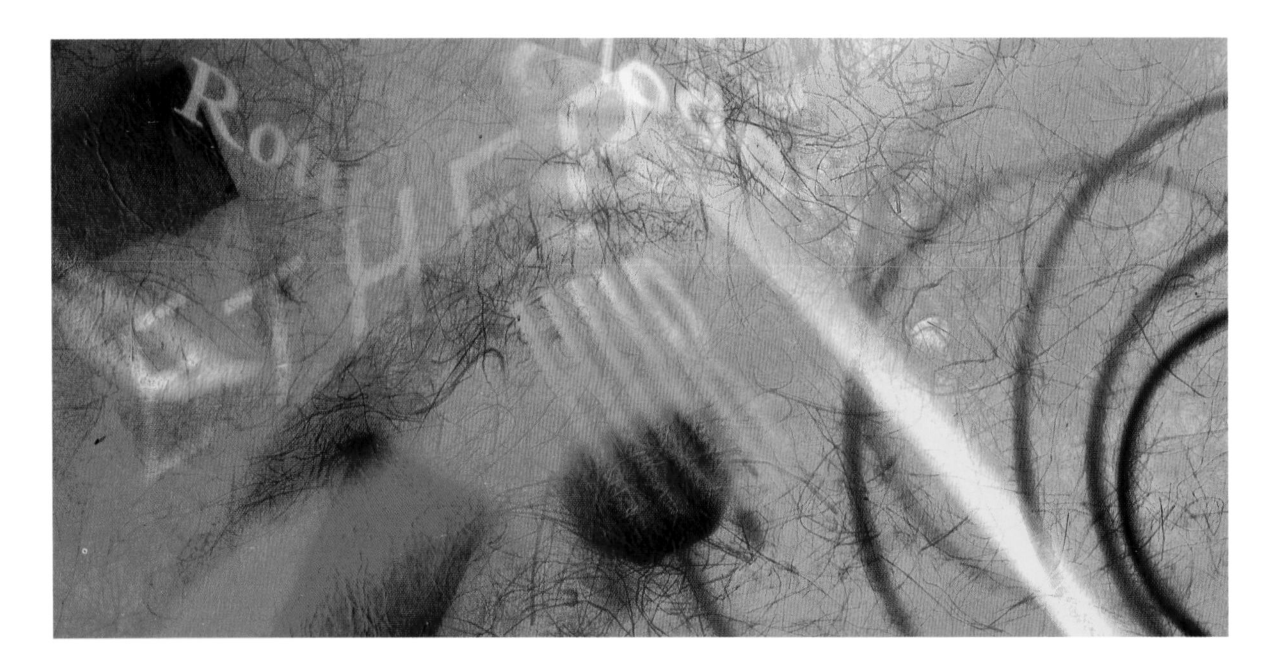

152 **Andrew Bret Wallis**

Castleton Mill
Armley Road
Leeds
West Yorkshire LS12 2DS

Tel: 0532 465584
Fax: 0532 341555
Mobile Tel: 0850 712028

Creative Corporate Images for Brochure, Annual Report, Advertising and Exhibition.

Geoff Sumner ABIPP

2a French Place
London E1 6JQ

Tel: 071 613 2672
Mobile Tel: 0836 252804

Richard Bradbury

27 Heddon Street
London W1R 7LG

Tel: 071 734 9585
Fax: 071 439 4891

Leon Morris

Tel: 071 267 6959
Fax: 071 284 3233

Represented by: Agent Watts
Tel: 081 533 5253

Leon Morris continues to build his archive of contemporary Britain with a recent focus on the personality of the British workforce. He is comfortable with models or real people and is capable of working independently or to strict art direction.

His work has been widely exhibited and won numerous awards including the Kodak UK European Award and Kodak Fine Art Award.
Clients include: London Electricity, British Gas, Royal Mail, Royal Bank of Scotland, etc.

London Electricity

Royal Mail Parcels

Tim Motion

91 St. Mark's Road
London W10 6JS

Tel/Fax: 081 960 6102
Mobile Tel: 0836 551136

Represented by: Agent Watts
Tel: 081 533 5253

Experienced in Architectural, Location, Interior, Travel and Aerial Photography worldwide: I speak Portuguese, French and Spanish. I maintain a Stock Library of Jazz, Blues and other Musicians. Travel Stock with Ace Photo Agency.
Member of Association of Photographers.

David Burch

11 Highbury Terrace Mews
London N5 1UT

Tel: 071 359 7435

Represented by: Agent Watts
Tel: 081 533 5253

Coneyl Jay & Gary Marsh

Coneyl Jay (Photographer)
Tel: 071 226 0683
Tel: 081 883 8034

Gary Marsh (Photo-computer illustrator)
Tel: 071 585 3616
Fax: 071 924 1668

Work together designing the image from concept to completion, shooting in the studio or on location to state-of-the-art post production.

Coneyl & Gary work: 10 x 8/5 x 4
6 x 9 / 6 x 6 / 35mm digital + analogue.

Work includes: GQ, ID, Touche Ross, BT, Stella, A&M, WEA, CBS, Virgin, Epic, BMG, Onu-Japan, TSBW, BBC, BBH, Sony, Polygram, Barcardi, Vauxhall.

Arista – Bmg

Stella Artois 'dry'

Ian Dare

33 Battersea Park Road
London SW8 5BH

Tel: 071 627 5195

Clients include:
BMW
Ford
Citroën
Renault
Fiat
Lancia
Honda
Daihatsu
Volkswagen
United Distillers
Campbell Distillers

Sandra Lousada

Susan Griggs Agency
43 Mary Place
London W11 4PL

Tel: 071 229 2092
Fax: 071 727 1263
Studio Tel: 071 727 7488
Studio Fax: 071 792 2306

Advertising, corporate and editorial, studio and location: children, fashion, health and beauty, portraits, crafts.
Clients include: Abbey National, Birthright, Boots, Brides, Clarks Shoes, Country Living, Cow & Gate, Ebury Press, Farleys, Fisher Price, Good Housekeeping, Great Ormond Street Hospital, IBM, Michael Peters, Next, Peper Harow, Random Century, St. Thomas Hospital, Tatler, Wolff Olins, Woman's Journal, Xtend.

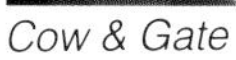

Cow & Gate

Cow & Gate

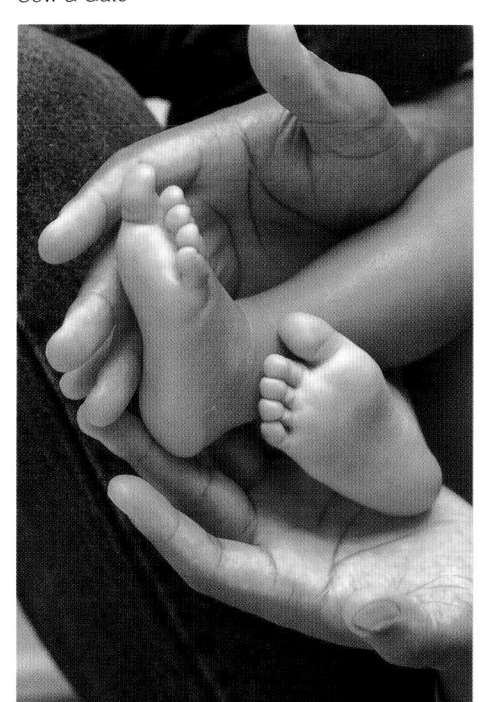

Clarks Shoes

Cow & Gate

Adam Woolfitt

Tel: 081 444 6516
Fax: 081 442 0604

Represented by: Susan Griggs
43 Mary Place
London W11 4PL

Tel: 071 229 2092
Fax: 071 727 1263

Corporate and editorial; People and places worldwide; 360° Panoramics; Aerials; Lighting of difficult interiors; Hotels; Location food.

Clients include: British Tourist Authority, Cameramen UK, Country Life, Gourmet, Mitsubishi Bank, National Geographic, Readers Digest, Travel & Leisure, Travel Holiday, Weldon Owen, "Over Europe".

Gourmet

Travel Holiday

Cameramen UK

Julian Nieman

Susan Griggs Agency
43 Mary Place
London W11 4PL

Tel: 071 229 2092
Fax: 071 727 1263

Corporate and editorial, studio and location: travel, architecture, industry, hotels and restaurants, portraits, children, still life, food.

Clients include: British Tourist Authority, Coca-Cola, Conrad Hotels, Country Life, Food & Wine, Gourmet, The Independent, Marriott Hotels, The National Trust, Nightingales, Reader's Digest, Smithsonian, Sony, Thames Water, Travel Holiday, Wechsler & Partners.

Coca-Cola Amatil

Country Life

Struan Wallace

The Studio
16 Gibraltar Walk
London E2

Tel: 071 739 4406
Fax: 071 739 8784

Represented by: Lisa Ellis
Tel: 071 431 6911
Mobile Tel: 0836 311339

Areas of expertise: Food, drink and still-life. Picture on facing page is using polaroid technique, for more examples see folio. Many thanks to model, Nancy from Matthews & Powell and Make-up, Aimee Adams.

Struan Wallace

Tel: 071 739 4406
Fax: 071 739 8784

Charlie Fawell

173 Consort Road
London SE15 3RX

Tel: 071 639 1798

Portrait & Location photography

Bay Hippisley

16 Lion Yard
Tremadoc Road
London SW4 7NQ

Tel: 071 978 2552

Alan Hampson

Foulis Cottage
Ingleby Greenhow
North Yorkshire TS9 6LL

Tel: 0642 722711
Mobile Tel: 0831 694248

My work covers Still-life, Product, Publishing, Editorial and Corporate. I specialise in intricate lighting and awkward sets.
18th Century studio with no infinity coves, no floating ceilings, and definitely not drive-in. However, plenty of free and easy parking by courtesy of the North Yorkshire Moors.
For further examples of my work see Contact 8, page 86 and European Contact 4, page 288 or call me direct.

Andrew Olney

32 Great Sutton Street
London EC1V 0DX

Tel: 071 253 0771
Fax: 071 253 3104

Client: Carré Noir, London

Norman Hollands

The Rochester Place Studio
55 Rochester Place
London NW1 9JU

Represented by: Rosie Beckett
Tel: 071 482 3400
Fax: 071 284 0458

Still Life & Food.

Recent clients: Sainsburys, Justerini & Brooks, Croft, Dunhill, Lloyds of London, W.V. Publications, Comet, LDDC, Earls Court & Olympia, Embassy.

Also Roomsets & Interiors.

Recent clients: Armitage, Twyfords, Camargue Kitchens, St. Thomas's Hospital, Ideal Home, Le Meridien Hotel, Zanussi, P & O.

Alex Wilson

The Rochester Place Studio
55 Rochester Place
London NW1 9JU

Represented by: Rosie Beckett
Tel: 071 482 3400
Fax: 071 284 0458

Still Life.

Recent clients: Selfridges,
Marks & Spencer, BHS, IDV, D.K. Direct,
Carling Black Label, Molton Brown,
Alfred Dunhill, Crabtree & Evelyn,
The Dorchester Hotel, Homes & Gardens.

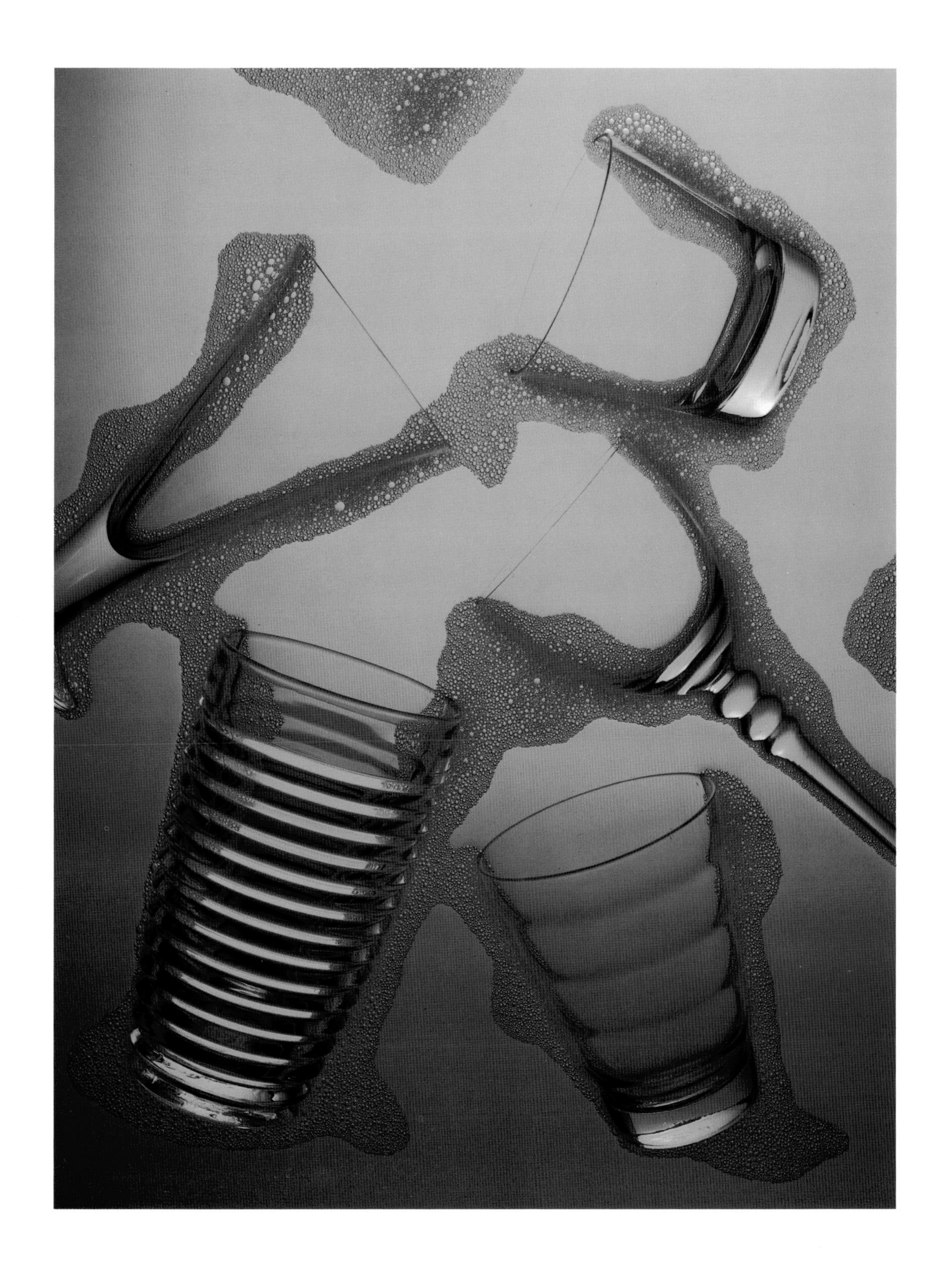

Mark Davison

217 North End Road
London W14 9NP

Tel: 071 381 6707
Mobile Tel: 0831 825169

Agent: Jo Clark
Tel: 071 722 4883
Fax: 071 586 1592

Mark Davison

Simon Potter

13a Lambrook Terrace
London SW6 6TF

Tel: 071 736 9245

People,
Location,
Reportage,
Business,
Literature.

Matthew May

111 Camden Mews
London NW1 9AH

Tel: 071 267 8827
Fax: 071 267 8837
Mobile Tel: 0860 600490

Chris Ridley

6 Pindock Mews
London W9 2PY

Tel: 071 286 4843
Mobile Tel: 0836 558082

Alan Marsh

11 Lever Street
London EC1V 3QU

Tel: 071 490 0952
Fax: 071 490 1895

Areas of expertise: Food/Still-Life

Tim O'Leary

63a Montagu Square
London W1H 1TG

Tel: 071 402 2924

People
See also Contact 8 page 142.

Eitan Lee Al

Agents: Debut Art

52 Barbauld Road
London N16 0ST

Tel: 071 254 2856
Fax: 071 241 6049

Recent clients include: British Gas, Lloyds Shipping, Reuters, Rutland plc, Tartan plc, Expamet International plc, VW, Cosmopolitan Magazine, GH Magazine, Ideal Home Magazine, Personal Computer World Magazine, Penguin Publishing, Collins Publishing, Hutchinson Publishing.

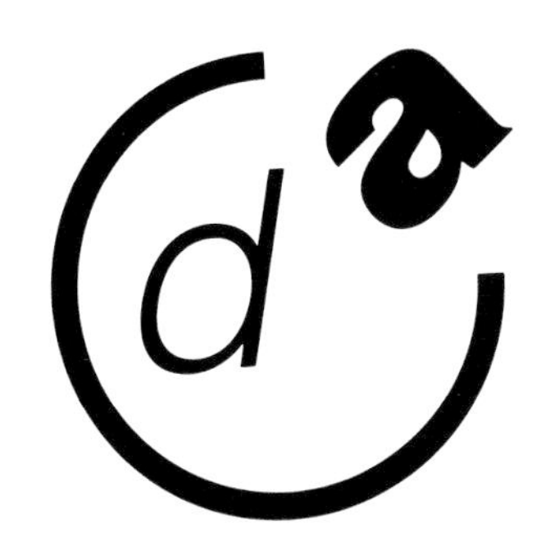

Commissioned by Radley Yeldar Design for Cheltenham & Gloucester BSOC

Commissioned by Addison Design for Globe Investments

Commissioned by VNU for Personal Computer World

Matthew Weinreb

The Studio
16 Millfield Lane
London N6 6JD

Tel: 081 340 6690
Fax: 081 341 0441
Portfolio Tel: 071 792 0128
Mobile Tel: 0836 679694
France Tel: 62 65 21 43

An award-winning photographer specialising in architecture, interiors, landscapes and cityscapes.
Weinreb's clients include many British and foreign design groups, advertising agencies, architects and blue-chip companies. A forthcoming book on London architecture (Phaidon Press Autumn 1993) features 350 of his colour photographs.

Folio, video and exemplar pack available on request.

Alex McNeill

Agents: Debut Art

52 Barbauld Road
London N16 0ST

Tel: 071 254 2856
Fax: 071 241 6049
Studio Tel: 081 347 8021

Alex specialises in producing imagery for the corporate and business to business market. He works on location, in working environments and in the studio. His extensive portfolio includes architectural, interior, industrial and 'people' imagery. He has developed post production multi image combination techniques. Recent clients include: TSB, Leeds Building Society, Prudential, National Power, Conrad Ritblat, London Transport.

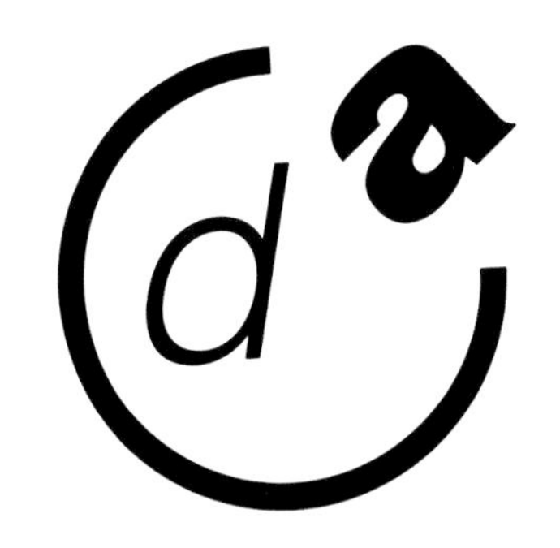

Commissioned by Prudential

Commissioned by McColl Design Limited

Nadia Mackenzie

1 Swindon Street
London W12 7HN

Tel: 081 743 8228
Mobile Tel: 0831 284473

Interiors
Location
Studio
People
Lifestyle

Imagination

Ebury Press

Coté Sud

Richard Ivey

202B Camberwell New Road
Camberwell
London SE5 0RR
Tel: 071 582 9978

Clive Frost

Tel: +44 (0) 81 673 6962
Fax: +44 (0) 81 673 6962

UK and International Locations.

Landscapes
People
Portraits
Travel
Architecture
Interiors
Products

Portfolio available on request.
For further work see Contact 6, page 150.

Advertising, Design, Corporate, Editorial, PR, Clients include: AMEX, Athena International, BA, Condé Nast Traveler, Conran Octopus, Cornhill Insurance, Country Living, Departures, Electrolux, Forte Hotels, Gillette, GQ, Harpers & Queen, House & Garden, The Observer Colour Magazine, Pedigree Pet Foods, Relais & Chateaux, Rowntree, Saatchi & Saatchi, The Savoy Group, Smith & Milton, The Sunday Times Magazine, The Telegraph Magazine, Vanity Fair, Vogue, Walker Izard, William Grant & Sons, The World of Interiors.

Condé Nast Traveler

Michel Roux/The Waterside Inn

Glenfiddich Distillery/William Grant & Sons

Pete Gardner

5 Charterhouse Works
Eltringham Street
London SW18 1TD

Tel: 081 871 3975
Fax: 081 877 0799

Still Life
Corporate
Interiors
Architecture

David Gill

7 Aberdeen Studios
22 Highbury Grove
London N5

Tel: 071 354 1561
Fax: 071 354 1552

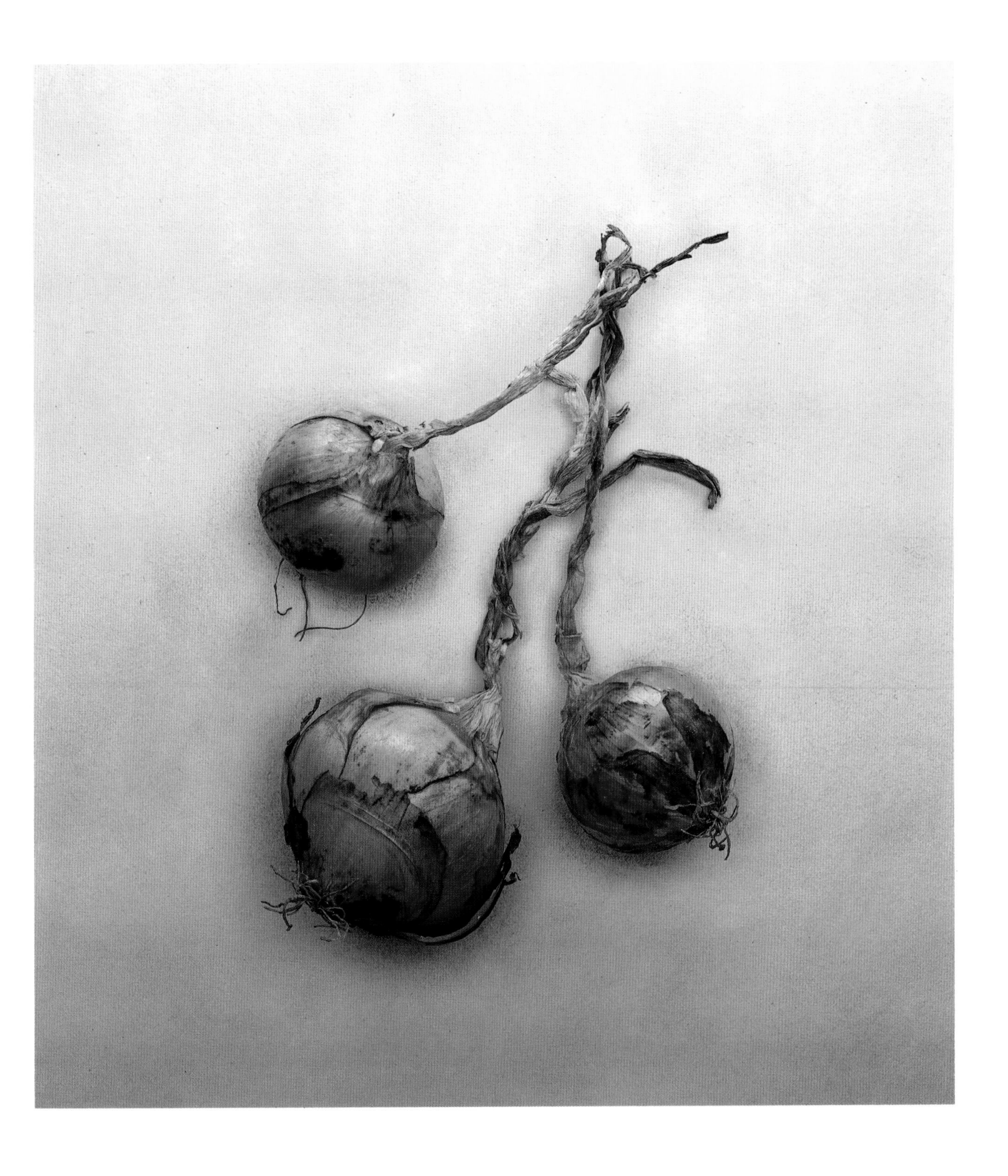

Daniel Allan

Tel: 071 582 3230
Fax: 071 820 0812

Agent: Sue Young
Tel: 071 262 0189
Fax: 071 262 2160

Neill Menneer BA Hons AFAEP

1 Postscript Publishing
1 Argyle Street, Bath
Avon BA2 4BA

Tel: 0225 460063
Fax: 0225 442456

Agents: Debut Art
Tel: 071 254 2856
Fax: 071 241 6049

Neill specialises in producing imagery for the corporate market. He works on location and in studio.

Clients include: Midland Bank, Coutts Bank, TSB, Rank Xerox, Unilever, Northern Telecom, Royal Caribbean, Peat Marwick McLintock, Coopers and Lybrand, BAT, Autoglass, Sunday Times, Observer, Elle.

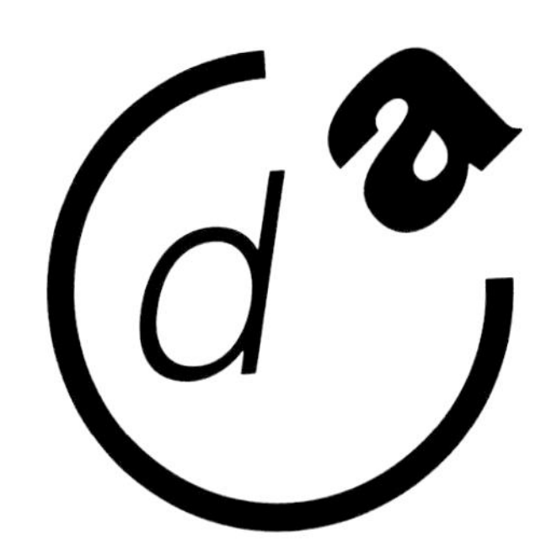

Commissioned by BSB Dorland Adv. for BAT Industries

Commissioned by Lapot Design

Larry Bray

7 Kensington High Street
London W8 5NP

Tel: 071 938 3402
Fax: 0273 439129
Mobile Tel: 0860 800180

10 years experience in location photography for Corporate, Design, Advertising and Editorial.

Clients worked for in the past twelve months include: BP, Burberrys, Cunard Lines, Europa Hotels, Homepride, ICL, Jones Shoes, Lloyds Bank, National Westminster Bank, Rodenstock and Seeboard.

See also Contact editions 6, 7 & 8.

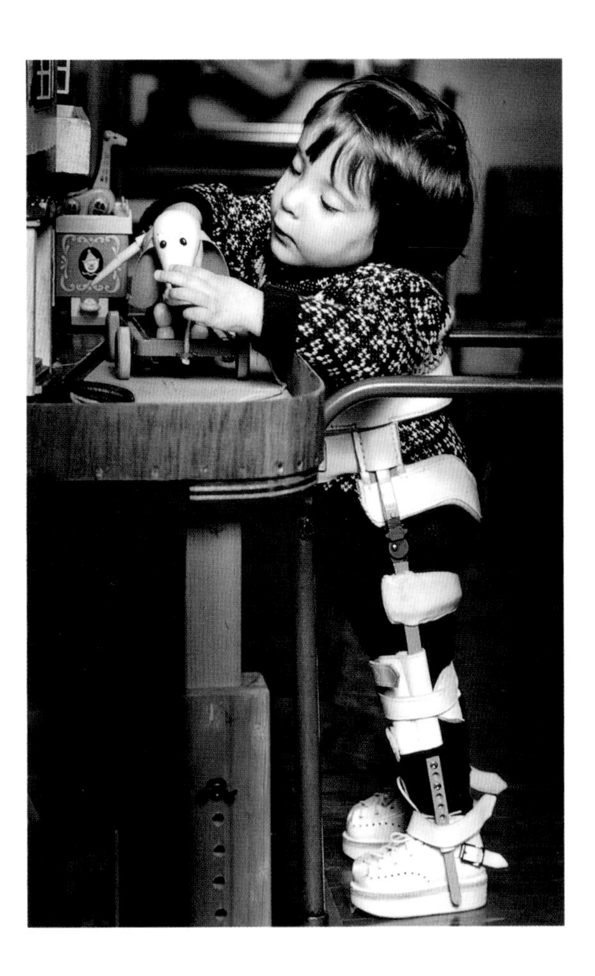

Phil Trost

53-55 Bayham Place
London NW1 0ET

Tel: 071 383 2073
Fax: 071 383 2109
Mobile Tel: 0860 538800

Still Life/Sets/Effects

Simon Warren

Studio 28 Waterside
44-48 Wharf Road
London
N1 7SH

Tel: 071 253 1711
Fax: 071 248 3248
Mobile: 0836 322711

Architectural
Interiors
Location
People in the workplace

Represented by: Julian Cotton
Tel: 071 486 3307
Fax: 071 486 6565

1. Connell Wilson
2. Danish Pavillion Expo 92
3. The Criterion. George Wimpey plc
4. Merril Lynch
5. Baltic Quay. LDHB Arcitects
6. UK Pavillion Expo 92

Barry Willis

8 Woodland Hill
London SE19 1NY

Tel: 081 761 7735
Mobile Tel: 0831 553250

People and location photography in corporate, editorial and advertising. Refer to Contact 8 for further examples of my work.

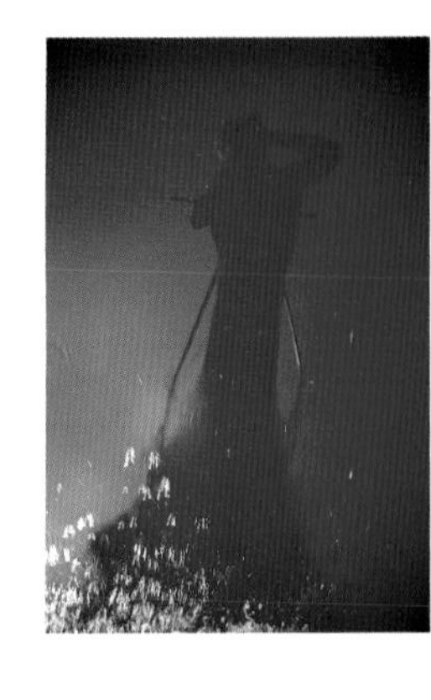

Beds TEC Annual Report

Jon H Hamilton

Tel: 081 672 8896
Tel: 081 788 3072

Clients include: Ford, ICI, Digital, Scottish Hydro Electric, Henley Centre, Mercury Communications, Tinsley Robor, Decca, Central Television, Barclay Card, Sappi Graphics, Harper Collins Publishing.

Selection of stock images available.

Also see Contact Illustration 8, page 128 and illustration 9, page 129.

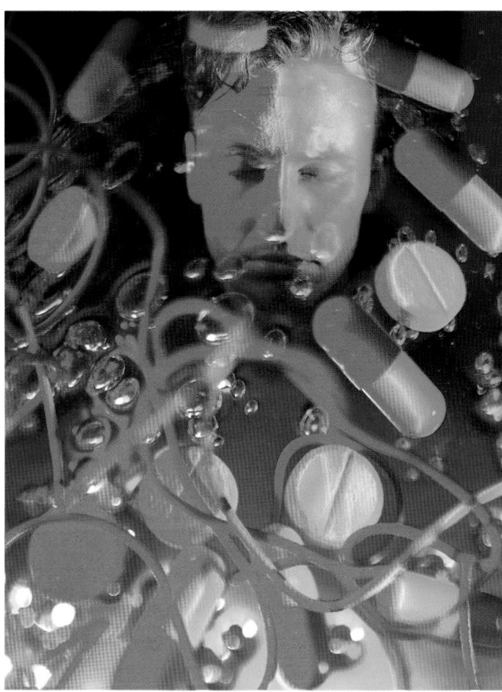

Commissioned by Harper Collins Publishing

Commissioned by Sampson Tyrrell for Intertech

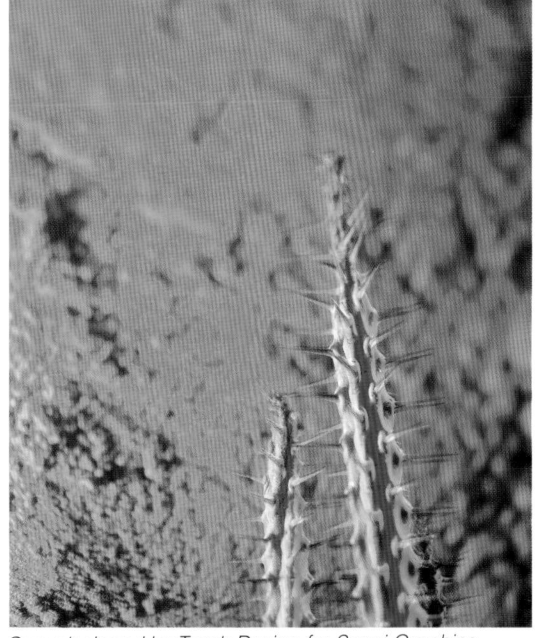

Commissioned by Torch Design for Sappi Graphics

Bruce Miller

River Watch Studios
Chilbolton
Hampshire SO20 6AZ

Tel: 0264 860366
Fax: 0264 860829

Represented in Paris by: Cosmos
Tel: 45 06 1880

Represented in London by: Bos & Company
Tel: 071 287 8860

Graham Tann

17/21 Emerald Street
London WC1N 3QL

Tel: 071 405 7900
Fax: 071 404 2072

Work currently in hand for:
Reuters
Rover Group
Renault UK
Landis & Gyr
Ebury Press
Dairy Crest

Tom Leighton

Tel: 081 876 8497
Mobile Tel: 0831 591969

Interiors
Still Life
Room Sets

Chris Hopper

60 St. Stephens Gardens
London W2 5NJ

Tel: 071 221 1621

People/Fashion

Courtesy of AXA Equity and Law

Mike Russell

7 Canham Mews
Canham Road
London W3 7SR

Tel: 081 740 5357

Represented by: David Lambert
Tel: 071 262 1774

George Logan

50A Rosebery Avenue
London EC1

Tel: 071 833 0799/8189

Agent: Noelle Pickford
Tel: 071 584 0908

Below:
Non Commissioned

Top right:
Art Director: Brett James/David Hughes
Client: Thomas Cook
Agency: Alterego

Centre right:
Art Director: Al Morris
Client: Philips
Agency: GGT

Bottom right:
Art Director: Jim Salter
Client: Silk Cut
Agency: Saatchi and Saatchi

Daniel T. Pangbourne

39 Tintern Street
Clapham
London SW4 7QQ

Tel: 071 733 7623
Fax: 071 738 5739
Mobile Tel: 0831 444217

Daniel Pangbourne has specialised in Children's Photography for the past six years. His experience covers everything from national advertising campaigns and magazine front covers to extensive catalogue/fashion work. Clients include major advertising and P.R. companies and publishing houses.
Ability to work within a fixed layout or originate creative ideas.
Comprehensive London studio facilities.
Undertaken location work throughout U.K., U.S.A. and Europe. Portfolio available on request.

David Sherwin

Agent: Mary Mackillop
Tel: 071 622 4111

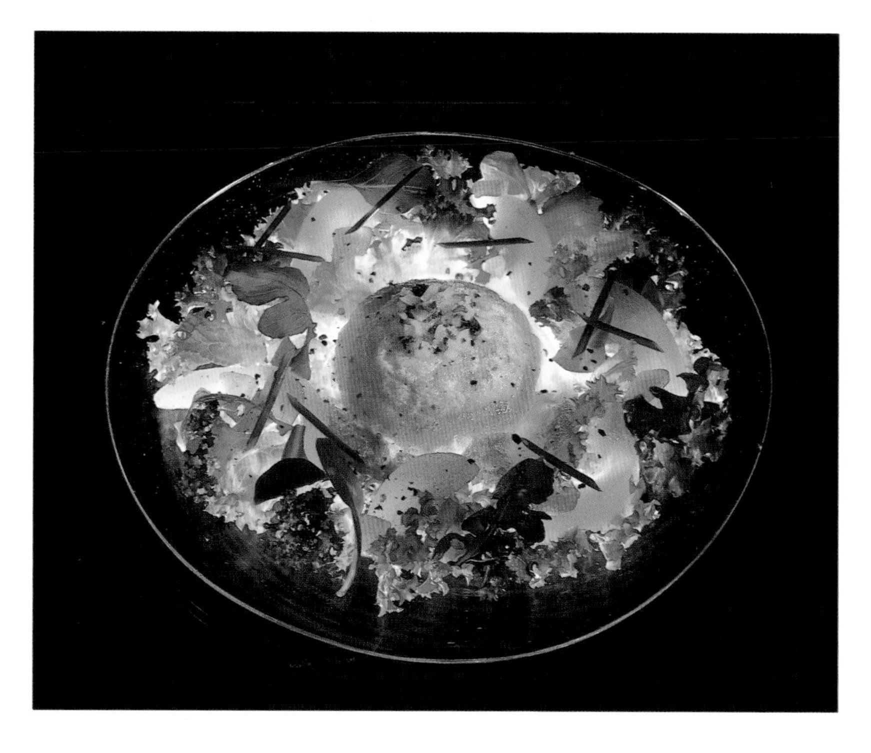

Nick Dolding

28/29 Great Sutton Street
London EC1V 0DS

Tel: 071 490 2454
Fax: 071 251 3843

Agents:
London
Sue Young
Tel: 071 262 0189
Fax: 071 262 2160

Hamburg
Marion Enste-Jaspers
Tel: 040 222 226
Fax: 040 221 062

MARKETING
MARKETING
MERCADEO

ARTWORK REFERENCES
REFERENCES D'ELEMENTS ARTISTIQUES
REFERENCIAS DEL ARTE FINAL

PRODUCT SPECIFICATION
SPECIFICATIONS DU PRODUIT
ESPECIFICACION DEL PRODUCTO

INTERNATIONAL ADVERTISING
PUBLICITE INTERNATIONALE
PUBLICIDAD INTERNACIONAL

208 Stuart Chorley

69 Lambeth Walk
London SE11 6DX

Tel: 071 793 0053
Fax: 071 582 2379

Malcolm Russell

Duthy Hall
Great Guildford Street
London SE1 0ES

Tel: 071 261 0360
Fax: 071 620 0602

Smosarski and Partners

Smosarski and Partners

Sears Davies

Smosarski and Partners

Howard Bartrop

56 Whitfield Street
London W1P 5RN

Tel: 071 637 4786

Represented by: Schelley Kiah
Tel: 071 351 0371
Fax: 071 352 6124

Recent clients include:
Kleenex, Mercury, Clarks Shoes, Hewlett Packard, Sensodyne, Courage, Marks & Spencer, Guinness, Jeyes, TSB and British Telecom.

Andrew Cameron

29 Waterside
44-48 Wharf Road
London N1 7SH

Tel/Fax: 071 608 0606

Still life
Studio
Location

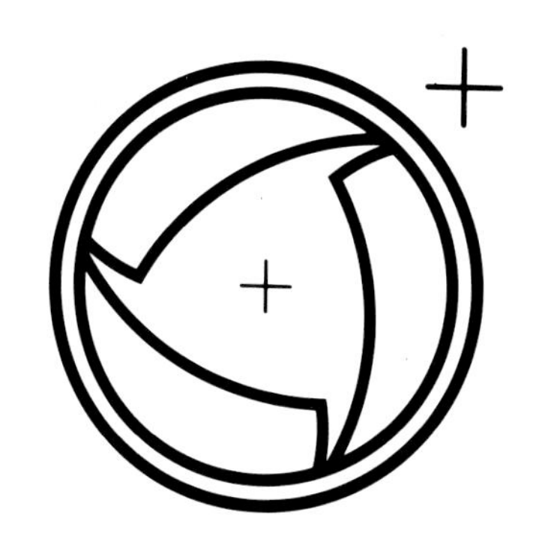

James Murphy

27 Swinton Street
London WC1X 9NW

Tel: 071 278 4770
Fax: 071 278 4581

Food

Ben Rice

1 Rushworth Studios
63 Webber Street
London SE1 0QW

Tel: 071 261 9753
Fax: 071 401 2206

Represented by: Suzanne Davies
No 5 Hillgate Street
London W8 7SP

Tel: 071 221 5623
Fax: 071 221 6212

214 Freddie Brazil

Tel: 071 494 4623
Fax: 071 287 1255

Representing
Martyn J Adelman
Christopher Joyce
Geoff Smyth
Graham Young

GEOFF SMYTH

TEL: 071- 831 3084 FAX: 071 287 1255

MARTYN J ADELMAN

TEL: 081 771 6669 FAX: 071 287 1255

CHRISTOPHER JOYCE

TEL: 071 287 6118 FAX: 071 287 1255

GRAHAM YOUNG

TEL: 071 240 9000   FAX: 071 928 8525

Barbara & Zafer Baran

Tel: 081 948 3050
071 627 4225

Abstract and experimental photography: still life, product, people, architectural, in colour and b/w.

Recent clients include: Andersen Consulting, British Telecom, Creative Circle, Decca, Dorling Kindersley, English National Opera, Forward Publishing, Gruppo Rinascente, Guinness, IBM, London Business School, Michael Conrad/Leo Burnett (Germany), Nationwide, Nat West, NEC, Our Price, Penguin, Redwood Publishing, Rutland Group, Scottish Television, Stanhope, 3i, United Airlines, United Distillers, Viking Books.

See also pp. 72/73

PARKER

220 **Gill Orsman**

The Tea Warehouse
10a Lant Street
London SE1 1QA

Tel/Fax: 071 378 1867
Pager: 0459 11 4680

Client: Laura Ashley

Andy Collison

75 Clarence Road
Teddington
Middlesex TW11 0BN

Tel/Fax: 081 943 1013
Studio Tel: 071 625 6844

Food offers the photographer an abundance of natural shapes, textures and colours to explore. Exploiting these qualities and stimulating the salivary glands is the challenge.

Jonathan Root

Units 51 & 52
50-56 Wharf Road
London N1 7SF

Tel: 071 250 1713
Fax: 071 250 3282

Agent: Claire Sparksman
Tel: 071 250 3282

Bare – Knuckle Boxer

Gus Filgate

Studio Six
The Peoples Hall
92-97 Freston Road
London W11 4BH

Tel: 071 229 6644

Represented by: Suzanne Davies
No 5 Hillgate Street
London W8 7SP

Tel: 071 221 5623
Fax: 071 221 6212

 The Peter Bailey Company

Tel: 071 935 2626
Fax: 071 935 7557

FIONA PRAGOFF

TELEPHONE 071 935 2626 FACSIMILE 071 935 7557

GULLACHSEN

LORENTZ GULLACHSEN

TELEPHONE 071 935 2626 FACSIMILE 071 935 7557

GULLACHSEN

LORENTZ GULLACHSEN

TELEPHONE 071 935 2626 FACSIMILE 071 9[illegible] 7557

JAN BALDWIN

TELEPHONE 071 935 2626 FACSIMILE 071 935 7557

TELEPHONE 071 935 2626 FACSIMILE 071 935 7557

MARTIN LANGFIELD

TELEPHONE 071 935 2626 FACSIMILE 071 935 7557

Liz Artindale

Tel: 081 674 4081

Specialises in Landscape, Architecture and People on location.

Clients include:
Northumbrian Water, South Bank Enterprises, Sampson Tyrrell, David Lock Design, Mc Ilroy Coates, BBC Books, Country Home & Interiors.

Tim Platt

12a Peacock Yard
London SE17 3LH

Tel: 071 703 2779
Fax: 071 701 0026

Inventive people orientated work, including fashion, portraits and accessories. Specialising in strong, vivid colour, classic black and white and creative 'effects' often achieved in camera. Wide experience of working in both advertising and design.

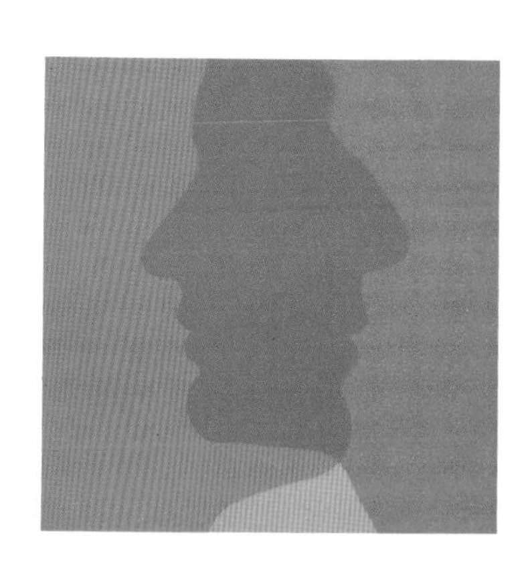

Boots Hosiery Packs (Lewis Moberly)

Martin Chaffer

Battersea Park Studios
2 Shuttleworth Road
London SW11 3EA

Tel: 071 223 7119
Fax: 071 924 2958

Martin specialises in roomsets and locations for brochures, advertising and editorial clients.
This page: one of a series of fourteen roomsets for the International Wool Secretariat's European promotion of carpets.
Opposite: small can also be beautiful! Promotional shot for Wood Bros 'Old Charm' furniture.

Exceptional studio facilities in Battersea enable us to handle every assignment efficiently and cost-effectively. We have 4000 sq ft of ground floor studios, free parking, on-site processing, and a long list of satisfied clients.

Steve Gale

Canalside Studios
2A Orsman Road
London N1 5QJ

Studio Tel: 071 729 3871
Fax: 071 729 1698
Mobile Tel: 0831 372198

Still-life
Property/Architecture
Corporate

Steve's large, well-equipped Studio is situated on the banks of the Regents Canal. It incorporates a very wide variety of props and has a Set-building facility on the premises.

Jonathan Knowles

37 Delaford Street
London SW6 7LT

Tel: 071 385 0188
Fax: 071 386 8785
Mobile: 0836 533933

Photographs below commissioned by the Quentin Bell Organisation for a corporate brochure for ADAS (a consultancy in food, farming, land & leisure).

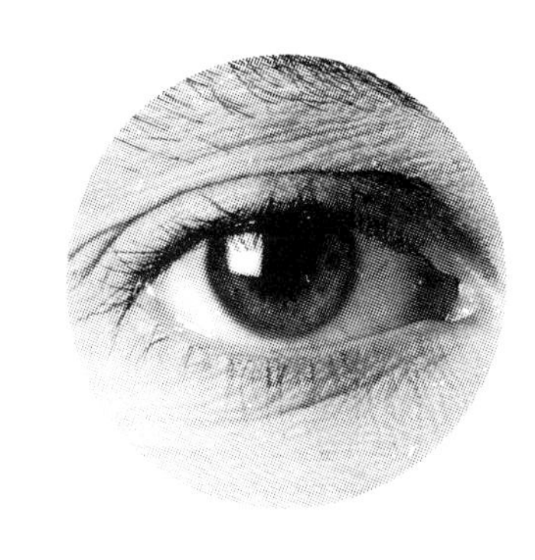

Julian Calder

2 Alma Studios
32 Stratford Road
Kensington
London W8 6QF

Tel: 071 937 3533
Fax: 071 938 2610
Mobile Tel: 0831 511640

Portraits of chairmen, directors, politicians, authors, artists and people at work worldwide.

The Board of Inchcape plc

Lord Jenkins: The cover of his autobiography

Sir Dirk Bogarde

Dye manufacture for Ciba-Geigy

Tea tasting at Tetleys for Allied-Lyons

Steve Lee

1 Rosoman Place
London EC1R 0YJ

Tel: 071 837 5204
Fax: 071 278 2507

Area of expertise:
Food and Still Life.
Location work undertaken.

The Studio consists of a fully equipped modern kitchen and props area.

Barry Meekums

1 Marylebone Mews
New Cavendish Street
London W1M 7LF

Tel: 071 487 5233

Mark Wragg

Gate Studios
Walkers Place
London SW15

Tel: 081 780 1186
Fax: 081 789 0140
Mobile Tel: 0836 238225

CASIO
FEED

The Royal Bank of Scotland
BANCO DE SANTANDER
RATP

244 **Peter Beavis**

Flat 3
100 Brondesbury Villas
London NW6 6AD

Tel: 071 624 4884
Fax: 071 625 4884
Mobile Tel: 0860 758861

Studio/Location.

Clients include: British Airways
National Grid, British Gas, Bayer, BP, DHL,
American Express, TSB, Bristol & West, ICL,
Mercury Communications, AGFA, Rank Xerox,
Air Canada, British Telecom.

246 Dean Marsh

19 Vardens Road
London SW11 1RQ

Tel: 071 223 3778

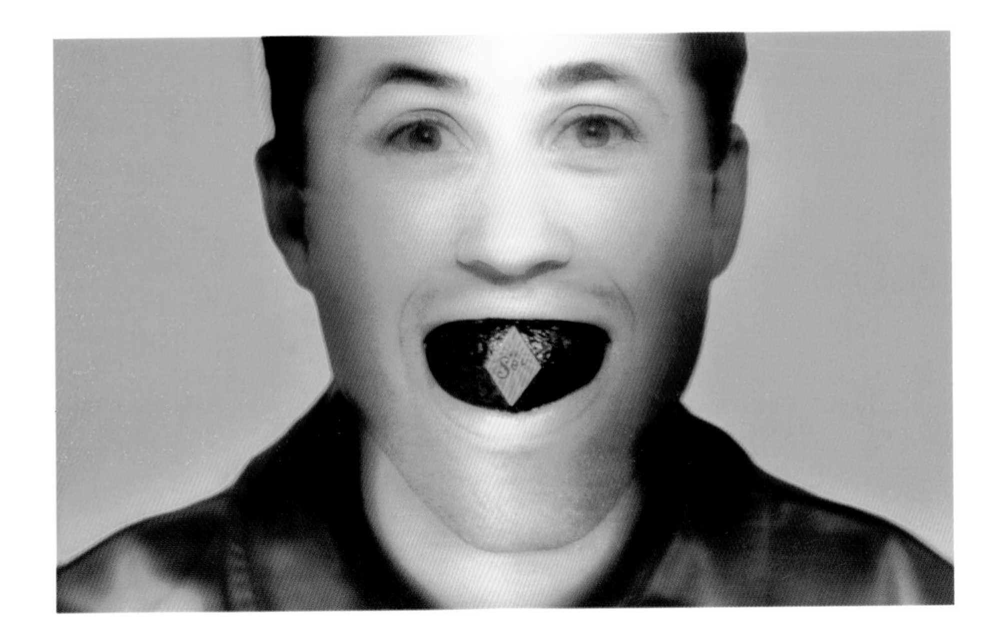

David Chambers

14a Hesper Mews
London SW5 0HH

Tel: 071 373 3183
Fax: 071 373 9313

Simon Battensby

Studio 28 Waterside
44-48 Wharf Road
London N1 7SH

Tel: 071 251 4223
Fax: 071 250 0044
Mobile Tel: 0850 210303

Ray Moller

West Point
Unit GD
36-37 Warple Way
London W3 0RX

Tel: 081 743 7679
Fax: 081 743 7751

Steve Jukes

Tel: 081 594 8262
Fax: 081 594 3313

Agent: Julian Cotton
12 Thorton Place
off York Street
London W1H 1FL

Tel: 071 486 3307
Fax: 071 486 6565

Specialist Studio Car Photographer

Paul Webster

2C MacFarlane Road
London W12 7JY

Tel: 081 749 0264

Food and Drink for clients including: Marks & Spencer, Safeways (New Ice Cream Range), Tesco, Asda, Sainsbury's, Heinz, Nestle, Batchelors, Weetabix (Alpen & cereals), Ross Youngs, Masterfoods, Brooke Bond and many others.

Still life for Mappin & Webb, Carvela, Lentheric, Kurt Geiger, Glade, Prestons (jewellery), Lloyds Bank and many more.

Portfolio

For Ziggurat Design. Client: Heinz.

For Clark & Taylor Advertising. Client: Ross Youngs.

Graham Precey

Studio 4
Kingsley House
Avonmore Place
London W14 8RY

Tel: 071 603 2690
Fax: 071 602 8616

Still Life and food photography for advertising and design in both the UK and Europe.

256 Ian Fraser

Fraser Studios
Unit 15/4 Botley Works
Botley
Oxford OX2 0LX

Tel: 0865 250088
Fax: 0865 791402

FRASER

Frederique Lefort

21 Brewster Gardens
North Kensington
London W10 6AQ

Tel: 081 968 7250
Mobile Tel: 0831 514401
Paris Tel: 49 30 97 74

Simon Wood

4 Murray Street
Camden
London NW1 9RE

Tel: 071 482 2173

People
Locations
Worldwide

Paul Venning

1 Stable Yard
Danemere Street
London SW15 1LT

Tel: 081 780 0442
Fax: 081 785 7017

Unisys/H.D.&A.

Unisys/H.D.&A.

I.B.M./The Frameworks

Telegraph Colour Library

Ed Pritchard

The Studio
144 Shaftesbury Avenue
Covent Garden
London WC2H 8HL

Tel: 071 836 0512
Fax: 071 839 7509

Photography worldwide for advertising and corporate clients.
Studio photography in Central London.
Stock available via TSW.

Pete Seaward

Holborn Studios
49 Eagle Wharf Road
London N1 7ED

Tel: 071 608 3064

Agent: Sue Allatt
Tel: 071 608 3064

264 **Alistair Morrison**

30c Great Sutton Street
London EC1

Tel: 071 608 3064

Agent: Sue Allatt
Tel: 071 608 3064

Tif Hunter

18a Wilds Rents
London SE1 4QG

Tel: 071 403 8879
Fax: 071 403 8881

Agent: Sue Allatt

Tel: 071 608 3064
Mobile Tel: 0860 224735
Fax: 071 250 0181

Jonathon Davis Design

Citygate Marketing

Alan Newnham

Unit 2
40-48 Bromell's Road
Clapham Common
London SW4 0BG

Tel: 071 498 2399
Fax: 071 498 2238

Richard Dean

Tel: 071 354 3755
Mobile Tel: 0831 420156

David Kelly

Cassidy Road
London SW6 5QH

Tel: 071 736 6205
Fax: 071 384 2240

Benedict Campbell

Fraser Studios
Unit 15/4 Botley Works
Botley
Oxford OX2 0LX

Tel: 0865 250088
Fax: 0865 791402

Malcolm Piers

Agent: Geoff Elliott

73 St. John Street
London EC1M 4AR

Tel: 071 490 7308

GEOFF ELLIOTT
TEL 081 444 0665
FAX 081 883 3895

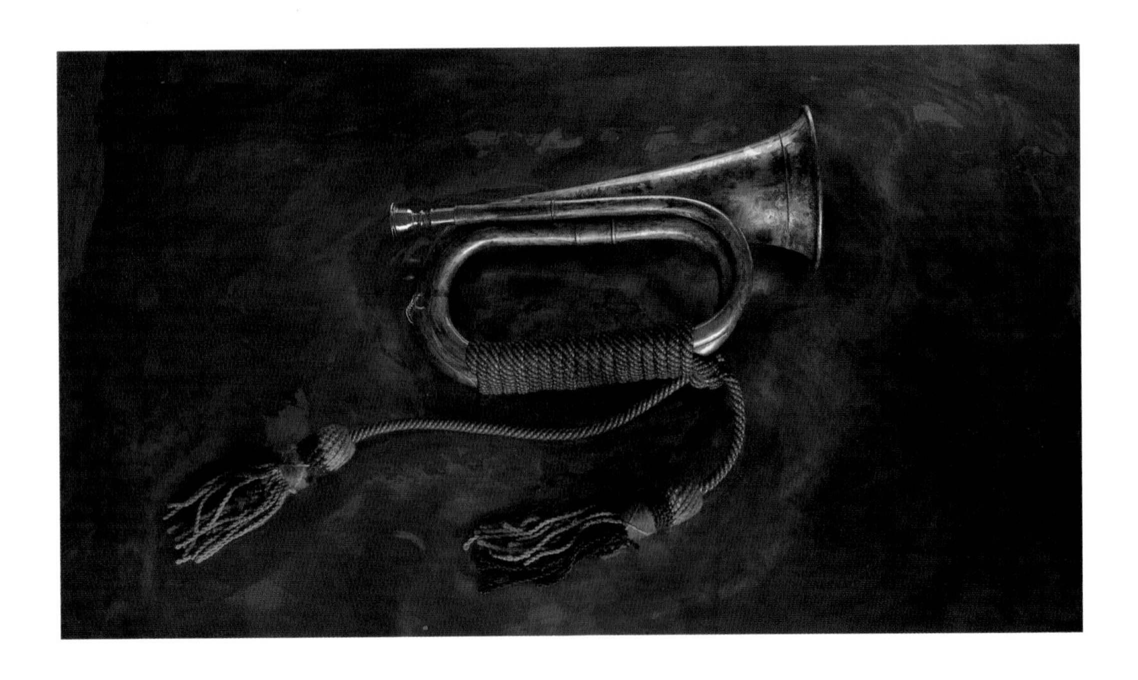

Steve Slayford

The Old House
Headley
Epsom
Surrey KT18 6JS

Tel: 0372 363436
Mobile Tel: 0836 537961

Represented by: Geoff Elliott
Tel: 081 444 0665

Prefers people.

English Apple Association

Bass Brewers

Colin Thomas

56 Whitfield Street
London W1P 5RN

Tel: 071 637 4786/0551
Fax: 071 323 5512

Agent: Geoff Elliott
Tel: 081 444 0665
Fax: 081 883 3895

Stephen Coe

Studio
6 Windmill Street
London W1P 1HF

Tel: 071 580 1703

38A Denning Road
London NW3 1SU
Tel: 071 431 1044
Fax: 071 435 4546

Advertising , Corporate & Editorial,
Portrait & People with Product, on
Location or Studio (with Darkroom).
Extensive Client List & Awards.
Work accepted AFAEP Awards '89 & '90.
D&AD Silver Awards & still hoping!
I enjoy making pictures which truly
express feelings & communicate.
I make my own prints - notably
for a growing number of collectors.
Call me, I look forward to your project.

Martin Barraud

160-162 Old South Lambeth Road
London SW8 1XX

Tel: 071 735 7737
Fax: 071 793 7361

Simon Murrell

Margrave Studios
25 Heathmans Road
London SW6 4TJ

Tel: 071 736 7200
Fax: 071 371 0138

Stephen Piotrowski

28-29 Great Sutton Street
London EC1V 0DS

Tel: 071 253 0169
Fax: 071 251 3843

David Timmis

50a Rosebery Avenue
London EC1R 4RP

Tel: 071 833 4482

Paddy Eckersley

90 Banner Street
London EC1Y 8JU

Tel: 071 606 1622
Fax: 071 490 2373

Rob Brown

Unit 2
18-22 Barnsbury Street
London N1 1PN

Tel: 071 354 3713
Fax: 071 704 1234
Pager: 081 884 3344 Code 3333

People, Architecture and Interiors,
UK and abroad.

For corporate brochures, annual reports, letting brochures & advertising.

To see my portfolio or discuss your photographic needs ring for a chat.

Top left clockwise:
Business Design Group.
Corporation of London.
Kajima UK
Holmes & Marchant for Lovells.

Right top: Carré Noir
Bottom: Félix Construction sa

Jim Forrest

82 Chestnut Grove
London SW12 8JJ

Tel: 081 673 0936
Fax: 081 675 0091
Mobile Tel: 0836 738841

FIRE

Connections
Posting box
First class
Mail only
Royal Mail Travelling Post Office

Derek Seaward

2-4 Vestry Street
London N1 7RE

Tel: 071 253 3109
Fax: 071 490 1317

New York Agent: Julia Kirk
Tel: 010 212 420 1794

Peter Beavis

Flat 3
100 Brondesbury Villas
London NW6 6AD

Tel: 071 624 4884
Fax: 071 625 4884
Mobile Tel: 0860 758861

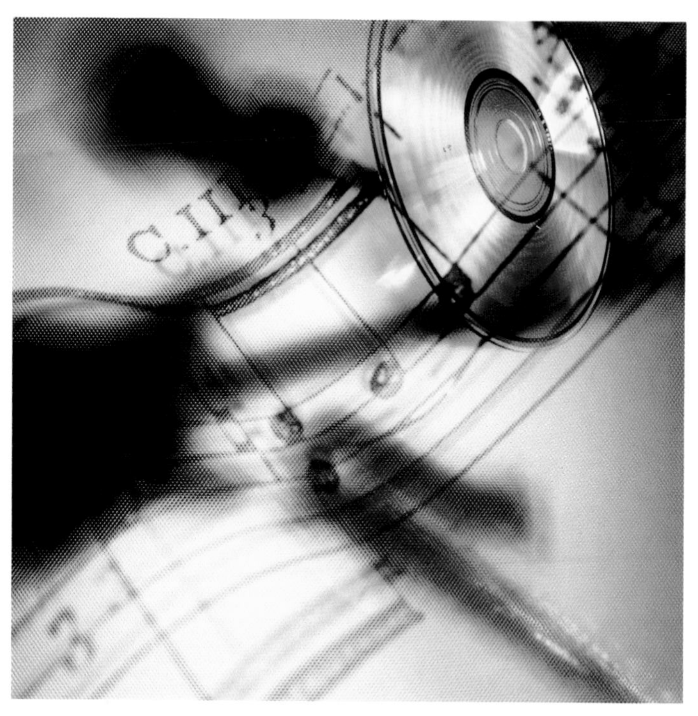

Trevor Hurst

Unit 301
203-213 Mare Street
Hackney
London E8 3QE

Tel: 081 533 5635
Fax: 081 533 5637
Pager: 081 528 9001 No. 804298

Debi Treloar

92 Brondesbury Road
London NW6 6RX

Tel: 071 328 0809
Fax: 071 328 0809

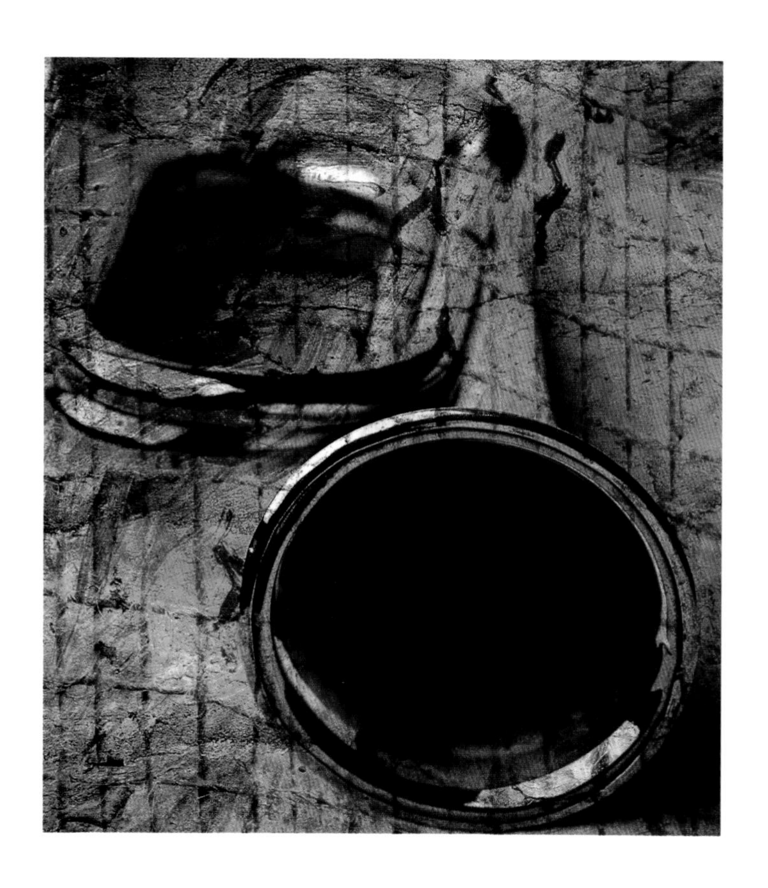

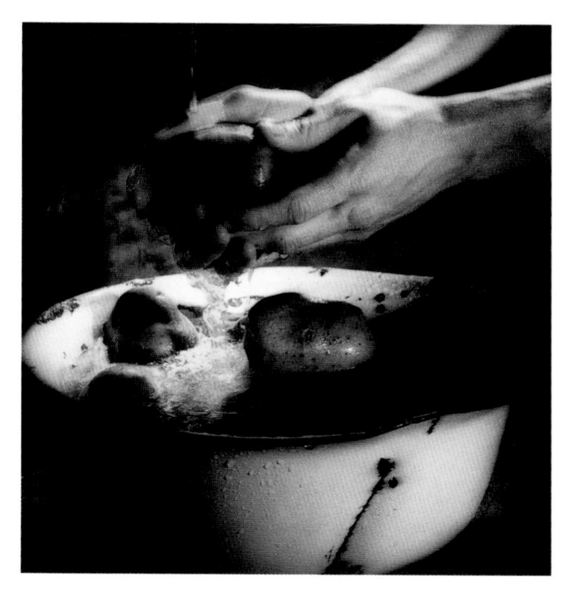

Andy Seymour

82 Princedale Road
Holland Park
London W11 4NL

Tel: 071 221 2021
Fax: 071 792 0702

Food
Still Life
Children

Carol Sharp

2-4 Vestry Street
London N1 7RE

Tel: 071 490 1347

From her design background Carol is inspired by shapes and colours, shown in her meticulous arrangements of food and still life.

Tim Wren

Tel: 081 673 9368
Mobile Tel: 0860 786228

Agent: Julian Cotton
Tel: 071 486 3307
Fax: 071 486 6565

Clients:
Land Rover UK
Chriysler Jeep
Rolls Royce Bentley
VW Audi UK
Honda UK
Sunday Times Magazine
Car Magazine
Automobile USA
Car Japan

Mike Laye

252 Belsize Road
London NW6 4BT

Tel: 071 328 0312
Fax: 071 372 0043
Mobile Tel: 0831 096822
24 hour word pager: 081 884 3344 ID-F951

Advertising, editorial and corporate: portraits and still-life of every description on formats from 35mm to 10 x 8, with a unique knowledge of image manipulation, both conventional and electronic, having worked on all the major computer systems. Clients include: American Express, Blue Circle, CGI, Channel Four, Design Department, Dew Rogerson, Guinness, Gestetner, Harvey Nichols, Johnson Mathey, KwikSave, Lloyds, Logica, Lotus Magazine, MacWorld, Observer Magazine, Pontins, Publitek, Sunday Times Magazine, Stocks Austin Sice, Sygma, Telegraph Weekend Magazine, Tesco, Vanity Fair.

M. R. RAMPRAKASH
(MIDDLESEX)

Malcolm Hulme

Unit 1
6A Pratt Street
Camden
London NW1 0LT

Tel: 071 388 7314
Fax: 071 387 4694
Mobile Tel: 0836 274790

Represented by: Lincoln & Mavolwane

Tel: 071 326 1711
Fax: 071 326 1711

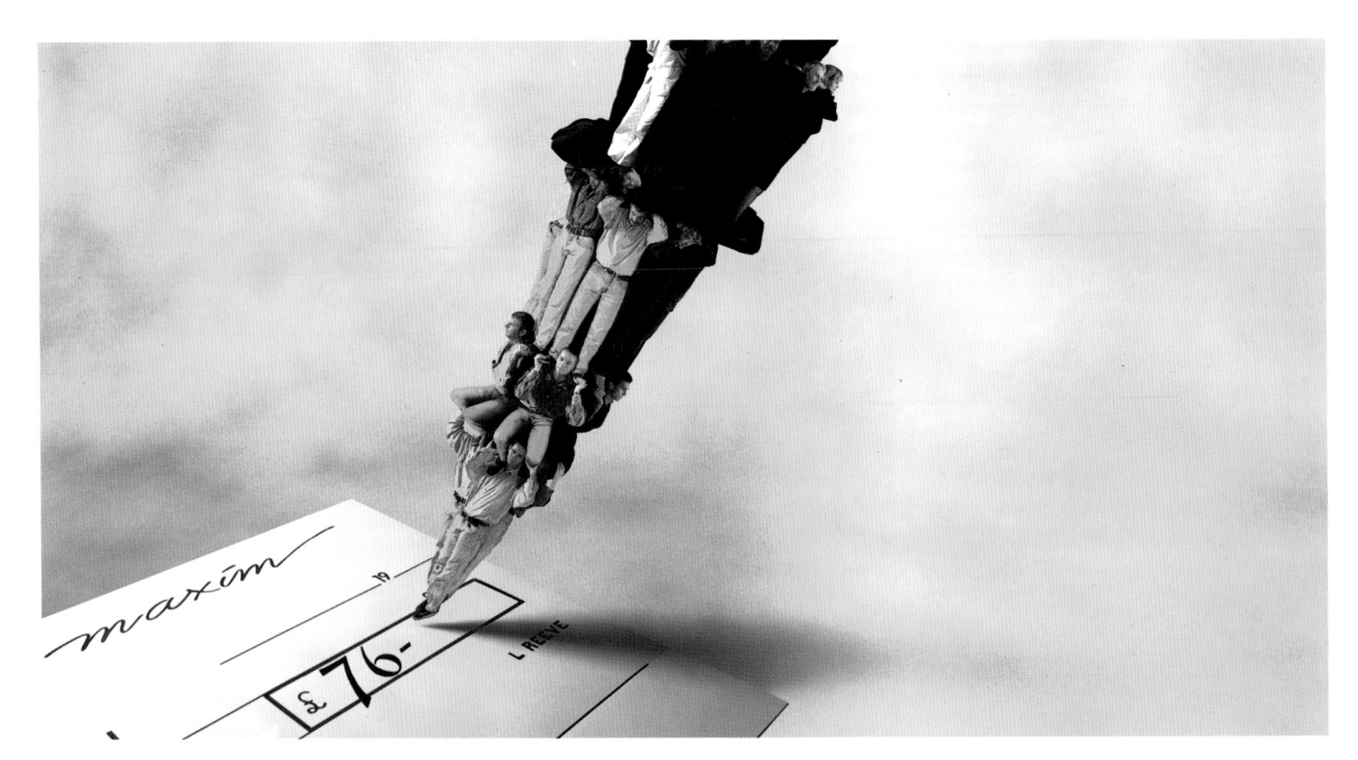

Sara Taylor

160-162 Old South Lambeth Road
London SW8 1XX

Tel: 071 735 7737
Fax: 071 793 7361

Represented by Europe Unlimited
Tel: 071 267 6862
Fax: 071 485 9423

Client: Elle magazine

David Bramley

Tel: 081 340 1238

Represented by:
Julian Cotton
Tel 071 486 3307

People photography for advertising and annual reports.

Compaq Computers Ogilvy & Mather

Royal Mail

Cornhill Insurance

James Jackson

2a Greenside Road
Sheperds Bush
London W12 9JQ
Tel: 081 749 7145
Fax: 081 743 3387

Represented by: Julian Cotton
12 Thornton Place, London W1H 1FL
Tel: 071 486 3307
Fax: 071 486 6565

James Jackson is best known for his creative food photography, having specialised in this field for many years. In his large, well equipped, Shepherds Bush studio he also shoots roomsets and more recently has developed a unique multi-image technique.

In the past year James has worked for such clients as Marks & Spencer, Waitrose, Safeway, Tesco, Sommerfield, British Telecom, The Dutch Dairy Bureau, Sanderson, The Pentos Group and Boots.

Malcolm Leyland

Unit 1
St. James's Mews
276 St. James's Road
London SE1 5JX

Tel: 071 378 7544
Mobile Tel: 0831 879764

Menu
Leek and Watercress Soup
Trio of Smoked Fish
Linguini with Cream and Oyster Mushrooms
Galia Melon with Seasonal Fruits
Pâté of Chicken Livers with Cumberland Sauce
Fried Avocado with Crab
Scottish Smoked Salmon
Roast Sirloin of Aberdeen Angus
Shallow Fried Calves Liver with Bacon and Onion
Lamb Sauté Bourguignon
Grilled Pork Chop with Cox's Apple
Casserole of Seafood Pernod Sauce and Braised Rice
Baked Aubergine with a Tomato and Basil Sauce
Platter of Assorted Cold Meats
Selection of Fresh Vegetables
English and Continental
Cheeses

300 Jonathan Knowles

37 Delaford Street
London SW6 7LT

Tel: 071 385 0188
Fax: 071 386 8785
Mobile: 0836 533933

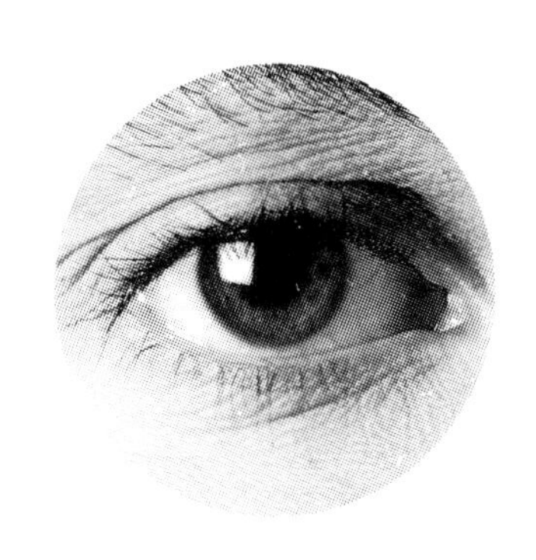

Earl Beesley ABIPP

Agent: Janice Beesley

E.J. Associates
P.O. Box 335
West Drayton
Middlesex UB7 7PJ

Tel: 0895 447473
Mobile Tel: 0860 794360

Based conveniently near Heathrow Airport and within twenty minutes of the West End. Earl Beesley specialises in Architectural, Landscape, Interiors, Cookery, Theatre, and Ariel photography. Working both in the studio and on location at home and abroad, for the Advertising, Editorial, Tourism and Corporate markets.

Jay Myrdal

Jam Studios
11 London Mews
Paddington
London W2 1HY

Tel: 071 262 7441
Fax: 071 262 7476

BONUS 90
10 MONTHS
8 MONTHS
6 MONTHS

Neal Wilson

33 Great Sutton Street
London EC1V 0DX

Tel: 071 253 7491
Fax: 071 490 2558

Clients include:
Abbey National, Midland, Euro-Tunnel, Fisons, IBM, ICL, LWT, Mercantile Credit, Mercury, Northumbria Water, Post Office, PowerGen, Smith & Nephew, Securicor, Sun Life, Enterprise Oil, Plessey, BUPA and British Gas.

James Meyer

Wells Street Studios
70 Wells Street
London W1P 3RD

Tel: 071 637 8209

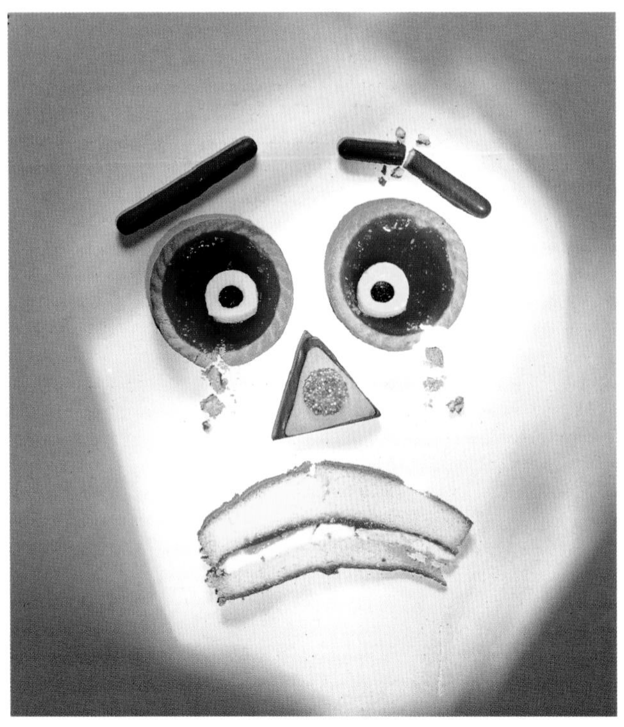

Bob Komar

The Soap Factory
9 Park Hill
London SW4 9NS

Tel: +44 71 622 3242
Fax: +44 71 498 6445

.... a few of my favourite things.

Patrick Blake

8 Chippenham Mews
London W9 2AW

Tel: 071 286 5148

Pans
Prawns
Other things too.

Johnny Boylan

The Soap Factory
No. 9 Park Hill
London SW4 9NS

Tel: 071 622 1214
Fax: 071 498 6445

"Still here,
Still photographing people."

Tim Hazael

25 Astwood Mews
South Kensington
London SW7 4DE

Tel: 071 370 6137
Fax: 071 373 9665

Work covers general still life, food, special effects and abstract, people, landscapes and corporate photography, for use in advertising, packaging, brochures and annual reports.
Superb studio and kitchen facilities with own black and white printing and hand colouring an additional speciality, (as shown here).
Contact direct for portfolio.

Photograph below: A.D. Michele Chaffe / GA International / SmithKline Beecham.
Opposite top left: Loranjo Associates / Portuguese cork.
Top right: Paper Moon Ltd / London Transport Advertising.
Bottom left: A.D. Michele Chaffe / GA International / Eli Lilley Ltd.
Bottom right: A.D. Ian Scott / Arc Advertising Ltd / The Times.

70 cl
12% Vol.

Chris Bell

Unit 8 Cedar Way
Elm Village Industrial Estate
Camley Street
London NW1 0PD

Tel: 071 388 4500
Fax: 071 388 4119
Mobile Tel: 0850 652911

It's both possible and affordable with no nonsense, common sense in-camera photography.

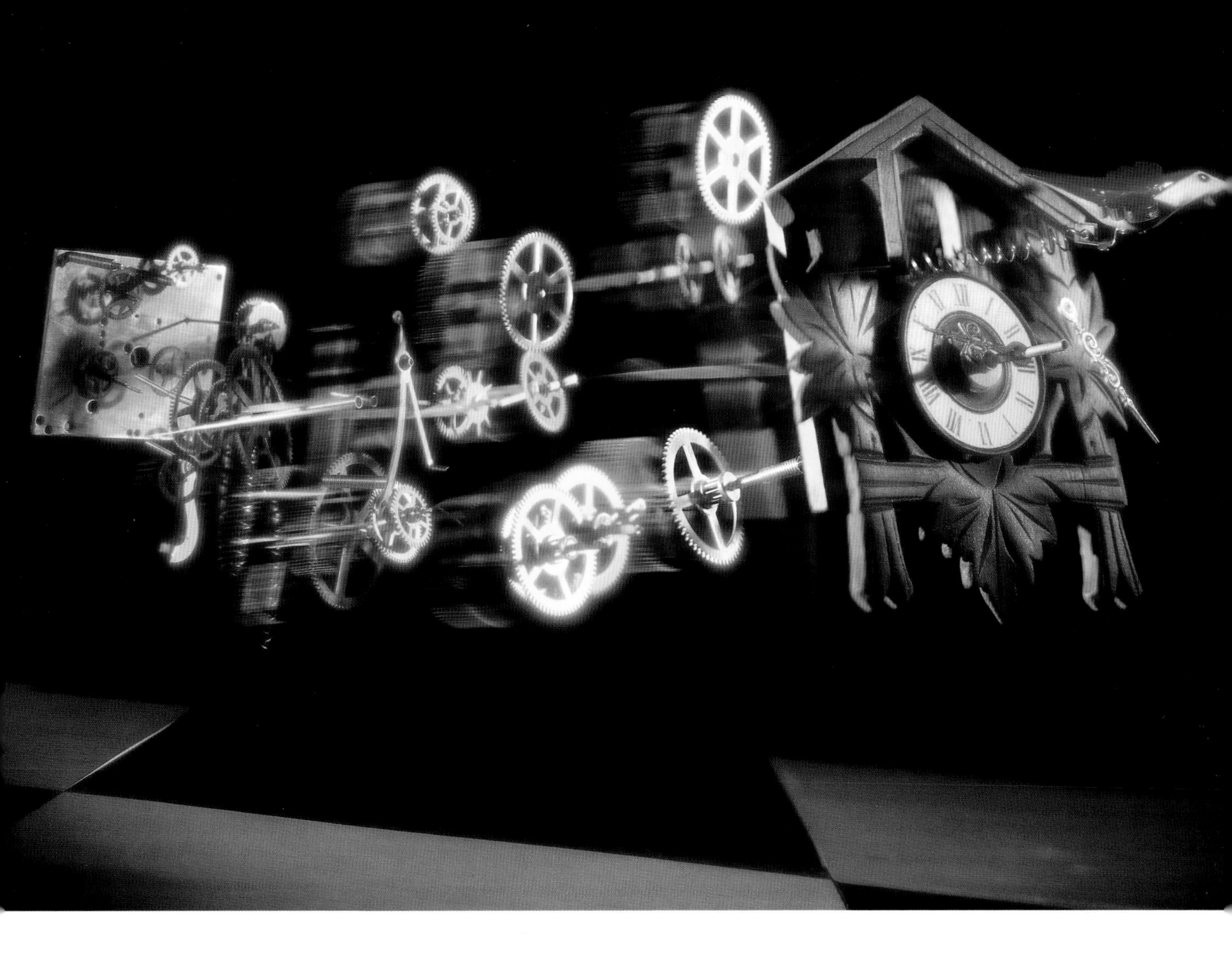

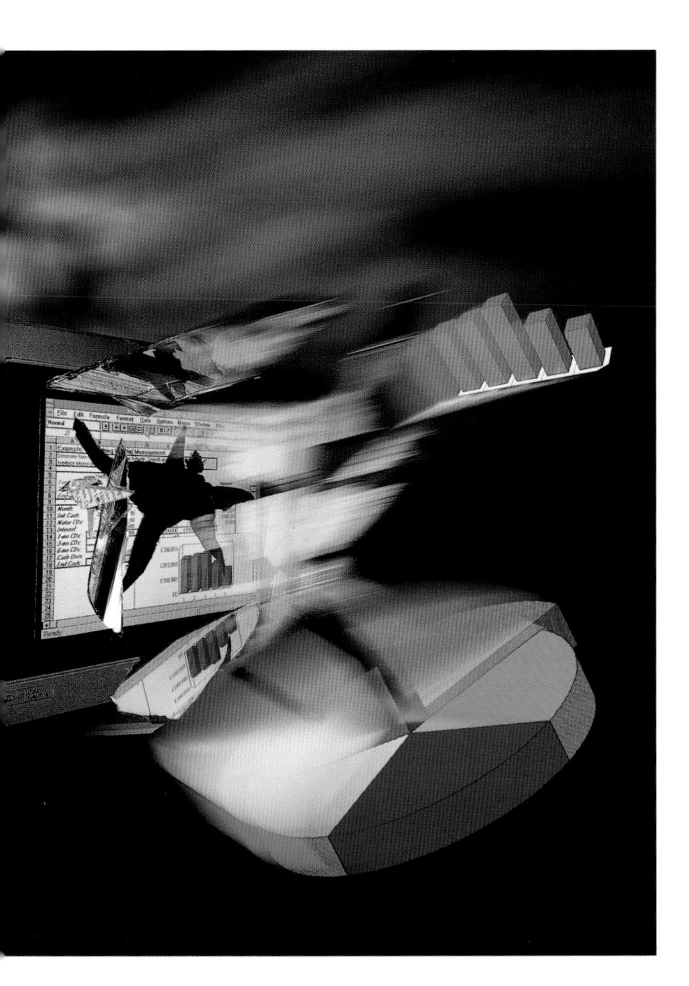

Michael Dunning

18 West Central Street
London WC1A 1JJ

Tel: 071 836 3110
Fax: 071 240 3992

Below:
Client: John Menzies
Agency: Oliver & Co.
A.D: Alastair Brown

Opposite:
Client: Tesco
Agency: Charles Barker
A.D: Andy Reddon

Marie-Louise Avery

7 Camden Terrace
London NW1 9BP

Tel: 071 267 1393
Mobile Tel: 0860 436668

My subjects range from food to fashion, via still life, interiors and children. Having been a designer and then Art Director of Good Housekeeping I particularly enjoy jobs where I can respond with a high level of creative input and can use my styling skills and contacts.
Clients include: Asda, Conran Octopus, Country Living, Country Homes & Interiors, Ebury Press, Esquire, Good Housekeeping, House Beautiful, National Dairy Council, Options, Parents, Period Living, Salamander, She, Taste, Tesco, VandenBurg Associates, Weidenfeld.

Dale Durfee

The Gallery
Unit 2
38 St. Oswalds Place
London SE11 5JE

Tel: 071 735 8766

Susan Ford
European Agent
071-603 6320

Stock images – Tony Stone Worldwide

Children, people and fashion photography.
Studio and location.

Guy Ryecart

20 Wilbury Grove
Hove
East Sussex BN3 3JQ

Tel: 0273 204371
Fax: 0273 329786
Mobile Tel: 0836 237761

During the last year clients have included:

Dorling Kindersley
Griffin Factors
Johnson & Johnson Critikon
3M
Neutrogena
The Parker Pen Co.
Renault
The Royal Mail

Model Maker: **MARK JAMIESON**

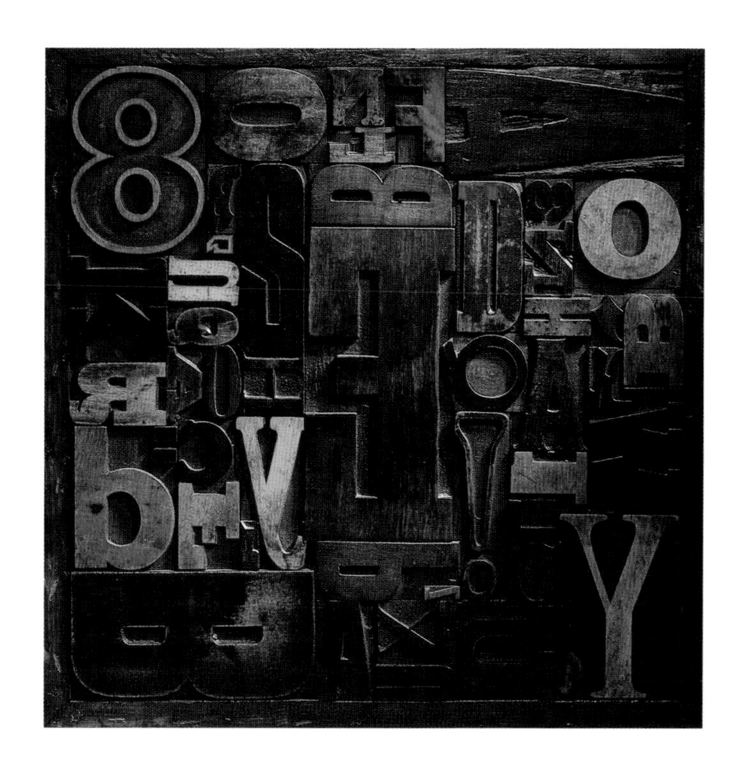

Brian Phipps

Peregrine House
Enborne Street
Newbury
Berkshire RG14 6RP

Tel: 0635 42585
Tel: 071 386 9428
Fax: 0635 528775

Now working from a large, well equipped Studio in the countryside near Newbury as well as a base in London.
Please telephone for Brochure and Video or Portfolio.

Heritage

Locktite

'W

nnah

Southern Wines

324 **Geoff Smith**

The Old School
No. 1 Thirsk Street
Ardwick Green
Manchester M12 6HP

Tel: 061 273 7489
Fax: 061 274 3449

Emma Parker

Agent: Début Art

52 Barbauld Road
London N16 0ST

Tel: 071 254 2856
Fax: 071 241 6049

Clients include: IBM, ICL, Fletcher King Property Division, Asda, Crookes Healthcare, Peaudouce, Vogue UK, Vogue Germany, Waterstones, New Scientist, Penguin Publishing, Viking Publishing, Harper Collins Publishing, Jonathan Cape Publishing, XYZ Magazine, Dorling Kindersley.

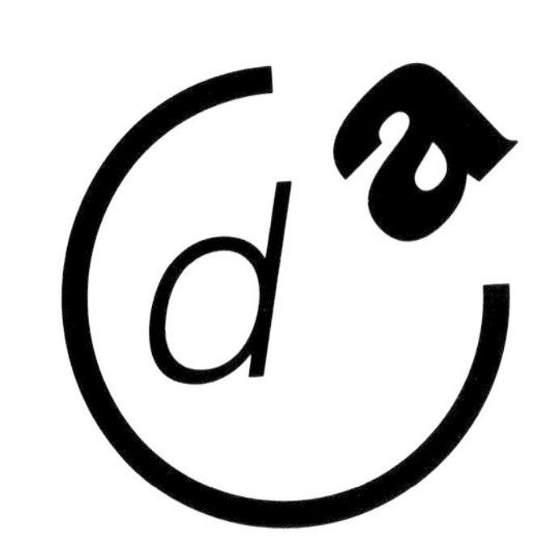

Self-initiated

Commissioned by XYZ Magazine

Commissioned by Fletcher King for cover of a property brochure

Sanders

Sanders Nicolson and Associates
Resolution House
19 Perseverance Works
38 Kingsland Road
London E2 8DD

Tel: 071 739 6987
Fax: 071 729 4056

Shoots: Fashion, Beauty,
Lifestyle and Landscape

Will White

83-93 Shepperton Road
London N1 3DF

Tel: 071 226 4811
Fax: 071 226 9810

Nick Carman

32 Great Sutton Street
London EC1V 0DX

Tel: 071 253 2863
Fax: 071 250 3375

Areas of expertise:
Food Specialist

Clients include:
Sainsbury, Tesco, Gateway, Mars,
Lyons, Findus, Allied Bakeries,
Del Monte, Nestle, Heinz.

Michael Crockett

29 Westover Road
London SW18 2RE

Tel: 081 874 7156

Life style.
Interiors.
Room sets.

Laura Ashley

Romilly Lockyer

Tel/Fax: 081 399 1041

People, Places and Still Life
UK and abroad, location and studio.

Above all, images expressing life
and movement.

332 Adrian Mott Photography

Mill House
Chapel Place
Rivington Street
London EC2A 3DQ

Tel: 071 729 5910
Fax: 071 729 2386

Rob Mitchell

Home Farm Studio
Shere Road
Albury
Surrey GU5 9BL

Tel: 048641 2655
Fax: 048641 3703

Clients include: Proctor & Gamble – Dulux – Birdseye Walls – RAC – London City Airport – Thorn Securities – Seiko – Continental Airlines – BMW – Colgate Palmolive – Sunday Times.

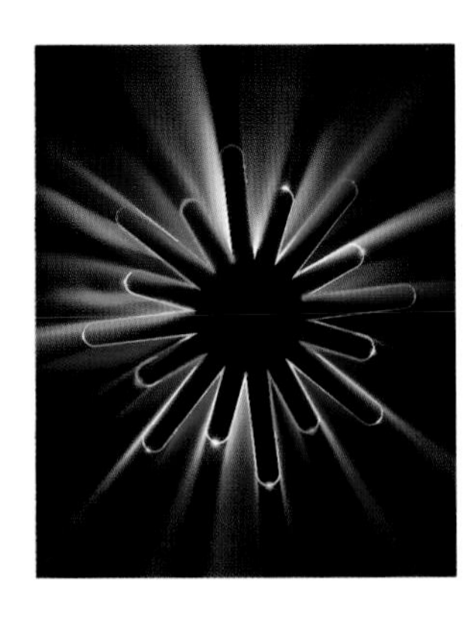

Andrew Putler
Jo Putler

46 Highbury Hill
London N5 1AP

Tel: 071 226 9911
Fax: 071 354 8503
Mobile Tel: 0836 283284

336 David Kampfner

69 Briarwood Road
London SW4 9PJ

Tel/Fax: 071 498 0868
Mobile Tel: 0836 231347

Represented by: Emma Beaugearde
Tel: 071 226 4354

People
Locations

UK Foreign Office — *Delhi*

Prague

Tim Bowden

2nd Floor
65-69 East Road
London N1 6AH

Tel: 071 490 3500
Fax: 071 490 3500
Mobile Tel: 0831 397096

Still Life
Food
People

Hugh Burden

3 The Stoneyard
Ninian Park Road
Cardiff CF1 8HE

Tel: 0222 225679
Fax: 0222 394804

Represented by:
Margaret Davies/V.I.P.
Tel: 0222 374301

Shoots in the studio and on location.
Member AFAEP

Hugh
Burden

Jon Stigner

Hoxton Towers
51 Hoxton Square
London N1 6PB

Tel/Fax: 071 613 0603

Still life, portraits and location work.
Colour and monochrome.

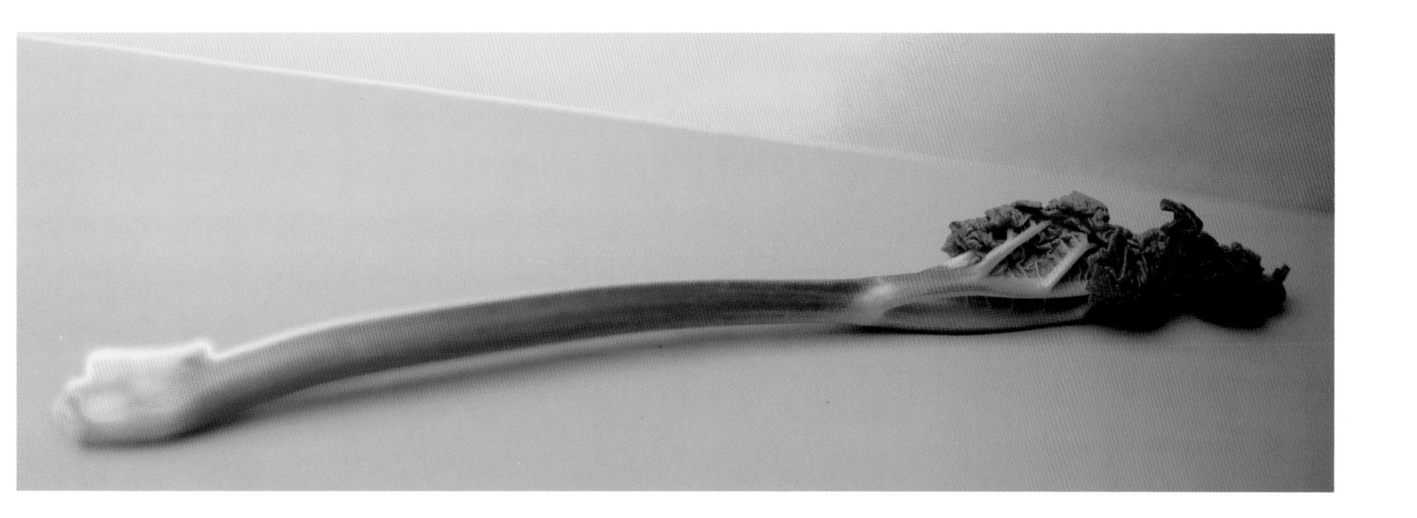

340 David Ash

Shaftesbury House
13-14 Hoxton Market
Coronet Street
London N1 6HG

Tel: 071 739 0990
Fax: 071 739 2321

Clients include: AB Littleman, Britvic, Enterprise Oil, KP, Marks & Spencer, Nat West, Pepsi, 7 Up, Mr Wobbler, Stuart Adams, Glaxo, James Daniels, Tiffany Sharwoods, Minale Tattersfield, Cooper Rose, SHE Magazine, Nelson Books, Aricot Vert Design.

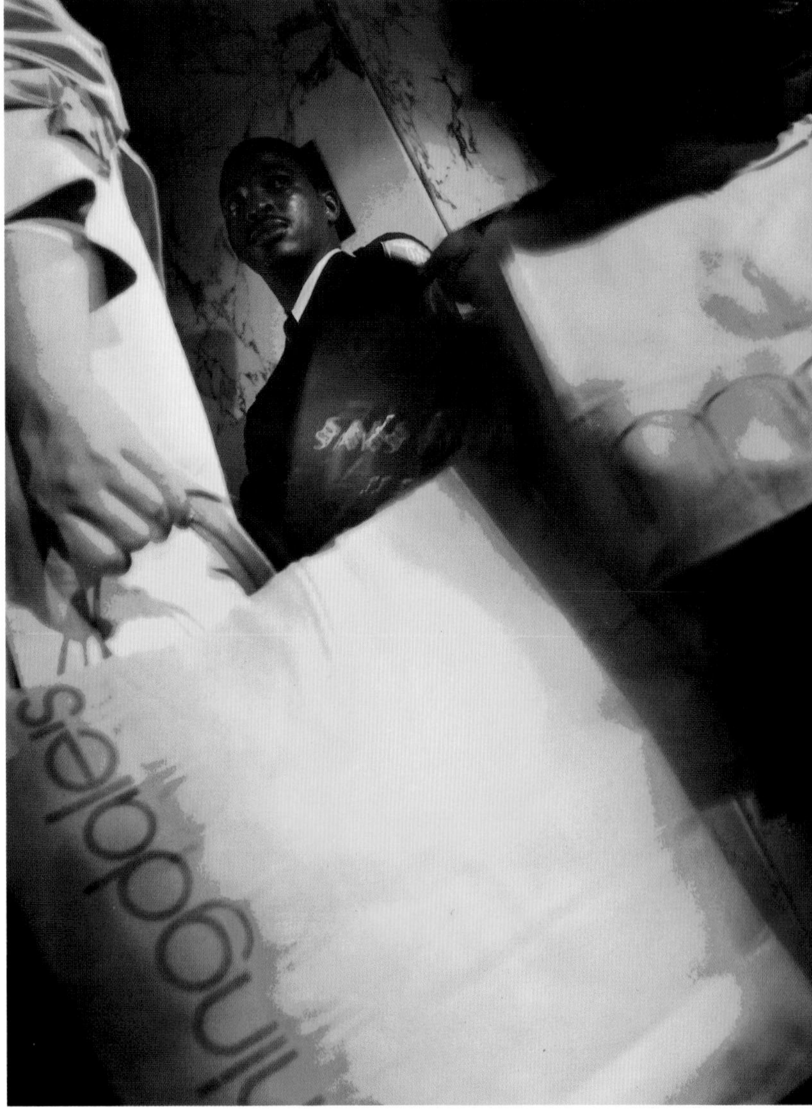

VIA AIR MAIL

Barry Jell

Barry Jell Productions
Bishops Hall
8 Ayres Street
London SE1 1ES

Agent: Su Turner
Fax/Tel: 071 407 2158
Mobile Tel: 0831 137308

Studio and location worldwide.

FLH 548C

Graham Oliver and Eric Murphy

Level 2
BI House
Carliol Square
Newcastle Upon Tyne NE1 6UF

Tel: 091 261 2612
Fax: 091 230 3963

Q. Knock Knock
A. Who's there?
R. Some Photographer's from Newcastle who want to show you their book.
A. Go Away.

Nick Bailey

33A Shacklewell Street
London E2 7EG

Tel: 071 729 9986
Mobile Tel: 0831 308713

Still life
Food
Advertising &
Design.

Scenic Artwork by Chris Brown

The Image Bank

7 Langley Street
London WC2H 9JA

Tel: 071 240 9621
Fax: 071 831 1489
Manchester Tel: 061 236 9226

The Image Bank is the world's leading photo library. And that's due in no small part to the fact we represent the work of the world's best photographers.
Outstanding talents like Jody Dole, Hans Neleman, Bob Elsdale and Paul Biddle supply us with some of the most dramatic and exciting photography available today. It's work that defies anyone's traditional misconceptions of library images and signifies a brand new era for the industry. Call us if you'd like to see more.

THE WORLD'S BEST PHOTOGRAPHERS

THE IMAGE BANK.

BOB ELSDALE

JODY DOLE

HANS NELEMAN

STOMACH
PANCREAS
SMALL INTESTINE
CAECUM
RECTUM

British Association of Picture Libraries and Agencies

13 Woodberry Crescent
Muswell Hill
London N10 1PJ
Telephone: 081 444 7913
Fax: 081 883 9215

The 1992/3 Directory of the British Association of Picture Libraries and Agencies gives access to over 250 million pictures from over three hundred libraries and agencies, some very large and some very small. A description of each member library with details of how to make contact, is followed by a subject index of specialist collections and a number of easy to use charts to enable users to discover easily, which library or agency holds the type of material required.

Using this Directory
Quantity Under each entry in the alphabetical listings is a line giving additional information which may be of some use to picture users. The first item, Quantity, gives some idea of the size of each library; under 10,000 images *, 10,000 – 75,000 images **, 75,000 – 250,000 images *** and over 250,000 images ****. The size of a library is no indication of the quality of the collection and for specialist material a small library may be the only source.

Formats
The most common formats you are likely to come across when getting material from a library are; S, normally 35mm; M, normally material shot on 120 film such as 6 x 4.5cm, 6 x 6cm and 6 x 7cm; L, material shot on 5 x 4ins or larger. When viewing large format transparencies you should note that if you hold the image with the notches at the top, they should always be in the left hand corner.

Colour
Virtually every library has colour material. This code indicates the range of dates covered by each library; Pre 1960 A, 1960-1969 B, 1970-1979 C, 1980 Onwards D.

B/W, Illustration
This indicates whether a library holds any black and white material or illustrative material, such as old engravings, magazines, art works or computer generated images. A + after the B/W indicates that the material is part of an expanding contemporary collection, B/W without the + may be dated or historical material only.

A-Z Botanical Collection Ltd
Bedwell Lodge, Cucumber Lane, Essendon, Hatfield, Hertfordshire AL9 6JB
Tel: 0707 49091
Contact: Jeremy Finlay
Fax: 0707 46613,

A wide ranging and continually expanding specialist photo library of 35mm and medium format transparencies of worldwide plant life. Flowers, trees, shrubs, vegetables, crops, gardens and garden features. Horticulture and agriculture. Fruit, fungi, lichens and wild flowers. Many overseas contributors.
Quantity * Format S/M Colour C-D B/W**

Ace Photo Agency
22 Maddox Street, Mayfair, London W1R 9PG
Tel: 071 629 0303
Contact: John Panton
Fax: 071 495 6100

In-depth colour files on people and life-styles, business, industry, technology, sports, skies and sunsets, beaches, glamour, animals, abstracts, textures, still-life, special effects, transport, UK and world travel, music and arts, celebrities, natural history, moods and concepts, plus many more. Pin-reg AV sequences also available. Formats 35mm to 10 x 8, mostly originals. Regular stock shoots organised by Ace to anticipate future demand. Worldwide network of photographers and sub-agents. Bulk discounts by negotiation. Central London location – visits are most welcome. Deluxe stock catalogues (Vols 2, 3, 4 & 5), featuring over 3,800 images, available free on application. Office hours 9.30 to 6.00. Assignment work in own studios. Stock illustrations also available.
Quantity ** Format S/M/L Colour D Illustration**

Abstracts Michael Banks Photography
3rd Floor, Colonial Buildings, 59-61 Hatton Gardens, London EC1N 8LS
Tel: 071 831 2547
Contact: Michael Banks
Fax: 071 405 3922

Abstracts is a unique photo library dealing only in graphic, abstract images. The stock of the library has all been shot by corporate specialist Michael Banks, and covers areas such as architecture, industry, travel, textures, organic, music through to very experimental images. Commisions are undertaken, again with the emphasis on graphic, abstract images.
Quantity * Format S/M Colour D

Action Images
74 Willoughby Lane, London N17 0SP
Tel: 081 885 3000
Contact: David Jacobs
Fax: 081 808 6167

Action Images supplies worldwide sports photo services for editorial, TV, advertising, etc. Colour and B/W library with half a million images on file. Computerised retrieval service and immediate dispatch. File includes personalities in sport, major events and leisure activities. Picture researchers welcome. Commissions undertaken.
Quantity ** Format M Colour B/C/D B/W+**

Action Plus Photographic
54/58 Tanner Street, London SE1 3LL
Tel: 071 403 1558
Contact: Julian Ravilious
Fax: 071 403 1526
Telex: 8951182 GECOMS G

An extensive and constantly expanding library of professional and amateur sports, leisure and action images. Colour and B/W, suitable for editorial and commercial use. Imaginative coverage of over 100 international sports and leisure activities. Original photographic commissions undertaken worldwide by our British and American based photographers. Fast and friendly service for visitors and telephone callers.
Quantity ** Format S Colour D B/W**

Adams Picture Library
156 New Cavendish Street, London W1M 7FJ
Tel: 071 636 1468
Contact: Carol Adams
Fax: 071 436 7131

Conveniently situated in Central London, in the shadow of the Telecom Tower, Adams Picture Library is a general library housing some 500,000 transparencies in various formats, selected from the work of over 400 photographers. To satisfy the ever-increasing visual needs of commerce and professional communicators, APL is constantly developing its worldwide sources, adding new material to the wide range of subjects and categories in its collection including computer graphics, abstracts and space frontier etc. This and a fast, efficient service makes Adams Picture Library first call to those seeking top quality pictures ASAP. Commissions and assignments undertaken by our own photographers in our own fully equipped studio and on location, plus our own art department available for creative and finished artwork. Visitors welcome. Please ask for free brochure.
Quantity ** Format S/M/L Colour D**

The Advertising Archives
45 Lyndale Avenue, London NW2 2QB
Tel: 071 435 6540/837 6743
Contact: Suzanne Viner
Fax: 071 794 6584

The largest archive of 20th Century American and British press advertising and magazine cover illustration in Europe. Over 1 million images categorised and cross-referenced for easy access. Clients can visit by appointment or alternatively we research projects and present a selection of relevant material. Clients include advertising agencies, newspapers, magazines and retail display departments, interior designers, academic researchers, props departments and private researchers. An inspiration source for a variety of creative fields. Images sent all over the world. Several languages spoken. Rapid service available.
Quantity ** B/W+ Illustration**

AFP & EPA (Agence-France Presse & European Pressphoto Agency
Available from Popperfoto, The Old Mill, Overstone Farm, Overstone, Northampton NN6 0AB
Tel: 0604 670670
Fax: 0604 670635

Daily news coverage on international events. B/W pictures are transmitted, but good quality 35mm colour transparencies are also available. B/W commences August 1989 and colour from April 1990. Subjects cover personalities, Royalty, crime, politics, demonstrations and up-to-date sporting events worldwide. European current affairs are especially well covered as well as worldwide events.
Quantity ** Format S Colour D B/W**

Malcolm Aird Associates
Falcon House, 12/14 Swan Street, Boxford, Colchester, Essex CO6 5NZ
Tel: 0787 210111
Contact: Robert Estall
Fax: 0787 211440

Landscapes, cities, towns and villages of Britain. Industry, crafts and people at work. Modern commercial aircraft and new transport. All material supplied as originals.
Quantity ** Format S/M Colour C-D

Bryan and Cherry Alexander Photography
Higher Cottage, Manston, Sturminster Newton, Dorset DT10 1EZ
Tel: 0258 73006
Contact: Cherry Alexander
Fax: 0747 51474

Specialist collection covering the Arctic, the lifestyles of its indigenous peoples, and the technology that is changing their lives and their lands. Polar bears, walrus and all aspects of natural history in the north are covered. Our Antarctic file offers not only penguins and seals but tourism and rubbish. We are constantly adding to our files on British Fieldsports and because of our magazine assignment work we have in-depth coverage on subjects as diverse as releasing humpback whales from fishermans nets in Newfoundland and the lives of rainforest people in Irian Jaya. In the UK photos are also available from NHPA.
Quantity * Format S Colour C-D**

All-Action
32 Great Sutton Street, London EC1V ODX
Tel: 071 608 2988
Contact: Duncan Raban
Fax: 071 250 3376

This is a London based picture and press agency with an expanding library of over 200,000 colour transparencies and providing a daily syndication service to 20 countries worldwide. Founded by sports photographer Duncan Raban, it covers a varied range of personalities in all fields of show-business, acting, pop music, politics and Royalty. All-Action also specialises in world football as well as a wide variety of all major sports and people at leisure. Commissions undertaken subject to individual requirements.
Quantity * Format S Colour D B/W**

All-Sport (U.K.) Ltd
All-Sport House, 3 Greenlea Park, Prince Georges Road, London SW19 2JD
Tel: 081 685 1010
Contact: Adrian Murrell
Fax: 081 648 5240
Telex: 8955022 ASPORT G

The world's largest specialist sports library, covering 130 different sports and all the world's top sports personalities. 35mm colour transparencies available for editorial and commercial use. Represented in 27 countries worldwide. Featuring the work of Tony Duffy, Steve Powell, Adrian Murrell, Dave Cannon, Bob Martin, Mike Powell, Simon Bruty, Russell Cheyne, Pascal Rondeau, Ben Radford, Dan Smith. Also available is the archive from the British Olympic Association including B/W material from the end of the 19th Century to the present. Large in-house studio facility.
Quantity ** Format S Colour B-C-D B/W**

Chris Allan Aviation Library
21-22 St Albans Place, Upper Street, Islington, London N1 0NX
Tel: 071 226 1508
Contact: Anna Kafetz
Fax: 071 359 8523

This library specialises in pictures from the world's finest aviation photographers who are based in the UK, the Far East and the USA. We offer a collection of colour transparencies covering all significant combat aircraft in service in the UK, North America and Asia, including rare air shots of modern, fast jets. A comprehensive selection of civil aircraft is available, including jets, propeller and helicopters, plus a selection of unique shots of the Red Arrows Display Team. Much of the material has been shot on medium format resulting in an increase in quality. The collection is continually updated, includes original material from the Gulf conflict and offers a fast, efficient service.
Quantity * Format S/M Colour D

Ancient Art & Architecture Collection
6 Kenton Road, Harrow-on-the-Hill, London HA1 2BL
Tel: 081 422 1214
Contact: The Librarian
Fax: 081 426 9479

Dramatic and informative worldwide images from our computerised photo library of pictures in colour and B/W covering travel, painting, sculpture, engraving and woodcuts, stained glass, wood and stone carving, enamels, jewellery, tapestries, mosaics, weapons, archaeology, architecture including castles, temples, chateaux, palaces, houses, pyramids, tombs, megaliths, industrial archaeology, geographical and historical material from pre-history to the present.
Quantity ** Format S/M/L Colour B-C-D B/W+ Illustration**

Andes Press Agency
26 Padbury Court, London E2 7EH
Tel: 071 739 3159
Contact: Val Baker
Fax: 071 739 3159

A rapidly expanding library in B/W and colour covering social, religious, political, economic and environmental issues in Asia, Africa, Europe and Latin America, with regular contributions from photographers around the world. A specialist section on Latin America covering a wide range of subjects. Extensive coverage of Britain especially on contemporary social documentary issues. Detailed section on world religions. A subject list is available and picture researchers are welcome by appointment. Worldwide assignments undertaken.
Quantity ** Format S/M Colour C-D B/W+**

Heather Angel/Biofotos
Highways, 6 Vicarage Hill, Farnham, Surrey GU9 8HJ
Tel: 0252 716700
Contact: Heather Angel
Fax: 0252 727464

Comprehensive expanding library of original transparencies, 35mm and medium format and some B/W. Worldwide landscapes, wildlife, natural history, plants, animals, and close-ups from Africa, Asia (notably China), Australia, Central and South America and USA. Amphibians, birds, insects, pond and marine life, fish, fossils, reptiles, mammals, seaweeds, fungi, lichens, mosses, ferns, flowers, trees, gardens and garden plants, whales, polar regions, urban wildlife and pollution. Associated photographers include Brian Rogers' tropical rain forest fauna and flora. Commissions undertaken. Detailed subject catalogue available on request.
Quantity ** Format S/M Colour C-D B/W**

Animal Photography Ltd
4 Marylebone Mews, New Cavendish Street, London W1M 7LF
Tel: 071 935 0503
Contact: John Thompson
Fax: 071 487 3038

Colour and B/W photographs of most breeds of horses and dogs. Large selection of cats. Galapagos Islands, animals in Zoos, some East African animals and French subjects. Commissions undertaken.
Quantity ** Format S/M Colour B-C-D B/W

Aquarius Picture Library
PO Box 5, Hastings, East Sussex TN34 1HR
Tel: 0424 721196
Contact: Gilbert Gibson
Fax: 0424 717704

Initially formed as an extension of Aquarius Literary Agency, the library, with nearly 1 million images in colour and B/W, operates as a separate entity supplying publishing, television and advertising agencies with a specialised service. Stills from films dating from the start of the century to the present with movie colour in 10 x 8 as well as candids. Opera, ballet, TV and pop. Requests by phone dispatched same day. Over 4,000 personalities represented with new images added every week. Collection includes Hollywood Press Service.
Quantity ** Format S/M/L Colour A-B-C-D B/W**

Aquila Photographics Ltd
Haydon House, Alcester Road, Studley, Warwickshire B80 7AN
Tel: 052785 2357
Contact: Alan Richards
Fax: 052785 7507

We cover the whole spectrum of natural history from liverworts and mosses through to flowers, insects, amphibia, reptiles, birds and mammals. We have colour and B/W of many forms of British and European wildlife and a good coverage of many other parts of the world, especially North America, Africa and Australia. Birds are our speciality on which subject we can also advise and help if required.
Quantity * Format S/M Colour C-D B/W**

Architectural Association Slide Library
36 Bedford Square, London WC1B 3ES
Tel: 071 636 0974
Contact: Valerie Bennett
Fax: 071 414 0782

A collection of architectural images built up since the end of the 19th Century. 65,000 35mm colour transparencies and some B/W divided broadly into historical and 20th Century building. Other areas covered include town planning, gardens and landscape. As well as the colour transparencies in the main collection, the library has an archive of B/W negatives and prints dating from the 1920's and some lantern slides.
Quantity * Format S/M Colour A-B-C-D B/W**

Ardea London Ltd
35 Brodrick Road, London SW17 7DX
Tel: 081 672 2067
Contact: Su Gooders
Fax: 081 672 8787
Telex: 896691 TLX1RG prefix Ardeaphotos

A specialist natural history photographic library with over 100,000 original transparencies of animals, birds, plants, fish, insects and reptiles from all over the world. Most of the creatures have been taken wild and free in their natural habitat but we also have cats, dogs and horses; in fact, everything to do with the natural world. Many of our contributors live and work in wild, remote areas, providing desert sands, Antarctic ice cliffs, tropical rainforests and Aborigines as well as farming, pollution, conservation, sunsets and scenery. Colour and B/W.
Quantity * Format S/M/L Colour C-D B/W**

Arcaid
The Factory, Rear of 2 Acre Road, Kingston-on-Thames, Surrey KT2 6EF
Tel: 081 546 4352
Contact: Barbara Godzikowska
Fax: 081 541 5230

Arcaid's architectural and interior design picture library incorporates material from leading architectural photographers. The collection covers international subjects and includes an extensive collection on Britain. Historic and contemporary subjects have been photographed during the last 25 years and encompass civic, residential and commercial architecture, interior and garden design. Coverage ranges from a single image to comprehensive series. Commissions undertaken. Visitors welcome by appointment.
Quantity ** Format S/M/L Colour B-C-D B/W+

Art Directors Photo Library
Image House, 86 Haverstock Hill, London NW3 2BD
Tel: 071 485 9325/267 6930
Contact: David Harding
Fax: 071 485 7776

A constantly expanding library of over a quarter million transparencies from top international photographers. Includes backgrounds for advertising, incorporating many of the best lensmen of US National Geographic Magazine. Computer graphics, Hi-Tech, industry and business, space, personalities, families, couples, life-style, travel, landscapes, skies, food and drink, entertainment, fashion, faces, animals, flowers, nature, vintage and modern cars and an outstanding quality and depth of coverage on USA, Europe, Asia, Africa and the Tropics. Art Directors has acquired an outstanding up-to-the-minute collection of medical, pharmaceutical and scientific shots. They are featured in our new catalogue, Art Directors 4, which is now available free of charge to commercial users of photography, publishers or other bona fide would-be customers.
Quantity ** Format S/M Colour C-D**

Art Resource Illustration Library
28 Shelton Street, London WC2H 9JN
Tel: 071 240 1447
Contact: Ruth Wood
Fax: 071 836 0199

High quality illustrations produced by well known illustrators at a fraction of the cost of commissioned prices. The library has over 2,000 images which are constantly being added to, covering everything from abstract to still-life, animals to architecture, sport to science fiction, people and travel. Styles vary from ultra realistic to highly stylised. All contributors work in the field of advertising and their material is of the highest quality. We are one of the leading suppliers of images to poster, greeting cards and jigsaw companies. Commissions undertaken.
Quantity * Format S Illustration

Aspect Picture Library Ltd
40 Rostrevor Road, London SW6 5AD
Tel: 071 736 1998/731 7362
Contact: Derek Bayes
Fax: 071 731 7362
Telex: 934999 TXLINK G quoting MBX 219994671

Specialising in reportage features and essays around the world. Covering countries, events, industry, travel. An extensive stock file of colour photographs suitable for advertising, audio-visual, books, brochures, company reports, calendars, magazines, packaging and posters. Large files on art, paintings, space, China, Middle East. Colour and B/W.
Quantity * Format S/M/L Colour C-D B/W Illustration**

Audio-Visual Services
St Mary's Hospital Medical School, Norfolk Place, Paddington, London W2 1PG
Tel: 071 725 1739
Contact: Miss B Tallon
Fax: 071 724 7349

This library, established in 1948 and regularly updated, contains approximately 35,000 colour and B/W transparencies of medical conditions, some now very rare. Also pictures allied to medicine, the best of which have been incorporated into the National Medical Slide Bank qv. Material is available to bona fide borrowers only and is in constant demand from publishers and TV. Viewing by appointment only. Please telephone to enquire about specific pictures or to request photographs to be taken.
Quantity ** Format S/M Colour A-B-C-D B/W

Aviation Photographs International
15 Downs View Road, Swindon, Wilts SN3 1NS
Tel: 0793 497179
Contact: Jeremy Flack
Fax: 0739 497179

An extensive collection of aviation photographs mainly in colour. Included are many associated subjects including internal views, airport buildings, radar and weapons as well as views from aircraft. Both civil and military subjects are covered and the collection is expanding to include ships and vehicles. Subjects are catalogued on computer giving a comprehensive and easy cross-reference facility. We are able to assist with editorial content and accept commissions for photography and additional picture research if required.
Quantity * Format S Colour B-C-D**

Aviation Picture Library
35 Kingsley Avenue, West Ealing, London W13 0EQ
Tel: 081 566 7712
Contact: Austin J Brown
Fax: 081 566 7714

A specialised source of over 100,000 original aviation transparencies covering all aspects of the industry with an increasing bias towards dynamic shots of aircraft. The collection consists of atmospheric views from the ground and in the air, high and low altitude obliques of Europe, Africa, the Caribbean and the USA and travel photographs from these areas. We are an active photographic unit specialising in air-to-air commissions for commercial operators and air-to-ground obliques for land development. Architectural photography of modern buildings and town planning, is available through the library. Some archival material available. From contacts, almost anything can be found.
Quantity * Format S/M Colour C-D B/W**

Aviemore Photographic
Main Road, Aviemore, Highland PH22 1RH
Tel: 0479 810371
Contact: Stewart Grant
Fax: 0479 811351

Scotland in summer and winter. Winter sports, tourism, landscapes and mood shots. Our proximity to the centre of the Scottish winter sports area has provided us with a large selection of skiing and curling. Developing collection on the Scotch Whisky industry. Colour and B/W

Axiom Picture Library
58-60 Lowesmoor, Worcester WR1 2SE
Tel: 0905 616412
Contact: David Newham
Fax: 0905 616412

A small but rapidly expanding general library holding stock colour transparencies specialising mainly in UK landscapes, cities, villages, coastline and the major tourist attractions. Other smaller sections include transport, military aviation and agriculture. All the existing files are constantly updated and new subjects such as events, people, backgrounds, occupations and industry are being swiftly added to the list. A phone call or fax is all it takes to discover exactly what is in the files. Visitors welcome by appointment.
Quantity ** Format S/M/L Colour D

Barnaby's Picture Library
19 Rathbone Street, London W1P 1AF
Tel: 071 636 6128/9
Contact: Mary Buckland
Fax: 071 637 4317

One of London's oldest established agencies with a stock of over 4 million colour and B/W pictures, all formats, embracing a wide variety of subjects ranging from nature, animals, geology, commerce, aircraft, maritime, industry, oil and most countries of the world. Varied historical subjects, suffragettes, an extensive collection on Hitler, World Wars I and II. Commissions undertaken.
Quantity ** Format S/M/L Colour A-B-C-D B/W+**

Bart's Medical Picture Library
Medical Illustration, St Bartholomew's Hospital, West Smithfield, London EC1A 7BE
Tel: 071 601 8080/1
Contact: Jason Burns
Fax: 071 796 3753

Possibly the longest pedigree of any medical illustration department in the UK. Our huge resource has appreciated in teaching, illustrative and historical value and is drawn on by authors, picture researchers from lay, medical and scientific journals, text book publishers and TV and other media property buyers. Scene setting pictures provide editors with shots to inject interest into news items. Reference shots for dramas and documentaries to guide simulation of injury or disease, for the accurate replication of equipment and uniforms or backgrounds for sets. Historical collection of personalities in medicine and past hospital scenes. Commissions undertaken.
Quantity ** Format S/M Colour A-B-C-D B/W Illustration

James Bartholomew's London
13 Woodberry Crescent, London N10 1PJ
Tel: 081 883 0083
Contact: Laura Boswell
Fax: 081 883 9215

James Bartholomew is concerned with representing London. With books published on these subjects he has exclusive and wide ranging files on the Tower of London, Kew Gardens and the City. His aim is to represent and document the essential London life and landscape.
Quantity ** Format S/M/L Colour D B/W+

Colin Baxter Photography Ltd
Unit 2/3, Block 6, Caldwellside Industrial Estate, Lanark ML11 6SR
Tel: 0555 65022
Contact: Mike Rensner
Fax: 0555 4775

The distinctive atmospheric landscapes of Colin Baxter. Large collections on Scotland – our speciality – the Lake District, Yorkshire, the Cotswolds, Bath, France and Iceland. Also a special collection on the work of Scottish architect and designer, Charles Rennie Mackintosh.
Quantity ** Format S Colour D

BBC Photograph Library
Unit 1, 29 North Acton Road, Harlesden, London NW10 6PE
Tel: 081 743 8000 ext 2988
Contact: Margaret Kirby
Fax: 081 965 2485

The library is the BBC's unique archive collection of stills, dating back to 1922 and the earliest days of radio and television broadcasting. It includes stills of programmes, personalities, broadcasting equipment and premises. The library retains mainly BBC copyright material and consists of over 2 million colour and B/W images, constantly updated with new material from all parts of the BBC. Stills can be researched by name, programme title or subject. No original material is loaned. Visitors welcome by appointment from 9.30 – 5.30, Monday – Friday.
Quantity ** Format S/M Colour A-B-C-D B/W**

Beken of Cowes Ltd
16 Birmingham Road, Cowes, Isle of Wight PO31 7BH
Tel: 0983 297311
Contact: Kenneth J Beken
Fax: 0983 29 10 59

Specialists in maritime subjects from 1888 to the present day. 100,000 medium format transparencies plus 75,000 B/W images. Subjects include worldwide ocean racing, Americas Cup, J-Class era, schooners, steam yachts, liners, power boats, cruising, Tall ships, etc. Worldwide commissions undertaken.
Quantity * Format M/L Colour A-B-C-D B/W**

Ivan J. Belcher Colour Picture Library
15 Gibson Close, Abingdon, Oxfordshire OX14 1XS
Tel: 0235 521524
Contact: Ivan J Belcher

Extensive colour picture library specialising in top quality colour transparencies depicting the British scene in sizes 6 x 6 and 5 x 4, mainly of recent origin and constantly updated. Thousands of pictures of famous cities, towns, picturesque harbours, rivers and canals, castles, villages, cottages, rural scenes and traditions, photographed throughout the seasons. In-depth coverage of many locations and subjects, especially the major UK tourist areas including London, the Cotswolds, Thames Valley, Lake District and many others, plus steam traction engines and victorian fairground equipment pictures. Suitable for brochures, books, advertising, calendars greeting cards, jig-saw puzzles, etc.
Quantity ** Format M Colour D

Andrew Besley Photolibrary
The Cross, Lelant, Cornwall TR26 3LJ
Tel: 0736 756756
Contact: Andrew Besley
Fax: 0736 756555

Andrew Besley has been a stock photographer for 30 years and has worked with major London based photolibraries. In 1985 he established his own Library based in St Ives, West Cornwall. He specialises in Somerset, Devon and Cornwall including the Isles of Scilly, faces and places and has coverage of towns and villages, rural landscapes, harbours, boats, ships, leisure activities, gardens and flowers, sea, sky and beaches in every mood. Mostly on large and medium format. An historical b/w section includes steam trains and shipwrecks plus some news coverage of events from 1975 to 1990.
Quantity * Format S/M/L Colour B-C-D B/W**

John Bethell Photography
89 Fishpool Street, St Albans, Hertfordshire AL3 4RU
Tel: 0727 50112
Contact: John Bethell
Fax: 0727 50112

Specialist architectural photographer John Bethell has been offering a library service since the late 1970's. All material is shot on the versatile 6 x 9 roll-film format. He is perhaps best known for country house interiors; but castles, gardens, churches and townscapes are well represented. Since the acquisition of a 6 x 9 hand-camera, landscapes have arrived in increasing numbers. Photographs taken for England's Historic Gardens (Headline), English Harbours (Weidenfeld), and King's College Carol Book (Penguin) will be available from the library in the near future. Bernard Cox's fine Kodachromes of architectural subjects worldwide are available through this library. Eastern Europe and the Middle East are particular strengths.
Quantity ** Format S/M Colour B-C-D B/W+

BFI Stills Posters and Designs
21 Stephen St, London W1P 1PL
Tel: 071 255 1444
Contact: Bridget Kinally
Fax: 071 323 9260
Telex: 27624

About 3 million B/W original photographs, colour transparencies, posters, set and costume designs, illustrating the history of world cinematography c1895 to the present day. Films by titles/personality, film studios, cinema buildings, history of television. Special emphasis throughout on British cinema and television. By appointment, Tuesday – Friday, 11.00 – 5.30. No loans. Duplicate B/W and colour transparencies available for a fee. Copyright clearance responsibility of the user. Printed catalogue available.
Quantity ** Format S/M/L Colour A-B-C-D B/W+**

Biotica Picture Library
Romney Cottage, Crossborough Hill, Basingstoke, Hampshire RG21 2AG
Tel: 0256 21093
Contact: David Carwardine
Fax: 0256 21093

This family run library has a substantial and growing stock of colour transparencies taken in over 80 different countries. The main emphasis is on wildlife and the collection includes unique pictures of endangered species. It also has a good coverage of a wide range of other natural history subjects and environmental issues, as well as people and places around the world.
Quantity ** Format S Colour D

John Birdsall Photography
75 Raleigh Street, Nottingham, Notts NG7 4DL
Tel: 0602 782645
Contact: Clare Marsh
Fax: 0602 785546

A multi-cultural, social-documentary library comprising a good collection of colour transparencies and prints and over 20,000 top quality B/W photographs. This collection, built up over twelve years, explores many contemporary social issues. Categories include children, housing, education, old age, youth, work and services and in addition, Nottingham and the surrounding areas, depicted in a wide range of colour and B/W images. A prompt and reliable picture search service operates. Free catalogue available. Commissions undertaken.
Quantity ** Format S Colour D B/W+

Birmingham Public Libraries
Central Library, Paradise Circus, Birmingham B3 3HQ
Tel: 021 235 4549
Contact: Phillip Allen
Fax: 021 236 2112

Several important topographical collections. The principal ones being prints and negatives by Sir Benjamin Stone (1838-1914), Francis Bedford (1816-1894) and Francis Frith (1822-1898). The Stone Collection comprises 22,000 images (1880-1910) including customs, occupations, events, portraits and topographical views. The Bedford Collection is 3,000 images of SW England, W Midlands and Wales (1860-1890). The Frith Collection is 310,000 negatives from 1886-1965, indexed. The library also holds topographical prints of China, India, Sri Lanka and some European countries. Also 100,000 prints and negatives relating to Birmingham and it's immediate environs and some railway material.
Quantity ** B/W**

Anthony Blake
54 Hill Rise, Richmond, Surrey TW10 6UB
Tel: 081 940 7583
Contact: Julia Cooper
Fax: 081 948 1224

Specialist in food and wine related images – cooking, finished dishes, chefs, restaurants, hotels, shops, markets, agriculture, trades, fishing, landscapes and travel worldwide. Representing over 20 top photographers. Original colour transparencies – all formats. Commissions undertaken from our studio for editorial and advertising. Free catalogue available.
Quantity * Format S/M/L Colour B-C-D**

John Blake Picture Library
The Georgian House, 6 The Plain, Thornbury, Bristol BS12 2AG
Tel: 0454 418321
Contact: John Blake
Fax: 0454 416636

The general topography of Britain, Europe and the rest of the world in all format transparencies and B/W. Constantly expanding stock includes landscapes, countryside, churches, architecture, cities, towns, villages, gardens, people at work and at play. Comprehensive collection on the Cotswolds and the Badminton and Gatcombe Horse Trials. Incorporated photographers available for commissions.
Quantity ** Format S/M/L Colour C-D B/W+

Bridgeman Art Library Ltd
19 Chepstow Road, London W2 5BP
Tel: 071 727 4065
Contact: Harriet Bridgeman
Fax: 071 792 8509

The largest source of fine art images in the UK, the Bridgeman Art Library hold large format colour transparencies of works of art from hundreds of collections around the world. The work of the greatest creative minds in history – paintings, sculpture, prints, manuscripts, antiques, antiquities and the decorative arts – from universally familiar masterpieces to the hidden treasures of provincial museums and private collections. All of our librarians are qualified art historians who, with the aid of our computerised search system, can quickly search through the entire library to fulfil your request.
Quantity ** Format M/L Colour C-D B/W+ Illustration

BMV Picturebank International Photo Library
79 Farringdon Road, London EC1M 3JY
Tel: 071 405 5021
Contact: Nigel Messett
Fax: 071 831 2982

Expanding collection of very good quality colour transparencies in all formats. Main area of specialisation is world travel. Good selection also available on many other subjects especially landscapes, agriculture, architecture, birds, flowers, watersports, industry and technology and sunsets and sunrises. Commissions undertaken, home and abroad. Colour poster and full list of covered subjects available on request.
Quantity ** Formats S/M/L Colour D

Chris Bonington Picture Library
Badger Hill, Hesket Newmarket, Wigton, Cumbria CA7 8LA
Tel: 06998 286
Contact: Frances Daltrey
Fax: 06998 238

Based on the personal collection of climber and author Chris Bonington and his extensive travels and mountaineering achievements, this library also offers photographs by other climbers and includes the Peter Boardman and Joe Tasker collections. Full picture coverage of the world's mountains from British hills to Everest, depicting expedition planning and management stages, the approach march showing inhabitants of the area, flora and fauna

Boys Syndication
Red House, Newbourn, Woodbridge, Suffolk IP12 4PX
Tel: 0473 36333
Contact: Pamela Boys
Fax: 0394 380483

Specialised collection of Michael Boys international interiors, gardens, wine and food, lighting and other creative images. NEW sections on Raymond Blanc, regions of France, period food and antiques. Formats 35mm and larger, all edited for quality. Ideas for whole books.
Quantity * Format S/M Colour B-C-D**

Britstock-IFA Ltd
41-42 Berners Street, London W1P 3AA
Tel: 071 255 2200
Contact: Liz Higgins
Fax: 071 637 4318

Britstock-IFA is a general photo library opened in October 1991, with a rapidly expanding stock of quality colour transparencies on all formats. We have four other European offices and many partnership agencies worldwide, plus our own production studio. Subjects include a very large people/lifestyle section, sports, still lives, computer graphics, wildlife, botany, architecture, scenics, economy and travel. Our third catalogue contains 470 pages and is available free of charge. All images on file are fully computerised and cross referenced for easy access. Free searches to visitors to the office, centrally located in London W1.
Quantity * Format S/M/L Colour D**

BT Pictures
426 Essex Road, London N1 3PJ
Tel: 071 704 2020
Contact: Roger Wemyss-Brooks
Fax: 071 704 2713
Formerly

Telefocus. Our comprehensive collection of telecommunication photographs covers a wide range of subjects from optical fibres, BT research labs, data link and satelite earth stations to remote services and rural locations, cable laying and BT staff at work. The historical collection records the history of telecommunications from Alexander Graham Bell's first telephone, early cable ships and 19th century telephone exchanges through to the present day.
Quantity * Format S/M Colour C-D B/W**

Bubbles Photolibrary
23a Benwell Road, London N7 7BL
Tel: 071 609 4547
Contact: Loisjoy Thurstun
Fax: 071 607 1410

Bubbles now specialises in all kinds of people including beautiful & fractious babies, child development, pregnancy & womens health, teenagers, middle & old age. We represent a large number of regularly contributing photographers who are happy to shoot `on spec' to a client's brief where relevant and if sufficient notice is given. The majority of the shots held on 35mm, the rest on medium format. We now exclusively hold colour except for B/W shots of childbirth.
Quantity ** Format S/M Colour D B/W

Builder Group Picture Library
Builder House, 1 Millharbour, London E14 9RA
Tel: 071 537 2222 ext 6243
Contact: Janet Lewis
Fax: 071 537 2019

A comprehensive collection of colour and B/W photographs on 35mm and medium format, based on the fourteen magazines published by the Group, specifically; Building, Chartered Surveyor Weekly, and Building Services. The collection includes images on the various aspects of construction, housing, building and building services as well as the personalities of the industry. Also, up-to-date images of current construction sites in Britain, primarily London.
Quantity ** Format S/M Colour D B/W

Michael Busselle's Photolibrary
18 Bayham Road, Sevenoaks, Kent TN13 3XD
Tel: 0732 455607
Contact: Michael or Pat Busselle

The collection consists exclusively of Michael Busselle's own photography. Most of the images were taken originally to illustrate books and magazine features. A number were taken specifically to illustrate books and articles on photographic techniques and special effects. Otherwise, the emphasis is on atmospheric landscapes and general travel subjects with a wide coverage of France, Spain and England. French Wine regions are covered extensively. Smaller collections cover India, Africa, Sri Lanka and USA to illustrate travel features, with landscapes, villages, markets, wildlife, people and cruising.
Quantity ** Format S/M Colour C/D

Cable and Wireless Visual Resource
Corporate Affairs, New Mercury House, 26 Red Lion Square, London WC1R 4UQ
Tel: 071 315 4885
Contact: Lesley A Wood
Fax: 071 315 5052
Telex: 920000 CANDWG

Cable and Wireless plc is one of the world's leading international telecommunications groups with business in some 50 countries. In support of our activities, slides are made of local scenes, cityscapes and general views as well as technical material such as telecommunications equipment, earth stations and cable ships. Our scope includes the Caribbean, Far East and the USA. Images are produced to a level suitable for corporate literature and display purposes. Joint photographic assignments may be considered. Enquiries can be taken by post, phone or personal visits by appointment.
Quantity ** Format S/M Colour C-D

Calendar Concepts & Design
33 Albury Avenue, Isleworth, Middx TW7 5HY
Tel: 081 847 3777
Contact: Michael Brown
Fax: 081 568 2402
Telex: 924150 ADLIB G

This specialist agency provides a unique service to calendar publishers and last year was responsible for the content of more than fifty calendars. Representing leading photographers who are pre-eminent in their field, they can deliver complete calendar concepts for retail, bespoke or stock advertising clients. All traditional calendar subjects are covered in depth – glamour – landscapes – transport – nature – sport. Innovative themes are being developed constantly to satisfy the increasing demand for new products. An illustrated book featuring the work of twelve photographers is available free of charge to calendar publishers. Please note this agency does not supply general stock requests.
Quantity ** Format S/M/L Colour C-D

Camera Press Ltd
Russell Court, Coram Street, London WC1H 0NB
Tel: 071 837 4488/9393/1300/0606
Fax: 071 278 5126
Telex: 21654

Founded in 1947 by the late Tom Blau, this collection has a vast range of high quality photographs, both B/W and colour. Subject coverage is general with particular strengths in portraits, Royalty and social history. A specialist department deals with Women's magazine material. Prestigious features on all kinds of subjects are syndicated every day to a large number of territories. New material is added daily from photographers and agencies around the world. Camera Press represents some of the best names in the business – Snowdon, Lichfield, Donovan, Beaton, Baron, Parkinson, Karsh of Ottawa, Dorothy Wilding, Prince Andrew ... The collection currently numbers some 8 million images. Staff photographers are available for commission work.
Quantity ** Format S/M/L Colour A-B-C-D B/W+ Illustration**

Camera Ways' Ltd
Court View, Egerton, Nr Ashford, Kent TN27 9BD
Tel: 023376 454
Contact: Derek Budd

An expanding collection of 35mm and 6 x 4.5 colour transparencies, exhibition prints and video footage by photographer and award-winning film-maker Derek Budd. Specialising in natural history and countryside programmes on ITV, his networked creative photography has won many international and Royal
Television Society awards during his 27 years experience. Subjects include advertising, aerials, journalism and travel. Specialising in wildlife habitats, flora and fauna of Britain and Europe, country crafts and people, village scenes, landscapes, aquatic life, storm damage and MOD reserves. Recent collection on cathedrals. Photographic commissions possible in all formats including standard and super 16mm as well as video.
Quantity * Format S Colour D B/W+

The Casement Collection
Erin Lodge, Jigs Lane, Warfield, Berkshire RG12 6DP
Tel: 0344 302067
Contact: Jack Casement
Fax: 0344 303158

Based on the personal collection of Jack Casement, but now being expanded with work by other photographers, the Casement Collection is an extensive international travel library of medium format colour transparencies and B/W prints of destinations from Abu Dhabi to Zimbabwe. Well noted for its creative element beyond the 'beach and palm tree' syndrome. The library contains only originals, no dupes, and is particularly strong on North America and the Gulf. General list available on request.
Quantity ** Format M Colour D B/W

Celtic Picture Agency
5 Llys Llannerch, St Asaph, Clwyd, North Wales LL17 0AZ
Tel: 0745 730395
Contact: Mike Thomas
Fax: 0745 730395

The library specialises in pictures relating to Wales, established in 1985 and growing daily, with contributions from some fifteen Welsh photographers dotted around the principality and happy to accept commissions for material not in stock. The library is extremely strong on environmental material including current issues relating to conservation, second homes, farming, development in the countryside and National Parks, tourism expansion, employment creation in rural areas, etc. It holds a wealth of scenic material, many depicting historical sites both inland and on the coast. Requests by phone between 9am and 9pm. Urgent orders despatched Datapost or according to clients' wishes.
Quantity ** Format S/M Colour D B/W

J Allan Cash Ltd
74 South Ealing Road, London W5 4QB
Tel: 081 840 4141
Contact: Alan Denny
Fax: 081 566 2568

From its origins, marketing J Allan Cash's extensive output, the library has undergone considerable change of direction over the past few years and now represents 300+ photographers, who contribute on a regular basis, introducing new material into the files. We stock approximately 250,000 colour transparencies in all formats and a similar number of B/W prints, all edited to reproduction standard, cross-indexed and filed for easy access. Coverage includes worldwide travel and documentary as well as large general sections on people, natural history, space, sport and activities and many other subjects.
Quantity ** Format S/M/L Colour B-C-D B/W+**

Cephas Picture Library
20 Bedster Gardens, West Molesey, Surrey KT8 1SZ
Tel: 081 979 8647
Contact: Mick Rock
Fax: 081 979 8647

The Wine Industry and Vineyards of the world is the subject on which this library has built its reputation. The collection is probably the most comprehensive to be found anywhere – mainly 6 x 7 originals, all with detailed captions and supported by specialist knowledge of the subject. Whisky, beer, cider and food are also included in the ever increasing files. Astute researchers have also discovered the general and travel section. Representing over 60 photographers, we are able to offer good selections from around the world. A fast, personal service is offered, with no search fee if any pictures are used. Should you prefer to visit (by appointment), we are only 40 minutes from central London. Coffee and sandwiches are dispensed free of charge!,
Quantity ** Format S/M Colour D B/W

The Chatsworth Collection
Chatsworth House, Edensor, Bakewell, Derbyshire DE4 1PJ
Tel: 0246 582242
Fax: 0246 583536

This is a photo library of the treasures of Chatsworth, home of the Duke and Duchess of Devonshire. The art collection and library, built up over four centuries, includes over a thousand old master and English paintings, about two thousand old master drawings and an outstanding series of hand coloured illustrated books on natural history, especially flowers. Among the many famous names represented are Rembrandt, Raphael, Van Dyke, Reynolds, RedoutÇ, Audubon and Gould. The great collection of decorative arts, including fine furniture, carvings, silver, ceramics and textiles, provides a wealth of imagery, especially surface decoration, of use in many commercial applications.
Quantity * Format M/L Colour D Illustration

Christel Clear Marine Photography
Roselea, Church Lane, Awbridge, Nr Romsey, Hampshire SO51 0HN
Tel: 0794 41081
Contact: Nigel Dowden
Fax: 0794 40890

Formed in 1986, this specialist library has grown from the partnership of photographer Christel Dowden and husband Nigel, a working writer. Both are experienced yachtsmen. The emphasis of the library is on yacht racing from international Grand Prix events to local regattas. Originally news orientated, the library now holds several thousand colour and B/W images of water related activities worldwide. Subjects covered include racing yachts, cruising and classic yachts, cruising grounds, coastal and travel scenes. Both sail and power yachting are covered in 35mm and medium format. Suppliers of illustrated feature articles to non specialist sources. Commissions undertaken worldwide.
Quantity ** Format S/M Colour D B/W+

Chorley & Handford Ltd
Stafford Studios, 129a Stafford Road, Wallington, Surrey SM6 9BN
Tel: 081 669 4900 (6 lines)
Contact: Paul Proctor
Fax: 081 773 0129

A comprehensive library of oblique aerial photographs dating from 1964. Specialising in Central London, The City, London Docklands and development areas, UK airports, railway stations, power stations, docks, rivers, town centres throughout the UK, historical buildings, major developments and new buildings. Commissions undertaken for new photography for subjects not already part of the library, or for special requirements. Clients and picture researchers welcome by appointment. All subjects available in 35mm or 5 x 4 transparencies or colour prints of any size, all produced in house. The library is constantly updated, and expanding by approximately 5,000 images per year, and can be retrieved easily by computer.
Quantity ** Colour B-C-D B/W

Christian Aid Photo Library
PO Box 100, London SE1 7RT
Tel: 071 620 4444
Contact: Joseph Cabon
Fax: 071 620 0719

A specialist library of pictures from Africa, Asia and Latin America. Most are on development themes, agriculture, health. education, urban and rural life etc. All relate to small scale, community-based programmes set up by people working to claim or keep their rights or to improve their environment.
Quantity * Format S Colour D B/W+**

Christie's Colour Library
1 Langley Lane, London SW8 1SX
Tel: 071 582 1282
Contact: Claudia Brigg

A library of 60,000 high quality transparencies of all subjects illustrated in colour in Christie's Sales Catalogues from Leonardo to Beuys and Japanese swords to Bugatti furniture. The main emphasis is on Art Nouveau and Art Deco, Japanese and Chinese Art, furniture, ceramics, jewellery, silver, sculpture and, of course, painting. Also cars, toys, musical instruments, books and manuscripts, clocks, antiquities, collectibles and others. More than 10,000 new images every year.
Quantity * Format M/L Colour B-C-D B/W+ Illustration**

The Cinema Museum incorporating the Ronald Grant Archive
The Old Fire Station, 46 Renfrew Rd, London SE11 4NA
Tel: 071 820 9991
Contact: Martin Humphries
Fax: 071 793 0849

A extensive collection of material covering the history of the motion picture industry from 1896 to the present day. Colour and B/W stills from films, portraits of important and obscure players, producers, directors, technicians, etc, film-making, cinema posters and ephemera. Material is filed according to film title or personality, there is a subject index. The collection also includes smaller sections on theatre, variety, popular music and television.
Quantity ** Format S/M/L Colour A-B-C-D B/W+**

Collections

13 Woodberry Crescent, London N10 1PJ
Tel: 081 883 0083
Contact: Laura Boswell
Fax: 081 883 9215

Collections is a collection of specialist collections on the British Isles. Based on Brian Shuel's long-standing British Customs and British Bridges qv, and Anthea Sieveking's extensive collection on pregnancy, children and education qv, Collections also includes Patrick Johns' Horticulture also qv, and extensive files on Castles, Railways, Funghi, the Police, 18 British Cities, Buses, the Brigade of Guards, the Tower of London, and several areas of Britain. We have three London collections. Our Overalls collection is for backgrounds. We have several other collections which are small but growing, with new ones promised, and we are always on the look out for really expert and comprehensive coverage of almost any British subject. A collection of antiquarian illustrations on Folklore and Bridges is emerging from the EFDSS and the Folklore Society.

Quantity * Format S/M Colour B-C-D B/W+ Illustration**

CIRCA (Part of ICOREC)
ICOREC,Didsbury College, Wilmslow Road, Manchester Polytechnic, Didsbury, Manchester M20 8RR
Tel: 061 434 8374/0828
Contact: Joanne O'Brian
Fax: 061 434 8374

Circa Photo Library specialises in religion and the environment. We cover worship in the community and at home, festivals, religious buildings, religious art and artifacts and faith as a part of everyday life. We have urban and rural environmental photographs including wildlife, landscapes and conservation activities by members of different religious communities. Our photographs are drawn from all continents and specialise in UK, Hong Kong, Turkey, Israel, Thailand, Bali, India, Philippines and Brazil. We deal mainly in colour transparencies although we do have B/W negatives of religious activities, environmental topics and landscapes in the UK. We are linked to a communications company in Geneva who hold part of our environmental collection and will provide the relevant transparencies within three days. Our religious transparencies and the rest of our environmental collection are held in Manchester.
Quantity * Format S/M Colour D B/W+

John Cleare/Mountain Camera
Hill Cottage, Fonthill Gifford, Salisbury, Wiltshire SP3 6QW
Tel: 0747 89320
Contact: John Cleare
Fax: 0747 89320

A working photographer/writer, John Cleare is also an experienced mountaineer and wilderness traveller and has climbed all over the world. While naturally specialising in mountain-related subjects, his library also features other adventurous pursuits such as trekking, ski mountaineering, desert-travel, coasteering, fell-running, kayaking, white-water rafting, safaris, sailing and so forth. Landscape too is a speciality, with pictures from all seven continents including extensive coverage of Britain's uplands and coasts, the Alps, the Himalayas and other major mountain ranges. There is wide coverage of geographical features and the natural world while general travel material encompasses many of the world's more interesting cities. John is currently shooting medium format panoramic colour material to add to the library.
Quantity * Format S/M Colour C-D B/W+**

Stephanie Colasanti
38 Hillside Court, 409 Finchley Road, London NW3 6HQ
Tel: 071 435 3695
Contact: Stephanie Colasanti
Fax: 071 435 9995

This established library contains over 50,000 images on medium format taken exclusively by Stephanie Colasanti, FBIPP. Extensive coverage of Austrian winter sports, France, Germany, Holland, Scandinavia, Senegal, Switzerland, Yugoslavia, Greece and the Islands, Italy, Cyprus, Madeira, Morocco, Tunisia, Turkey, Israel, Egypt, Kenya, Ivory Coast, Seychelles, Canada, USA, Mexico, Caribbean, Barbados, Bahamas, Hawaii, Jamaica, India, Thailand, China, Japan, Venezuela, Columbia, the Maldives, Australia, New Zealand, Tahiti, Dubai, Comores Islands and Mauritius. Children, people working and playing, animals, sports, carnivals, agriculture, landscapes, seascapes, sunsets, deserts, markets, archaeology, religion and ancient civilisations. Some B/W. Travel assignments undertaken worldwide.
Quantity ** Format M Colour C-D B/W

Colorific!
Visual House, 1 Mastmaker Road, London E14 9WT
Tel: 071 515 3000
Contact: Graham Cross
Fax: 071 538 3555

A long established colour library with over 400,000 images, supplying stock to both editorial and commercial markets. Subject files cover travel, science and technology, natural history, sport, politics, world events, leisure, animals, entertainment and extensive personality files. Current feature material is available by many of the world's top photographers from top agencies including Black Star, Contact, Sports Illustrated and Visages from USA and ANA, Odyssey and Regards in Europe. Our team of helpful researchers is here to help you find the best pictures.
Quantity ** Format S/M/L Colour A-B-C-D B/W**

Colorsport
44 St Peters Street, London N1 8JT
Tel: 071 359 2714
Contact: Stewart Fraser
Fax: 071 226 4328

Established in 1969, this expanding library, which represents the work of over 20 photographers in Europe and the USA, provides extensive coverage in colour and B/W of all aspects of sport. Coverage includes both summer and winter Olympic Games since 1972. Also football dating from 1881 – possibly the oldest library of football pictures in the world – and cricket from 1920 onwards. Pictures are readily available for both editorial and commercial use and can be selected personally in the library or sent on request by our experienced staff. Our specialist photographers are available for commission.
Quantity ** Format S Colour B-C-D B/W**

Compix
Commonwealth Institute, Kensington High Street, London W8 6NQ
Tel: 071 603 4535
Contact: Maria Ockenden
Fax: 071 602 7374
Telex: 895582

An expanding colour library specialising in Commonwealth countries in Africa, Asia, the Caribbean and the Pacific. Subjects include agriculture, crafts, education, festivals, food, industry, landscapes, markets, people, towns and village life. Information leaflet available. Visitors welcome by appointment.
Quantity ** Format S/M Colour C-D

Comstock
28 Chelsea Wharf, 15 Lots Road, Chelsea, London SW10 0QQ
Tel: 071 351 4448
Contact: Helena Kovac
Fax: 071 352 8414

The Comstock library collection contains over 3 million images covering all general subject areas as well as the Susan Griggs Collection of travel and editorial photography. A majority of the collection is colour transparencies with a growing collection of B/W. Call or write to receive our new free catalogue with a sample of over 3,000 colour images from our files.
Quantity ** Format S Colour D B/W**

Sylvia Cordaiy Picture Library
72 East Ham Road, Littlehampton, West Sussex BN17 7BQ
Tel: 0903 715297
Contact: Sylvia Cordaiy
Fax: 0903 731605

This fast growing library holds comprehensive files on the following subjects: architecture and travel worldwide; global environmental topics; the archive of Paul Kaye (specialising in animals and people) contributor to Picture Post and Reveille; UK counties, landscapes, cities, villages etc; the RSPCA at work with wild and domestic animals; the Pony Drift; people at play; the Tall Ships and yachting; large selection of images related to the card and calendar market. Photographers available for commissions. Clients and picture researchers welcome.
Quantity ** Format S/M Colour A-B-C-D B/W+

Country Life Library
Kings Reach Tower, Stamford Street, London SE1 9LS
Tel: 071 261 6337
Contact: Camilla Costello
Fax: 071 261 5139

A unique collection of photographs of exceptional quality, mainly black and white, dating back to 1897, of country houses, churches and houses in Britain and abroad. Interiors showing architectural details of ceilings, fireplaces, furniture, paintings and sculpture. Exteriors showing many fine landscaped gardens, including those by Gertrude Jekyll. The Library is open Tuesdays and Thursdays from 10.00am to 5.00pm. Visits by appointment only.
Quantity * Format S/M/L Colour A-B-C-D B/W+**

County Visuals
Planning Deptartment, Kent County Council, Springfield, Maidstone, Kent ME14 2LX
Tel: 0622 696171
Contact: Tony Hemsted
Fax: 0622 687620

A small but comprehensive library of colour transparencies specialising in the wide spectrum of attractions, activities, developments and general countryside scenes across the County of Kent. The 35mm and medium format material covers many topics from Kentish towns, villages, coastline and countryside to major tourist attractions and development projects such as the Channel Tunnel/ High Speed Rail Link. The material is constantly updated. Same day despatch. Personal visits are welcome by appointment. An archive of older material and Kentish postcards is also available.
Quantity * Format S/M Colour C-D B/W+

Philip Craven Worldwide Photo-Library
Surrey Studios, 21 Nork Way, Nork, Banstead, Surrey SM7 1PB
Tel: 0737 373737
Contact: Philip Craven

Colour transparencies in medium and large format including worldwide travel, wildlife and pictorial. Specialist coverage of British scenes, cities, towns, villages, countryside, gardens, historic buildings, castles, cottages, London, landscapes and wildlife, including a comprehensive collection on British frogs and toads. Commissions personally undertaken. Travel Material is available from James Davis Travel Photography qv.
Quantity ** Format M/L Colour C-D

CTC Publicity
Longfield, Midhurst Road, Fernhurst, Haslemere, Surrey GU27 3HA
Tel: 0428 655007
Contact: Neil Crighton
Fax: 0428 641071

The library consists of a unique and important collection of material gathered internationally over a period of more than 70 years containing pictorial, scientific and technical material relating to agricultural, horticultural and environmental issues. The resource base is constantly updated and in the past year has been extended to include two smaller collections of travel, sport and general material. The library also consists of a 16mm film and video archive.
Quantity * Format S/M/L Colour A-B-C-D B/W+**

Cumbria Picture Library
PO Box 33, Kendal, Cumbria LA9 4SU
Tel: 05396 21002
Contact: Eric Whitehead

Cumbria Picture Library holds pictures covering all aspects of Cumbria and The Lake District in colour and black and white. With pictures of people, places, events and landscapes around the area. There is also a large collection of outdoor pursuits pictures, from paragliding to mountaineering in Britain and Europe. The library also holds the World's leading snooker library with pictures by Eric Whitehead.
Quantity ** Format S Colour D B/W+

Lupe Cunha/Children Photography
Second Floor, 843-845 Green Lanes, London N21 2RX
Tel: 081 360 0144
Contact: Lupe Cunha
Fax: 081 886 6812

Children/Woman's interest/Health. Medium sized library concentrating on specially set up advertising style people illustrations (both studio and location) covering all aspects of child development – in particular babies, pregnancy and parenting, all aspects of women's interests (no fashion), and nursing and the health professions. Commissions undertaken. Also Brazil Photo-Agency – a collection of images on Brazilian life, tourism, nature and scenics. Regular trips to Brazil ensure new material. Portfolio and subject list available.
Quantity ** Format S/M Colour D B/W

Sue Cunningham Photographic
56 Chatham Road, Kingston-upon-Thames, Surrey KT1 3AA
Tel: 081 541 3024
Contact: Sue Cunningham
Fax: 081 541 5388

Coverage includes a specialist collection on Brazil, which is extended and updated regularly. The wide-ranging subject matter from Indians to industry and from Rio to rainforests is based on an intimate Knowledge of the country. Chile, Peru, Portugal, Spain, France, Germany, Hungary, Austria, Holland, Switzerland, Ireland and the United Kingdom – Cornwall, London (including aerial), Scotland and rural England – are also represented in this library of over 50,000 top-quality images. We provide an efficient, personal service, and enquiries about commissions and features are welcome – we write too!,
Quantity ** Format S/M Colour D B/W+

Peter Dazeley Photography
The Studios, 5 Heathman's Road, Parsons Green, Fulham, London SW6 4TJ
Tel: 071 736 3171
Contact: Peter Dazeley
Fax: 071 371 8876

Peter Dazeley, a top name in golf photography, has a large library with over 250,000 images covering the last two decades of the sport – from 1970. This constantly updated collection includes material from the major tournaments, with images of famous and unknown players both male and female, courses worldwide and hundreds of miscellaneous golfing images; balls, clubs. His library is manned 9.30-5.30 and staff will research the images or clients can visit, by appointment only. Courier service / Red Star can be arranged. Picture selections are normally supplied same day.
Quantity ** Format S/M Colour B-C-D B/W+**

James Davis Travel Photography
30 Hengistbury Road, New Milton, Hampshire BH25 7LU
Tel: 0425 610328
Contact: James Davis
Fax: 0425 638402

The James Davis library has been built up from over 20 years of his own travels combined more recently with the work of a team of photographers at home and abroad. This collection specialises in photographs of people, places, emotive and tourism. James Davis and his photographers continuously update the library with new material. Being located in the provinces, overheads are kept lower which reflect in the competitive fees.Picture selections are normally supplied same day, if necessary by courier or Red Star.
Quantity * Format S/M Colour B-C-D B/W**

Douglas Dickins Photo Library
2 Wessex Gardens, Golders Green, London NW11 9RT
Tel: 081 455 6221
Contact: Douglas Dickins

Worldwide library in colour, 35mm and medium format and B/W, specialising in educational work in Asia and especially India. Strong on Indonesia, Japan, USA and Canada. Also covered, Hong Kong, Burma, Cambodia (Angkor Wat), Sri Lanka, China, Pakistan (Karakorams), Iran, Egypt, Singapore, Thailand, South Korea, Taiwan, Tunisia, Morocco, Uganda, Kenya, Sierra Leone, South Africa, Australia, New Zealand, Fiji, Ecuador, Peru (Machhupicchu). Britain, with emphasis on historical sites and houses, scenics, people, religions, customs, archaeology, folklore and historic buildings.
Quantity * Format S/M Colour B-C-D B/W+**

C M Dixon/Photo Resources
The Orchard, Marley Lane, Kingston, Canterbury, Kent CT4 6JH
Tel: 0227 830075
Contact: Michael Dixon
Fax: 0227 830075

Colour transparencies in 35mm and medium format, specialising in ancient civilisations, archaeology and art, especially Stone, Bronze and Iron Ages, Greek, Roman, Scythian, Celtic, Byzantine, Viking, Egyptian and Mesopotamian. European birds, butterflies and trees. Ethnology, mythology, world religion, museum objects. Agriculture, architecture, geography, geology, meteorology, mountains, occupations, scenic, travel, people and places in most of Europe including the former Soviet Union, Egypt, Ethiopia, Iceland, Morocco, Sri Lanka, Tunisia and Turkey.
Quantity * Format S/M Colour A-B-C-D B/W+**

Dominic Photography
9a Netherton Grove, London SW10 9TQ
Tel: 071 352 6118
Contact: Catherine Ashmore
Fax: 071 351 0058

Dance, opera, theatre, ballet, musicals, some films and television – an extensive coverage in colour, 35mm and medium format and B/W of all aspects of the entertainment world. The library consists of over 250,000 transparencies and negatives shot from 1957 to the present day of live performance, back-stage, studio shots and portraits of dancers, singers, actors and musicians. Whilst mostly shot in the UK, the library includes material photographed in Europe, America and Japan.
Quantity ** Format S/M Colour A-B-C-D B/W+**

Philip Dunn Picture Library
Jasmine Cottage, Marston, Church Eaton, Staffordshire ST20 0AS
Tel: 0785 840674/0860 523599
Contact: Philip Dunn

After 15 years as a Fleet Street staff photographer, Philip Dunn started freelancing for British and overseas newspapers and magazines in 1986, the year he published his first book on photography. He works on commisions throughout the world as both writer and photographer. The basis of the black & white collection is work for The Sunday Times and The Daily Telegraph travel and feature pages. The colour collection is growing rapidly and much work is now done purely for stock.
Quantity ** Format S Colour D B/W+

The E.J. Panoramic Collection
PO Box 335, West Drayton, Middlesex UB7 7JL
Tel: 0895 447473
Contact: Janice Beesley
Fax: 0895 447473

Panoramic 6 x 17 colour transparencies are the basis for this newly established library. Subjects include architectural and rural landscape and interiors such as castles, palaces, stately homes, historic ruins, monasteries etc, of England, Scotland, Ireland, Russia and Australia. The library consists at present mainly of the work of Earl Beesley, but will be expanding to incorporate the panoramic work of other photographers. 35mm, 6 x 6, 5 x 4 and 6 x 4.5 transparencies are also included in the collection, on similar subjects, as well as a large variety of photographs of ballets and ballet companies throughout the world. Commissions undertaken. If you require any further information, please do not hesitate to telephone us.
Quantity * Format S/M/L Colour D

E.T. Archive
19 Albany Street, London NW1 4DX
Tel: 071 584 3137
Contact: Anne-Marie Ehrlich
Fax: 071 823 8996

History in Art. Large format colour transparencies and B/W prints. Paintings, engravings and sculpture and some contemporary photographs. Subjects range from archaeology, botany, fashion, manuscripts, portraits and topography to zoology. Special collection on ancient civilisations, Australiana, music and militaria. We handle the Elek Archive, The Garrick Club, Nicholas Sapieha's continental house and garden pictures, Staffordshire Polytechnic's ceramic collection, Paul Forrester's Gunshots as well as material from English and continental photographers. An up-to-date catalogue is always available as well as expert picture research.
Quantity ** Format L Colour C-D B/W Illustration

Patrick Eagar Photography
5 Ennerdale Road, Kew Gardens, Surrey TW9 3PG
Tel: 081 940 9269
Contact: Patrick Eagar
Fax: 081 332 1229

The Cricket Library comprises colour and B/W 35mm photographs dating from 1965, including detailed coverage of every Test match played in England since 1972. Overseas tours e covered in some detail. The material includes cricket grounds, yer portraits, action shots and historic moments from the village g n to the great Test arenas worldwide. It is well indexed. The Wine brary is in colour and concentrates on carefully captioned photogra s of the vineyards, grapes, cellars and winemakers of France, Au ralia, New Zealand, Italy, Spain, Portugal, Germany, England and reece.
Quantity ** Format S Colour B-C-D B/W+**

Ecoscene
The Oasts, Headley Road, Passfield, Liphook, Hampshire GU30 7RX
Tel: 0428 751056
Contact: Sally Morgan
Fax: 0428 751057

A rapidly expanding collection covering all aspects of natural history with particular emphasis on the effects of man on the environment throughout the world. Subjects include acid rain, animals, conservation, development, earth sciences, energy, flowers, fungi, global warming, "green consumerism", habitats, habitat loss, industry, pollution (all forms), rainforests, recycling, rubbish, transport and urban wildlife. New collections from Antarctica, Canada, Chile, Eastern Europe, Himalayas, Malaysia and Namibia. The library is run by a professional ecologist who has expert knowledge of environmental issues and can provide a comprehensive service to the picture researcher.
Quantity ** Format S/M/L Colour D

Edifice
14 Doughty Street, London WC1N 2PL
Tel: 071 405 9395
Contact: Philippa Lewis
Fax: 071 267 3632

Buildings of all kinds and their immediate surroundings. Types range from almshouses to watermills by way of bungalows and railway stations; materials from corrugated iron to marble. All varieties of architectural triumphs and horrors, conversions, dereliction, urban and rural features and gardens. Pictures are categorised by styles, periods, building materials and architects. We specialise in details and ornament, particularly vernacular – doors, windows, ironwork, fences, etc – and in providing accurate and detailed captions. Especially wide coverage of British and American domestic architecture. Good material from France, Spain, Italy and Japan and to a lesser extent Portugal, Ireland, Holland, Cyprus, Sweden, China, Russia, India, Finland and S. America. Visits welcome by appointment.
Quantity ** Format S Colour C-D

Edinburgh Photographic Library
54 Great King Street, Edinburgh EH3 6QY
Tel: 031 557 3405
Contact: Helen Henderson

The Edinburgh Photographic Library holds a wide selection of colour transparencies in all formats of Scottish subjects. Entirely formed from original images supplied by independent Scottish photographers recognised as leaders in their profession, the library is arranged in categories which include industry, buildings, landscapes, social and leisure activities, wildlife and matters of historic interest. Operating within an administrative framework designed to provide a swift and intelligent response to client needs, the library can also offer wider search facilities or arrange for one of its pedigree "stable" to fulfil a particular requirement.
Quantity ** Format S/M/L Colour C-D

Empics Ltd
26 Musters Road, West Bridgford, Nottinghamshire NG2 7PL
Tel: 0602 455885
Contact: Colin Panter
Fax: 0602 455243

Apart from covering national and international news and features our main strength is an extensive selection of images from worldwide sports including a specialist football collection dating back to the 60's taken by FIFA photographer Peter Robinson. Picture Researchers are welcome to visit. All material can be supplied in print or transparency format, in addition we can transmit pictures from our modern electronic picture desk to clients with a wire receiver. Photographers are available to undertake commissions.
Quantity * Format S Colour B-C-D B/W**

England Scene
Suite 212, The Business Design Centre, Islington Green, London N1 0QH
Tel: 071 288 6080
Contact: Ray Daffurn
Fax: 071 288 6094

England Scene holds the world's largest and finest collection of pictures of England, covering every region and county. This well known collection is complimented by specialist collections of Scotland, Ireland and Wales offered by Visionbank Library qv who also hold the international collection. If you require stock pictures for DTP we can supply your selection on Syquest for Quark Express, PageMaker and other programmes such as Photoshop/Illustrator. Images can also be supplied on 3 1/2 inch discs. Digitised images are provided in low or high resolution formats. Please ring for details of CD-ROM and On-Line ISDN services.
Quantity ** Format S/M/L Colour D**

English Heritage Picture Library
Room 517, Fortress House, 23 Savile Row, London W1X 1AB
Tel: 071 973 3338/9
Contact: Lucy Bunning
Fax: 071 973 3001

From ancient monuments to artifacts, from legendary castles to stone circles, elegant interiors to industrial architecture, garden landscapes to sculptural details, the English Heritage Photographic Library offers a wide selection of photographs reflecting a nation's rich past. Most of the material in the collection is 5 x 4 original colour transparencies and many photographs can be ordered as B/W prints. We also have a selection of historical re-enactments such as the English Civil War on 35mm. All requests are carefully researched and normally despatched the same day. Visitors are welcome.
Quantity * Format S/M/L Colour B-C-D B/W+ Illustration**

Environmental Investigation Agency
2 Pear Tree Court, London EC1 0DS
Tel: 071 490 7040
Contact: Steve Trent
Fax: 071 490 0436

The Environmental Investigation Agency is an independent non-profit making organisation set up to protect and put a stop to abuses to wildlife and the environment worldwide. Our approach involves undercover investigation and in depth research and relies heavily on photographic evidence. Our photographic library, set up in 1985, covers many highly specialised areas such as the ivory trade, whaling and dolphin kills throughout the world and the trade in live wildlife, especially birds and primates. As well as covering abuses to the environment and wildlife we also stock a wide range of pictures of animals in their natural habitats, from rare birds to endangered whales.
Quantity * Format S Colour D B/W+

The Environmental Picture Library
90 Queensland Road, London N7 7AW
Tel: 071 700 4990
Contact: Vanessa Miles
Fax: 071 700 1821

Rapidly growing stock of pictures on environmental issues worldwide. Categories include agriculture, fisheries, forestry, conservation, development and the Third World, development and planning, economics, energy, health and safety, pollution, politics, resources, transport and exploitation of wildlife. Images to illustrate the real problems of our crisis as well as "positive" practices from local to global. Colour transparencies on 35mm to 5 x 4 and B/W prints.
Quantity ** Format S/M Colour D B/W+

Robert Estall Photographs
Falcon House, 12/14 Swan Street, Boxford, Colchester, Essex CO6 5NZ
Tel: 0787 210111
Contact: Robert Estall
Fax: 0787 211440

This rapidly expanding collection of 35mm and medium format transparencies is almost entirely the work of Robert Estall and consists of diverse documentary and evocative photographs from Britain, Europe and North America. As well as a good general range of subjects, there are special collections on standing stones and megalithic sites, cheese and cheese-making, transport, domestic and farm animals and sites involving hauntings and legends. We now have the material on Africa from eight lush books by Angela Fisher, Carol Beckwith and David Coulson as well as their National Geographic features. The books concentrate on documenting the tribal aspects of Africa, but also include landscapes and natural history.
Quantity * Format S/M Colour B-C-D**

Greg Evans International (Photo Library)
91 Charlotte Street, London W1P 1LB
Tel: 071 636 8238 (3 lines)
Contact: Martha
Fax: 071 637 1439

Comprehensive general colour library with over 200,000 transparencies in all formats and constant updating of material. Featuring Greg Evans's own worldwide travel and skiing collection and general subjects from 300 photographers. Subjects covered include abstracts, aircraft, art, animals, antiques, beaches, business, children, computers, couples, families, food and restaurants, glamour, industry, natural history, skies, sunsets, soft focus, sports (action and leisure), UK scenics and worldwide travel. Visitors welcome. Combined commissions undertaken. Photographers' submissions welcome.
Quantity * Format S/M/L Colour D**

Mary Evans Picture Library
59 Tranquil Vale, Blackheath, London SE3 OBS
Tel: 081 318 0034
Contact: Mary Evans
Fax: 081 852 7211

General historic collection, all subjects and periods – prints, ephemera, photographs and medium format colour transparencies. Emphasis on social conditions, history of technology and visual documentation of the past. Specialist material on the paranormal, from levitation to UFOs. Long runs of illustrated periodicals, British and foreign. Special collections: Sigmund Freud photographs, Society for Psychical Research, London University Harry Price Collection, The Fawcett Library (women's rights), Bruce Castle Museum (daily life 1850-1950), Ernst Dryden Collection (fashion/publicity early 20th Century), Institution of Civil Engineers and several individual photographers from 1930's-1960's, including Roger Mayne, Thurston Hopkins

The Express Picture Library
Ludgate House, 245 Blackfriars Road, London SE1 9UX
Tel: 071 922 7902-3-4-5
Contact: Dennis Hart
Fax: 071 922 7966
Telex: 21841

A general agency handling pictures, text illustrations and cartoons from Express Newspapers (Daily Express, Sunday Express, Sunday Express Magazine, Daily Star). The library holds colour in most formats, and B/W on a range of subjects including Royalty, fashion, events, personalities, nostalgia, sport, cars, showbiz, etc. Pictures by staff photographers and handled on behalf of certain freelance photographers.
Quantity ** Format S/M Colour D B/W+ Illustration**

Eye Ubiquitous
1 Brunswick Road, Hove, East Sussex BN3 1DG
Tel: 0273 326135
Contact: Paul Seheult
Fax: 0273 820775

The collection is continually growing and now holds images from 60 photographers worldwide. Subject matter varies from UK landscapes through the opening of the Berlin Wall to a large collection on Japan. There is a strong emphasis on adults and children in all aspects of their lives. Where possible, pictures not on file will be shot in the studio or on location.
Quantity ** Format S/M Colour D

Chris Fairclough Colour Library
Studio 65, Smithbrook Kilns, Cranleigh, Surrey GU6 8JJ
Tel: 0483 277992
Contact: Bridget Sherlock
Fax: 0483 267984

The library handles the work of some 200 photographers, some from overseas and consists of over 80,000 colour transparencies from 90 countries – mostly 35mm and medium format. Subjects are varied and diverse, covering agriculture, education, industry, religion, sport, transport and wildlife (a particularly good coverage of British wild flowers). Our 'keyword' searching system can usually answer enquiries within minutes and despatch material the same day. Lists of subjects available. We have full studio facilities on site and can arrange a shoot of a particular shot not already covered, at the same cost as if supplied from stock. Researchers are welcome by appointment between 9.30 and 4.00 daily. The coffee is free.
Quantity * Format S/M Colour D**

Farmers Publishing Group
Picture Library Farmers Weekly, Quadrant House, The Quadrant, Sutton, Surrey SM2 5AS
Tel: 081 652 4914
Contact: Peggy Wilson

Paul Felix
Hornbeam House, Robinson Lane, Woodmancote, Nr Cirencester GL7 7EW
Tel: 0285 831703
Contact: Diana Alexander

A collection of colour transparencies of all aspects of modern country life, this small library specialises in high quality work on craftsman tradition and modern crafts from charcoal burning and stonewalling to baskets for hot-air balloons and acrylic jewellery, with portraits and activities of the men and women who work around the country. Most are available with full text. Also a large collection of landscapes of the Cotswolds and the Thames Valley, which have appeared in the book A Year on the Thames, a full colour portrait of the river throughout the seasons.
Quantity ** Format S/M/L Colour D

ffotograff
10 Kyveilog Street, Pontcanna, Cardiff CF1 9JA
Tel: 0222 236879
Contact: Patricia Aithie
Fax: 0222 236879

The photolibrary concentrates on the photographic work of Patricia and Charles Aithie. International colour material, particularly the Middle and Far East, China, Australia and extensive coverage of the Yemen and Wales. The library is also introducing work by other photographers, film makers and artists who specialise in travel, exploration and the arts. Foreign cultures, people, architecture and the natural environment. We can supply accompanying text if required. Commissions for photo features in Wales, UK and abroad are undertaken, if you have a specific brief, project or location.
Quantity ** Format S/M/L Colour D B/W+

Financial Times Picture Library
The Financial Times, No 1 Southwark Bridge, London SE1 9HL
Tel: 071 873 3484
Contact: Patricia Lee
Fax: 071 873 3927

The Financial Times Picture Collection consists of around 500,000 items and is extremely diverse in its subject matter. The great strength of the collection rests on the comprehensive personality files built up over the last ten years, covering key statesmen, politicians and financial figures worldwide. Our photographers tour the world covering the major financial centres and have built up a fascinating selection of pictures covering industry, banking and agriculture, in both the industrialised countries and the Third World.
Quantity ** Format S Colour D B/W+

Fine Art Photographic Library
2a Milner Street, London SW3 2PU
Tel: 071 589 3127/584 1944
Contact: Linda Hammerbeck

Around 20,000 large format transparencies of mainly 19th and early 20th Century paintings. Categories include genre, marine, landscape, seasonal, floral, religious and historical. Suitable for use in advertising, television, print, stationery and book publishing. Highly commercial, they are available also for the packaging of contemporary toiletries and cassettes, etc. Clients by appointment. Research carried out for a fee. Colour brochure available on request.
Quantity ** Format L Colour D Illustration

Floracolour
21 Oakleigh Road, Hillingdon, Uxbridge, Middlesex UB10 9EL
Tel: 0895 251831
Contact: H C W Shaw

A 15,000 colour transparency (35mm) library, built up over 34 years. The owner/photographer has spent his working life in television news and film processing. Coverage is to a large extent flowers and gardens, but there is a wide coverage of travel subjects – Caribbean, Rio, Russia, Bali, Singapore, Mediterranean, Tyrol. Also Transport (air, land and water), zoo birds and animals, period costumes, stately homes, church interiors and windows. Flower coverage is of close-ups, gardens (English, European and Worldwide), shows (including 16 years of Chelsea), arrangements, flower carpets, vases, paintings and thousands of roses.
Quantity ** Format S Colour A-B-C-D

Michael & Patricia Fogden
Mid Cambushinnie Cottage, Kinbuck, Dunblane, Perthshire FK15 9JU
Tel: 0786 822069
Contact: Susan Fogden
Fax: 0786 822069

The collection concentrates on natural history subjects with the emphasis on quality rather than quantity. Photographers and administrator are zoologists with extensive field research experience, hold a comprehensive stock on forests and deserts but also supply complete articles including text and pictures with strong behavioural content such as camouflage, warning colouration, mimicry, animal/plant relationships etc. The material is very widely published internationally.
Quantity ** Format S Colour C-D

FootPrints Colour Picture Library
Goldfin Cottage, Maidlands Farm, Broad Oak, Rye, East Sussex TN31 6BJ
Tel: 0424 883078
Contact: Paula Leaver
Fax: 0424 883078

FootPrints has a growing collection of 35mm colour transparencies covering travel and related subjects worldwide. We have an extensive collection on marine life, covering fish and invertebrates in their natural environment, photographed by marine biologists and u/w photographers from around the world. Travel subjects include holiday destinations, tropical beaches and islands, culture and beach sports. Coverage of Africa, the Americas, Asia, Caribbean, Indian Ocean, the Pacific and Europe available. Food and flowers coverage is another facet of the library, creatively styled pictures taken by Debbie Patterson of herbs, fruit, plants and flowers. Commissioned food and flower photography available.
Quantity * Format S Colour D

Werner Forman Archive Ltd
36 Camden Square, London NW1 9XA
Tel: 071 267 1034
Contact: Barbara Heller
Fax: 071 267 6026

Medium format colour and B/W photographs specialising in the art and cultures of ancient, oriental and primitive societies. Subjects comprehensively covered include ancient Egypt, ancient and islamic Africa, Celts, Vikings, Byzantium, ancient Rome, the Moors, pre-Columbian America, American Indian art and archaeology, Moghul India, medieval Japan and medieval China. Rare collections include myth, primitive and oriental erotica, "white man" as depicted in the art of Africa, Asia and the Americas, masks, puppets, embroideries, oriental and primitive jewellery and Scythian, Tantric, African, Korean, Vietnamese, Balinese, Kalimantan, Eskimo and Maori art. Photographs cross-referenced, books and lists available.
Quantity ** Format M Colour B/W+

Format Partners Photo Library
19 Arlington Way, London EC1R 1UY
Tel: 071 833 0292
Contact: Maggie Murray
Fax: 071 833 0381

Format is an all woman agency, which documents social, economic and political life in Britain and abroad. We specialise in work, health, education, women's issues, the elderly and the very young. Good coverage of Black and Asian cultures, people with disabilities, the environment, politics, religion, gay issues, trade unions, demonstrations, transport and leisure. Countries include Africa, Asia, the Americas, Caribbean, Europe, Middle East, Soviet Union, Eastern Europe, Yugoslavia, China, Japan and south east Asia. We are also agents for Impact Visuals, USA. Friendly and efficient service, researchers welcome by appointment. Photographers available for commission.
Quantity ** Format S Colour C-D B/W

Fortean Picture Library
Melysfan, Llangwm, Corwen, Clwyd LL21 0RD
Tel: 049 082 472
Contact: Janet Bord
Fax: 049 082 321

A pictorial archive of mysteries and strange phenomena worldwide including clairvoyance, cryptozoology, dowsing, dragons, ectoplasm, fairies, ghosts, giants, haunted sites, lake monsters, levitation, leys, manlike monsters (like Bigfoot), mediums, metal bending, poltergeists, PSI, sea monsters, shamanism, stigmata, UFOs, visions, werewolves, witchcraft and much more. The archive is managed by Janet and Colin Bord, authors of books on mysteries, whose photographs of prehistoric sites, antiquities, churches, countryside and folklore of Britain and Ireland are also available from the same address. Wales Scene is a growing collection of Welsh pictures – landscape, towns and villages, churches, rural life and nature.
Quantity ** Format S/M Colour C-D B/W+

The Fotomas Index
5 Highland Croft, Beckenham, Kent BR3 1TB
Tel: 081 663 6628
Contact: A. D. C. Allan
Fax: 081 650 7429

A large collection of negatives of prints, drawings, paintings, engravings, maps and plans, objets d'art and artefacts as well as original engravings and photographs. The greater number are of items in museums and galleries throughout the British Isles. They cover all aspects of life and history but of particular importance are the sections covering London, trades and industries, portraits, satire, maps and schools of art. The collection is restricted to items pre 1900.
Quantity ** Illustration**

The Garden Picture Library
Unit 30, Ransome's Dock, 35 Parkgate Road, London SW11 4NP
Tel: 071 228 4332
Contact: Sally Wood
Fax: 071 924 3267
Telex: 915270 SBOS G DP

A comprehensive source of high quality original colour transparencies; featuring inspirational images of gardens, plants, outdoor living, people in the garden, swimming pools, conservatories, patios, indoor planting, water features, decorative details, still life, landscapes and seasonal aspects. From individual stock photos to complete features, photographers submit material from the UK, Europe, USA and Australia. Selected with the discerning art director and designer in mind, we offer a fast knowledgable research service. Researchers welcome by appointment and our new catalogue is available on request.
Quantity * Format S/M Colour D**

Leslie Garland Picture Library
69 Fern Ave, Jesmond, Newcastle upon Tyne, Tyne and Wear NE2 2QU
Tel: 091 281 3442
Contact: Leslie Garland
Fax: 091 281 3442

NE England is our speciality – architecture, backpacking, bridges, construction, countryside, civil engineering, ecology, environment, geography and geology, heritage, industry, leisure, mountains, natural history, scenics, seas and skies, towns and villages, transport, travel, wild flowers, etc. Other areas covered include the Lake District and Scotland, Europe and the Far East. Pictures are available in colour and B/W, 35mm and medium format, suitable for advertising, books, brochures, exhibitions, magazines, etc. Qualified photographers available to undertake commissions.
Quantity ** Format S/M Colour C-D B/W+

Genesis Space Photo Library
Peppercombe Lodge, Horns Cross, Bideford, Devon EX39 5DH
Tel: 0237 451756
Contact: Tim Furniss
Fax: 0237 451600
Telex: 9312131285 TF G

Specialist service from Tim Furniss, spaceflight journalist and author, with 25 years experience in the spaceflight writing industry. Genesis holds a comprehensive library of historical and contemporary spaceflight photographs, backed up by an expert knowledge of the industry, to provide the right photographs to meet the tightest brief. Colour transparencies, colour and B/W prints. Rockets – spacecraft – spacemen – Earth – Moon and planets. Research and reproduction fees negotiable.
Quantity * Format S/M Colour A-B-C-D B/W

Geonex UK Ltd
92/94 Church Road, Mitchum, Surrey CR4 3TD
Tel: 081 685 9393
Contact: Terry Collier
Fax: 081 685 9479

Geonex UK Ltd (formerly JAS Photographic Ltd) has a library of over one million oblique and vertical aerial photographs, it is arguably the largest collection of aerial photographs commercially available. Areas include Europe, the United Kingdom, North America, Australia and Africa. To supplement this unique collection, Geonex has an extensive range of natural history photographs from around the world.
Quantity ** Format M/L Colour C-D**

GeoScience Features
6 Orchard Drive, Wye, Nr Ashford, Kent TN25 5AU
Tel: 0233 812707
Contact: Dr Basil Booth
Fax: 0233 812707

The world's principal source of images of volcanic phenomena and Earth sciences. Providing scientific detail with technical quality from a comprehensive and rapidly expanding computerised photolibrary. In addition to our vast collections of rocks, minerals, fossils and volcanos, we have extensive coverage of agriculture, animals, birds, chemistry, Earth science, ecology, environment, fungi, flowering plants, geology, geography, icebergs, landscapes, micro-biology, sky, trees, weather, wildlife, worldwide habitats, plus general subjects. Over 140,000 original colour transparencies in 6 x 7cm and 35mm format for advertising, audio visual, books and calendars.
Quantity * Format S/M Colour A-B-C-D Illustration**

Glamour International
Vision House, 16 Broadfield Road, Heeley, Sheffield S8 0XJ
Tel: 0742 589299
Contact: David Muscroft
Fax: 0742 550113

A major and rapidly expanding collection of glamour images of the highest quality. Medium format transparencies of the most beautiful models, ranging from "page 3" studio shots to girls on beaches, at stately homes and many other locations. Pictures syndicated directly to many editorial users worldwide and to the UK calendar market. Our files also include beauty shots, keep-fit themes, make-up and romantic boy-girl themes. Specific commissions can be accommodated either in our studio or on frequent location shoots. Pictures dispatched same day.
Quantity ** Format M Colour D

The Golf Picture Library
74a High Street, Tring, Hertfordshire HP23 4AB
Tel: 0442 890424
Contact: Wendy Seed
Fax: 0442 890847

The Golf Picture Library contains photographs taken by Matthew Harris, whose work appears in Todays Golfer magazine, Golf World and Golf Weekly together with magazines and newspapers across Europe, USA and Japan. The ever increasing collection includes action and profile shots of the worlds leading players as well as golf course shots from around the world. If you need to illustrate anything to do with golf then contact us.
Quantity ** Format S/L Colour D B/W

Martin & Dorothy Grace
40 Clipstone Avenue, Mapperley, Nottingham, Nottinghamshire NG3 5JZ
Tel: 0602 208248
Contact: Dorothy Grace
Fax: 0602 626802

A rapidly expanding personal collection of 35mm transparencies portraying Britain's natural history. Specialities are native trees, shrubs and wild flowers and of these we have a particularly comprehensive collection covering a significant proportion of the list and including many rare species. Also an extensive range of habitats, landscapes and illustrations of ecological principles and conservation. Other subjects include birds and butterflies and a small, unusually diverse collection of other fauna. Photographs taken in a wide variety of locations with emphasis on a natural yet striking presentation. Subject lists available on request.
Quantity ** Format S Colour D

Sally and Richard Greenhill
357a Liverpool Road, London N1 1NL
Tel: 071 607 8549
Contact: Sally Greenhill
Fax: 071 607 7151

A wide selection of social documentary photographs in colour and B/W, including especially large coverage of child development, education, family life, medical, pregnancy and birth, and urban scenes. Abroad we have comprehensive coverage of modern China and Hong Kong from 1971 and of the USA. The library covers, at home and abroad, such subjects as industry, agriculture, education, leisure, medicine, family life, teenagers, old people, everyday scenes, religion, transport, farming, poverty, environment etc. Some material from Borneo (longhouse life), Germany, Greece, India, Israel, Philippines, Sri Lanka and Singapore. The library now has on file a selection of the Chinese photos of Alain Le Garsmeur and also the Society of Anglo Chinese Understanding archive.
Quantity ** Format S Colour C-D B/W+**

Greenpeace Communications Ltd
5 Bakers Row, London EC1R 3DB
Tel: 071 833 0600
Contact: Liz Somerville
Fax: 071 837 6606
Telex: 8953660 GPCOMM G

Colour transparencies and B/W prints on environmental issues and Greenpeace campaigns. Subjects include industrial production and waste disposal, nuclear power – reprocessing and transport. Agriculture and land use, fisheries, marine life including whales, dolphins and seals, river and marine pollution, rainforests, nuclear testing and arms, acid rain, CFC's, renewable energy, the Gulf and Croatia. We have pictures of pollution and regional geography from selected areas, including the Pacific, Mediterranean, Antarctica and Eastern Europe.
Quantity ** Format S Colour C-D B/W+

Susan Griggs Collection
Comstock, 28 Chelsea Wharf, 15 Lots Road, Chelsea, London SW10 0QQ
Tel: 071 351 4448
Contact: Helena Kovac
Fax: 071 352 8414

Now being handled by Comstock, qv. Original colour transparencies, mainly 35mm, of scenics and people worldwide; extensive files on items such as antiquities, children, food, gardens, industry, seasons, sky, travel, wine. Subject list available on request. Susan Griggs herself continues to represent UK and overseas photographers for assignments; tel: 071 385 8112, fax: 071 381 0935.
Quantity ** Format S Colour C-D**

V.K. Guy Ltd
Silver Birches, Troutbeck, Windermere, Cumbria LA23 1PN
Tel: 05394 33519
Contact: Vic Guy
Fax: 05394 32971

20,000 (and increasing), medium and large format transparencies of British landscapes. Available for calendars, advertising, jigsaws, brochures, greeting cards, books, etc. We invite you to view this collection featuring the beautiful countryside and architectural heritage of Britain. The countryside is pictured throughout the year to catch the changing qualities and moods of the different seasons and includes dramatic atmospheric shots. Attractive studies of famous cities, towns and villages, traditional cottages, colourful gardens, scenic harbours and splendid castles and cathedrals. Colour brochure sent on request.
Quantity ** Format M/L Colour D

Sonia Halliday Photographs
Primrose Cottage, Weston Turville, Bucks HP22 5SL
Tel: 029 661 2266
Contact: Sonia Halliday
Fax: 029 661 2266

Over 100,000 original transparencies. Specialists in stained glass, Biblical subjects in all media and Middle Eastern archaeological sites. Coverage on Egypt, Cyprus, Greece, Israel, Jordan, Turkey in archaeology, ethnology, geography, industry, and illuminated manuscripts. Christian/Islamic manuscripts from Bibliothäque Nationale. Illuminated book of hours. Hand painted 1840 engravings, Tassili cave paintings, Bushmen and African wildlife, Chartres Cathedral, Angers tapestries, Byzantine/Roman mosaics, murals, mythology, cloudscapes, landscapes, seascapes, Afghanistan, China, Crete, France, Britain, India, Italy, Nepal, Persia, Sicily, Spain, Tunisia, Yugoslavia. Aerial coverage of Israel, Jordan, Kibris (Northern Cyprus), Cornwall and Cornish tin mines. Book jackets a speciality.
Quantity * Format S/M Colour C-D B/W Illustration**

Tom Hanley
61 Stephendale Road, Fulham, London SW6 2LT
Tel: 071 731 3525
Contact: Tom Hanley

Colour in 35mm and medium format and B/W covering people and places in London and many parts of England, Europe, Canada, India, the Philippines, Brazil, China, Japan, Korea, Taiwan, Seychelles, Cayman Islands and the USA. Also some sixties material including The Beatles and other pop artists, the sailing of the Atlantic by Ridgeway and Blyth, the removal of London Bridge to America and the destruction of cattle through foot and mouth disease. Also First World War trenches at Vimy Ridge.
Quantity ** Format S/M Colour B-C-D B/W+

Robert Harding Picture Library Ltd
1st Floor, 58-59 Great Marlborough Street, London W1V 1DD
Tel: 071 287 5414
Contact: Jenny Pate
Fax: 071 631 1070

Our files now exceed 1 million colour transparencies and we welcome researchers to browse. Ask for our free colour catalogue with examples of the following subjects: abstracts, activities, agriculture, animals, anthropology, archaeology, architecture, art, beauty, children, cities, commodities, computer graphics, crafts, customs, ecology, education, environment, families, farming, fashion, food and drink, geography, girls, hobbies, industry, interiors, landscapes, lifestyle, medicine, natural history, people, space, sport, technology, transport, travel, etc. Now syndicating IPC and French Marie Claire Group magazines. We represent the Rainbird Picture Library which includes extensive fine art and Tutankhamun, Alistair Cowen's Beauty Bank, Kodak Library, Equinox Picture Library, The Chinese Exhibition, Financial Times Colour, Explorer in France and Schuster In Germany.
Quantity ** Format S/M/L Colour B-C-D B/W**

Jim Henderson Photographer
Crooktree, Kincardine O'Neil, Aboyne, Aberdeenshire AB34 4JD
Tel: 0339 882149
Contact: Jim Henderson

A library of medium and large format colour transparencies and B/W of NE Scotland, taken over the past six years and suitable for postcards, calendars, tourist information, PR and design groups and editorial. Subjects include castles, both private and NTS and including some interiors, landscapes, woodlands, floral, forestry, agriculture, mountain scenery, the River Dee and its tributaries, local towns, Aberdeen, coastal views and castles, stone circles, Pictish carvings, Roman sites, Highland Games, agricultural shows, golf courses, fishing, water-skiing, canoeing and hill walking. Also available, a specialist collection on 35mm of Aurora Borealis displays.
Quantity * Format S/M/L Colour D B/W+

Harpur Garden Library
44 Roxwell Road, Chelmsford, Essex CM1 2NB
Tel: 0245 257527
Contact: Jerry & Marjorie Harpur
Fax: 0245 344101

This is a personal collection of Jerry Harpur's garden photographs, from Great Britain, France, Australia, United States, South Africa and Morocco, on 35mm and 6 x 7, mainly in colour but with some B/W. It is partly inspired by contemporary designers and plantsmen's work in small and large gardens, town and country, but also includes historic gardens. Subjects include front and back gardens, plant associations, all four seasons, formal, one-colour, containers, fences, hedges, herbs, hillside, seaside, lawns, paths, paving and steps, rock, arbours, scented, fruit and vegetables, ornaments, water and integrated gardens. Earlier photographs from this collection are held by Elizabeth Whiting & Associates (071 388 2828) qv.
Quantity ** Format S/M Colour D

John Heseltine
44f Nailsworth Mills, Nailsworth, Gloucestershire GL6 0BT
Tel: 0453 835792
Contact: John Heseltine
Fax: 0453 835792

A photographers collection of about 50,000 images, mainly colour transparencies on all formats, but also including a black and white section. Landscape, European cities, food and gardens are the main subject areas. Particularly well represented places include London, Rome, Paris, Venice, The Welsh Borders, North Wales, South West England, The Downs, The Peak District and Scotland. Also there is coverage of France, Greece, Italy, Portugal and Spain.
Quantity ** Format S/M/L Colour D B/W+

Hobbs Golf Collection
5 Winston Way, New Ridley, Stocksfield, Northumberland NE43 7RF
Tel: 0661 842933
Contact: Michael Hobbs

With twenty golf books published and many articles, Michael Hobbs knows the needs of writers, picture researchers and editors. A historian of the game from its beginnings at least seven centuries ago to the present day, he has unique insight into what pictures may be of use. Subjects include well known golfers since the 1840's, other golfing characters since 1502, paintings, other art forms and memorabilia from 1350, golf action from 1746, the written and printed word from 1457, early advertising from 1880 to 1930 and playing equipment from 1600. Golf course photography a speciality. Commissions accepted for tournaments and instruction.
Quantity ** Format S Colour A.D B/W Illustration

David Hoffman Photolibrary
21 Norman Grove, London E3 5EG
Tel: 081 981 5041
Contact: David Hoffman
Fax: 081 980 2041

A colour and B/W library built up from my 35mm journalistic and documentary work since the late seventies, specialising in social issues. Good fat files on drugs and drug use, policing, disorder, riots, major strikes and protest, race issues, racists and racism, housing and homelessness. Good range of recent pictures from UK, Europe and Thailand on ecology, environmental issues and pollution. General files cover a wide range of subjects and current affairs together with odd specialist files from leisure cycling to local authority services.
Quantity ** Format S Colour C/D B/W+

Michael Holford Picture Library
119 Queens Road, Loughton, Essex IG10 1RR
Tel: 081 508 4358
Contact: Michael Holford
Fax: 081 508 3359

Art history in colour on medium and large format. Architecture and objects from pre-history to the 19th Century. Prehistoric, Sumerian, Babylonian, Hittite, Assyrian, Egyptian, Greek, Roman, Coptic, Islamic, European, Chinese, Japanese, Indian, Mayan, Aztec, Inca, African, Melanesian, Polynesian. Tombs, temples, churches, cathedrals, castles, houses, sculpture, ceramics, coins, maps, manuscripts, paintings, prints, terracottas, mosaics, textiles, Greek vases, stained glass, the Bayeaux Tapestry (complete in 80 sections), ivories, enamels, jewellery, frescoes, altarpieces, bronzes, Mughal miniatures, Hindu miniatures, Persian miniatures, ikons, early scientific instruments, early navigational instruments, early toys.
Quantity * Format M/L Colour C-D**

Holt Studios International Ltd
The Courtyard, 24 High Street, Hungerford, Berks RG17 0NF
Tel: 0488 683523
Contact: Andy Morant
Fax: 0488 683511

Pictorial and technical photographs on 35mm and medium format of world agriculture and horticulture. All factors associated with crop production and crop protection including healthy crops, weeds, pests, diseases, deficiences. people and machines, livestock, husbandry and management, factors affecting the environment. Worldwide assignments undertaken.
Quantity ** Format S/M Colour D

Kit Houghton
Radlet Cottage, Spaxton, Bridgwater, Somerset TA5 1DE
Tel: 0278 671362
Contact: Kit Houghton or Debbie Cook
Fax: 0278 671739

This specialist library covers all aspects of the horse world in colour and B/W. Racing, polo, showjumping, eventing, dressage and long distance to breeds, working horses and romantic shots. Instructional pictures are available on all aspects of riding. Almost all major horse championships have been covered since 1978 as well as Olympic Games.
Quantity * Format S Colour C-D B/W**

Houses and Interiors Photographic Features Agency
Warwick House, 7 Nevill Street, Tunbridge Wells, Kent TN2 5RU
Tel: 0892 524404
Contact: Richard Wiles
Fax: 0892 523785

Rapidly expanding stock collection of top quality 35mm and medium format transparencies of stylish house interiors and exteriors, interior design, crafts, home renovation, practical step-by-step sequences, architectural details, regional building styles, gardens and general home interest topics. B/W also available. Dossiers on complete houses of all ages and styles plus their owners (including text). Commissions undertaken. Visiting researchers welcome; photographers submissions always sought. The agency are also experienced desktop publishing packagers producing partworks, magazines and books: full writing, design, photographic, typesetting and editing facilities provided.
Quantity ** Format S/M/L Colour D B/W

The Hulton Picture Company
Unique House, 21-31 Woodfield Road, London W9 2BA
Tel: 071 266 2662 (Pictures)
Contact: Anna Calvert
Fax: 071 289 6392

Perhaps the world's most comprehensive picture resource, the Hulton Deutsch Collection comprises over fifty collections dating from the birth of photography to the most recent news pictures. In addition to the Keystone, Fox, Central Press and Picture Post collections, news and features are now covered by the daily intake of over 80 Reuters News Pictures. These are complimented by Sasha and Baron for the theatre, Studio Lisa and Serge Lemoine for Royalty and Auerbach for music. The company is the sole UK agent for Bettman Archive, New York and has direct access to many agencies worldwide. The Syndication International qv library is managed and housed by the Hulton. Darkroom and research facilities are provided and a free 70 page catalogue is available on request.
Quantity ** Format S/M Colour A-B-C-D B/W+ Illustration**

Jacqui Hurst
219 Felsham Road, Putney, London SW15 1PD
Tel: 081 789 5008
Contact: Jacqui Hurst

This is a small library of 35mm colour transparencies specialising in regional foods, gardens and crafts. The photos form illustrated essays of how something is made and finish with a still life of the object. Subjects on file – Regional Foods: farmhouse cheese makers, millers and bakers, fish smokers, oyster farmers, cockle and mussel gatherers, bacon and ham curers, cider makers, homemade preserves, chocolates, fruit and vegetable farms in Britain, France and India. Crafts: paper marblers, rocking horses, brickmakers, thatcher, terra cotta pottery, quilting, weaving, smocking, linen, trugs and willow baskets, musical instruments, rugs, dying and knitting, a milliner and Indian textiles. This list is always being extended.
Quantity * Format S Colour D

The Hutchison Library
118b Holland Park Avenue, London W11 4UA
Tel: 071 229 2743/727 6410
Contact: Michael Lee
Fax: 071 792 0259

Over half a million worldwide photographs in 35mm colour and B/W covering agriculture, architecture, art, crafts, ethnic, industry, landscape, medicine, religion, customs, urban and country life, war, disasters, transport. Also, the following collections: Disappearing World (ethnic minorities), Puttkamer (Amazon Indians), Long Search (world religions), Moser/Taylor (South American Indians), Felix Greene (China, North Vietnam, Tibet), Tribal Eye (tribal), Shogun Experience (Japan), Spirit of Asia, New Pacific and Durrell-McKenna, Kitzinger and Stoppard Collections on pregnancy, birth and human relations. Also David Hodge/Academia Medica Collection.
Quantity ** Format S/M Colour C-D B/W**

ICCE Photo Library
Greenfield House, Guiting Power, Cheltenham, Glos GL54 5TZ
Tel: 0451 850 777
Contact: Kathleen Collier
Fax: 0451 850 705

The International Centre for Conservation Education collection of colour transparencies and B/W prints, specialising in conservation and environmental issues. Scenics and wildlife from Britain, Africa, South East Asia, the Middle East and more. Forests, mountains, grasslands, deserts, seas and rivers, animals in their natural habitats including good coverage of British and African wildlife. National parks and protected areas, forestry, agriculture and domestic livestock. People, cities, towns and villages, rich and poor. Environmental impact including pollution, poaching and trade in wildlife. All photo library income supports the work of the Centre in promoting conservation education especially in developing countries.
Quantity ** Format S Colour D B/W

The Illustrated London News Picture Library
20 Upper Ground, London SE1 9FP
Tel: 071 928 6969
Contact: Elaine Hart
Fax: 071 928 1469
Telex: 8955803 SCLDNG

A comprehensive collection of engravings, illustrations and photographs, colour and B/W from 1842 onwards. Based on nine titles – The Illustrated London News, The Illustrated Sporting and Dramatic News, The Illustrated War News (1914-1918), The Graphic, The Sphere, The Tatler, The Bystander, The Sketch and Britannia and Eve – it is strong on all aspects of 19th and 20th Century history – social, industrial and political, Royalty, war, London, etc. Also the Thomas Cook Collection – a colourful travel archive of posters, brochure covers etc. c1840-1950. Brochures and rate card are available on request and visitors are welcome by appointment.
Quantity ** Format S Colour A-B-C-D B/W Illustration**

The Image Bank
7 Langley Street, London WC2H 9JA
Tel: 071 240 9621
Contact: Mark Cass
Fax: 071 831 1489
55 Spring Gardens, Manchester M2 2BX
Tel: 061 236 9226
Contact: Andrew
Fax: 061 236 8723

The top source for stock photography and illustration, with over one million images. We represent over 450 photographers and 347 illustrators, through our network of 60 offices worldwide. We hold colour transparencies in all formats organised in over 800 categories including people, industry, travel, sports, agriculture, nature, food and special effects. We now also supply black and white images. For more details, please call for a free copy of our Picture Researchers Index, or our latest catalogues featuring over 2,500 new images. Our publishing department serves the needs of our editorial clients (with special price agreements for regular users). Visitors to our Covent Garden or Manchester offices can access our libraries without any service fee. Alternatively just fax or phone your brief and the images will be ready the same day. We look forward to hearing from you.
Quantity ** Format S Colour D B/W Illustration**

Image Resource Limited
Riverside, New Lumford, Bakewell, Derbyshire DE45 1JG
Tel: 0629 812569
Contact: Christine or Tony Marshall
Fax: 0629 812569

Image Resource Limited is a specialist library and we represent over 40 artists, photographers and designers. Our specialisation is bodies of themed work from our individual artists both in black and white and colour, this includes heritage material from around the world. We transpose images onto CD 'in house' at full reproduction quality and because we keep all our material in digital form we are able to create a whole range of computer manipulated imagery, store on CD and make colour separations direct, or supply as standart photographs and transparencies.
Quantity ** Format S/M Colour D B/W+ Illustration

Images Colour Library Ltd
Kingswood House, 180 Hunslet Road, Leeds, West Yorkshire LS10 1AF
Tel: 0532 433389
Contact: Diana Leppard
Fax: 0532 425605
9 Rosemont Road, London NW3 6NG
Tel: 071 435 8175
Contact: Gary Fisk
Fax: 071 794 8853

Images is a general, contemporary library, specialising in top quality advertising, editorial and travel photography. Our stock is constantly being expanded and updated with new material commissioned specifically for the library market and available from our Leeds and London offices. Specialist photographers cover all the main stock categories and we have affiliations with top libraries around the world. Our free brochure pack is available on request. Visitors are welcome to our offices to make their own picture selections.
Quantity * Format S/M/L Colour D**

Images of Africa Photo Bank
11 The Windings, Lichfield, Staffordshire WS13 7EX
Tel: 0543 262898
Contact: David Keith Jones
Fax: 0543 417154

60,000 transparencies and 50,000 B/W negatives of Africa. Kenya is covered in great detail. Excellent material on Botswana, Egypt, Rwanda, Tanzania, Uganda, Zaire, Zambia and Zimbabwe. The natural beauty, tourism attractions, landscapes, birds, animals, forests, mountains, lakes, coast, peoples, cities and towns of the region. Especially strong sections on African wildlife, National Parks and Reserves, tourism facilities, traditional peoples and their way of life. New material and areas regularly added to our files. Assignments undertaken.
Quantity ** Format S Colour B-C-D B/W

Impact Photos Ltd
26-27 Great Sutton Street, London EC1V 0DX
Tel: 071 251 5091
Contact: Hilary Genin
Fax: 071 608 0114

The Impact Library features high quality colour and B/W editorial material, specialising in people and places with a strong emphasis on reportage. It covers a wide spectrum of subjects at home and abroad including politics, health, society, industry, sports, business, the environment, agriculture and also Pamla Toler's specialist horticulture collection. Impact has a particularly strong reputation for world travel material, especially in developing countries together with current affairs having merged with Reflex. There are over 150 contributing photographers but this is constantly expanding. A free colour brochure is available on request. Assignments are undertaken by our photographers.
Quantity ** Format S/M Colour D B/W**

Imperial War Museum
Department of Photographs, Lambeth Road, London SE1 6HZ
Tel: 071 416 5000/5333
Contact: Jane Carmichael
Fax: 071 416 5374

A national archive of over 5 million photographs dealing with warfare in the 20th Century. The collection is mainly concerned with the two World Wars but also includes material on other conflicts involving the armed forces of Britain and the Commonwealth. The bulk of the collection is B/W but there are some colour transparencies dating from the Second World War and more is being acquired as the collection expands to cover more recent events such as the Falklands. The visitors room is open by appointment from Monday to Friday, 10 to 5. B/W prints are made to order (allow three weeks). Colour transparencies may be hired. Requests should be as specific as possible.
Quantity ** Format S/M/L Colour A-B-C-D B/W**

The Independent Picture Library
Independent Newspapers, 40 City Road, London EC1Y 2DB
Tel: 071 956 1777
Contact: Elizabeth Lynch
Fax: 071 962 0018

Since its launch in 1986, The Independent has been acclaimed for its use of B/W photographs. With the launch of The Independent on Sunday, we also have an extensive colour library. Both libraries have a wide selection of images including domestic and foreign events, fashion, sport, personalities, landscapes and business, adding up to over 400,000 photographs. We are able to wire our material to clients if they wish.
Quantity * Format S Colour D B/W+**

Innes Photographic Library
11-13 The Square, Hessle, N Humberside HU13 0AF
Tel: 0482 649271
Contact: Ivor Innes
Fax: 0482 647189

The library specialises, in depth, in its own location to include rural reference of East Yorkshire, Humberside and the Yorkshire and Lincolnshire Wolds, There is a unique and creative record of the construction and of the completed Humber Bridge. A B/W archive collection covers virtually the entire Hull based principal British deep water trawl fishing fleet and related topics from beginning to demise. Industrial and technological material, food, drink and cookery, sunsets, clouds and offshore and marine material, commercial and industrial requirements. Special requirements can be commissioned. Visitors are most welcome.
Quantity * Format S/M Colour C-D B/W**

International Photobank
Loscombe Barn Farmhouse, West Knighton, Dorchester, Dorset DT2 8LS
Tel: 0305 854145
Contact: Peter Baker
Fax: 0305 853065

A specialist library of travel pictures with worldwide coverage and British scenics in medium and large formats. There are over 180,000 transparencies as well as B/W prints in the collection. The photographs are of places, people, traditions, folklore and events around the world. Our British collection features stunning large formats of landscapes, towns, villages, historic castles and coastline.
Quantity * Format M/L Colour C-D B/W+ Illustration**

The International Stock Exchange Photo Library
PowerStock Ltd, Roman House, 9-10 College Street, London E3 5AN
Tel: 081 983 4222
Contact: Gaynor Lightfoot
Fax: 081 983 3846

The ISE Photo Library specialises in business and industry photography, worldwide. Trading rooms, exchanges, business situations, cities, high tech, heavy industry, power, agriculture, transport, space, computer graphics... Our latest aquisition is PowerStock, adding new files of superb images covering travel and general categories, for editorial, advertising and design. We are conveniently situated between the City and docklands

Camilla Jessel Photo Library
13 Woodberry Crescent, London N10 1PJ
Tel: 081 444 7913
Fax: 081 883 9215

A specialised archive of babies and children. Child development, psychological aspects as well as physical growth. Childbirth, newborns, children in hospital, handicapped children and adults, socially disadvantaged children (UK, some Africa, South America), race relations and general relationships amongst various generations. Also child and adult musicians and the Royal Ballet on stage. Usage restricted. 35mm colour and B/W.
Quantity ** Format S/M Colour C-D B/W

Joel Photographic Library
Unit 105, Blackfriars Foundry Annexe, 65 Glasshill Street, London SE1 0QR
Tel: 071 721 7274
Contact: Patrick Skinner
Fax: 071 721 7276

A library established in 1988, stocking only originals to ensure optimum reproduction quality. General subjects are covered but not press or personalities. The fastest growing section is travel with a good selection of skies also available. If we cannot fulfill your request we will gladly consider shooting to your specific requirements and supplying material at stock prices. Commissions undertaken worldwide. Studio facilities available. Prompt, personal service strengthened by many years experience with advertising and editorials. Visitors welcome but please try to phone first.
Quantity ** Format S/M Colour C-D

Patrick Johns
13 Woodberry Crescent, London N10 1PJ
Tel: 081 883 0083
Contact: Laura Boswell
Fax: 081 883 9215

A wide selection of horticultural subjects including cultural aspects of ornamentals and houseplants, lawns, fruit and vegetables, containers, pests, diseases, weed control and nutritional problems and practical step-by-step pictures of gardening operations. Complete subject list available of colour transparencies on 35mm and medium format. Assignments undertaken.
Quantity ** Format S/M Colour C-D

Trevor Jones Thoroughbred Photography
55 Ashridge Way, Morden, Surrey SM4 4ED
Tel: 081 542 3584
Contact: Trevor or Gill Jones
Fax: 081 395 4054

Trevor Jones has an extensive library of high quality colour photographs depicting all aspects of thoroughbred horse racing dating from 1987. This includes all English classic races and major group races. His work abroad covers the USA Breeders Cup, the Arc de Triomphe, the French Derby and unusual events such as racing on the sands at low tide at Laytown, Ireland and on the frozen lake of St Moritz. Also on file are photographs of studs, stallions, mares and foals and early morning scenes at Newmarket together with racing personalities, jockeys, trainers and prominent owners.
Quantity ** Format S/M Colour D

Katz Pictures Ltd
13/15 Vine Hill, London EC1R 5DX
Tel: 071 814 9898
Contact: Petra Hornsby
Fax: 071 814 9899
Telex: 927960 KATZ UK G

This is an international agency with a constantly expanding library. We have a wide selection of contemporary show business personalities, general stock and serious reportage on a national and international scale. Our photographers include some leading London photojournalists available for reportage, studio and corporate assignments. We receive material from agencies all over the world, Outline, Saba, Contrasto and REA. We syndicate material from New Woman, Hello, Sky, Time Magazine and Life Magazine. We have a team of helpful researchers and you will find the agency friendly, enthusiastic and very active.
Quantity ** Format S/M Colour D B/W+**

The Kennel Club Library
1/5 Clarges St, London W1Y 8AB
Tel: 071 499 0844
Contact: Teresa Slowik
Fax: 071 495 6162

A specialist and expanding library covering many aspects of dogs and the dog world. Extensive coverage of personalities and people, dog shows, dog breeds, champions, veterinary science and field sports. The collection is mainly B/W and contains material dating back to c1870.
Quantity ** B/W Illustration

Rayment Kirby Photography
Coggers Farm, Horam, Heathfield, East Sussex TN21 0LF
Tel: 0435 32148
Contact: Rayment Kirby

This is a photographic collection devoted to pictures of women. The material is used for the calendar market, book covers, magazines and advertising and ranges from glamour to beauty and special effects. Photographs are shot in studio or on location in the English Countryside and are either 6 x 6 or 6 x 7 with a small but increasing amount of 35mm.
Quantity ** Format S/M Colour C-D

The Kobal Collection Ltd
4th Floor, 184 Drummond Street, London NW1 3HP
Tel: 071 383 0011
Contact: Dave Kent
Fax: 071 383 0044

The collection is one of the world's most valuable sources of film imagery, with over 750,000 colour and B/W photographs covering some 40,000 historic and modern film titles from around the world. The cinema has, since the early 1900's, covered almost all of mankind's activities, situations, moods and emotions. Our knowledgeable staff can quickly provide an apt image for the most abstract concept or for that elusive situational shot not available elsewhere. There is also an outstanding collection of portraits of the movie stars by leading Hollywood photographers from the 1920's to the 1960's such as Clarence Sinclair Bull, Ted Allan, George Hurrell, Ernest Bachrach, Ruth Harriet Louise and Laszlo Willinger.
Quantity ** Format S/M/L Colour A-B-C-D B/W+**

Kos Picture Source Ltd
The Glider Centre, Bishop's Waltham, Hampshire SO3 1DH
Tel: 0489 8963117
Contact: Lizzie Green
Fax: 0489 8924165

A colour library established in 1980 specialising in worldwide marine subjects from yacht racing to seascapes. With over 85,000 images and representing some of the best marine photographers in Europe and the US, Kos Picture Source is one of the more comprehensive libraries specialising in this area, with stock constantly increasing and being updated.
Quantity ** Format S Colour D B/W

Landscape Only
14a Dufours Place, London W1V 1FE
Tel: 071 734 7344/437 2655
Contact: Trevor Parr
Fax: 071 287 0126

As its name implies, a company which concentrates on landscape and related subjects in colour and B/W. Originally based on the work of Charlie Waite, it has expanded to include the work of other fine landscape photographers. A growing collection of travel landscapes and cities from all corners of the world with a strong emphasis on the UK and Europe.
Quantity ** Format S/M Colour D B/W.

Frank Lane Picture Agency Ltd
Pages Green House, Wetheringsett, Stowmarket, Suffolk IP14 5QA
Tel: 0728 860789
Contact: Jean Lane
Fax: 0728 860222

FLPA is an extensive and rapidly expanding natural history and weather library. All our photographers are carefully chosen to supply the finest images from every aspect of nature as well as agriculture, conservation, ecology, geography, geology, habitats, pollution, rural life and weather. We represent some of the world's top photographers and have images suitable for both editorial and advertising use. The library now incorporates the large collection of Eric and David Hosking and represents Silvestris Fotoservice from Germany.
Quantity * Format S/M Colour C-D B/W+**

Andre Laubier Picture Library
4 St James Park, Bath, Avon BA1 2SS
Tel: 0225 420688
Contact: Andre Laubier

35mm and medium format photographs, illustrated maps, stereographs, posters, greeting cards dating from 1935 to the present day. Geography and UK travel, especially the West Country and Wales. France, Italy, Austria, Greece, Yugoslavia and Spain. Seasons, animals, birds, botany, agriculture, urban and country scenes, architecture, archaeology (UK, New Mexico, Indian, Pueblo, Mesa Verde Colorado), art and artists, industry, religious architecture, transport, canals, sport, people, customs and crafts, abstracts and special effects. Own coverage of allied forces during WWII. Researchers by appointment only. Stock lists on request. Photo assignments, artwork, design, line drawings undertaken with pleasure. English, French and German spoken (fluently),
Quantity ** Format S/M Colour A.C-D B/W+ Illustration

Andrew Lawson Photography
Gothic House, Church Street, Charlbury, Oxford OX7 3PP
Tel: 0608 810654
Contact: Andrew Lawson
Fax: 0608 811251

Andrew Lawson's wide ranging coverage of plants and gardens is filed under three headings – gardens, plants and special garden features, such as ponds, pergolas and containers. Small private gardens are featured as well as the larger famous ones. Individual plant portraits are available as well as associations of plants. A secondary, less comprehensive collection includes English towns, particularly London and Oxford, as well as landscape and seascape. Also country customs and crafts. Foreign travel material includes Australia, Italy, France, Switzerland, Maderia. Pictures sent out promptly on request, visitors by appointment.
Quantity * Format S/M Colour D**

Simon McBride Photographic Library
Please refer to BAPLA
Tel: 081 444 7913

Simon McBride's original colour transparencies include mainly 35mm and some medium format. Comprehensive coverage of the landscape of England, Scotland and Wales, with the West Country in detail. Cities, towns, villages, some aerial shots and the landscape of major literary writers. Also gardens, wild and dried flowers. A new section in this library is a growing collection on Italy, since the photographer lives there. Photographic commissions undertaken.
Quantity ** Format S/M Colour D

The MacQuitty International Photographic Collection
7 Elm Lodge, River Gardens, Stevenage Road, London SW6 6NZ
Tel: 071 385 6031/384 1781
Contact: Dr Miranda MacQuitty

250,000 colour and B/W photographs from the 1920's to the present day covering aspects of life in over 70 countries, people, customs, occupations, fishing, dancing, music, religion, funerals, archaeology, artifacts, art, crafts, museums, buildings, transport, surgery, acupuncture, food, drink, gardens, nature and scenery. Illustrated articles from the collection are circulated to 35 countries and the collection has produced 15 books. Brochure on request. Researchers welcome.
Quantity ** Format S Colour A-B-C-D B/W**

Magnum Photos Ltd
2nd Floor, Moreland Buildings, 23/25 Old Street, London EC1V 9HL
Tel: 071 490 1771
Contact: Heather Vickers
Fax: 071 608 0020

Magnum was founded in 1947 by Cartier-Bresson, George Rodger, David Seymour and Robert Capa. Over 40 years, the agency has developed into the premier agency for photojournalists. There are now over 40 photographers working with Magnum worldwide. The library covers world events from the Second World War to the present day. In addition to unique social, economic and political coverage in virtually every country, the library also contains a vast personalities file: Monroe to Mitterand, Dean to Diana, Ghadafi to Geldof. With helpful professional staff we aim to provide the best service to our clients along with what Magnum has always been renowned for – the best pictures.
Quantity ** Format S/M/L Colour A-B-C-D B/W+**

The Raymond Mander and Joe Mitchenson Theatre Collection
The Mansion, Beckenham Place Park, Beckenham, Kent BR3 2BP
Tel: 081 658 7725
Contact: Richard Mangan
Fax: 081 663 0313

The Mander and Mitchenson collection can supply pictures of all aspects of British theatre from its earliest days. Our files include theatres, plays, musicals, opera, ballet, pantomime, music hall and circus; we also have files on actors, singers, dancers, composers, conductors, musicians, dramatists, directors and designers. We have posters, programmes, paintings, engravings, set and costume designs, books, magazines and artifacts. We supply pictures to book, magazine and newspaper publishers, to film and TV companies, interior designers and academics. We have access to individuals with specific expertise as consultants. We also answer questions.
Quantity ** B/W+ Illustration**

Mantis Studio
124 Cornwall Road, London SE1 8TQ
Tel: 071 928 3448
Contact: David Usill
Fax: 071 620 0350

Mantis specialises in offbeat travel photography. Each scene captured through the lens of David Usill is not a tourist picture, but a unique insight into the culture and the history of each country and the people who live there. We also have a specialist collection on hot air ballooning. If we don't have the picture you want, then we are happy to take it for you, we can also fulfill all your photographic requirements for brochures, company reporst and newsletters.
Quantity ** Format S/M Colour D

The Martin Library
45 Stainforth Road, Newbury Park, Ilford, Essex IG2 7EL
Tel: 081 590 4144
Contact: Frank Martin
Fax: 081 599 1166

A colour library of wildlife photographed by Frank Martin. Animals, birds, reptiles and insects from various parts of the world; India, Africa, the Americas, the Antarctic and Europe.
Quantity ** Format S Colour D

Ingrid Mason Pictures
Hill House, The Hill, Cranbrook, Kent TN17 3AD
Tel: 0580 713647
Contact: Ingrid Mason
Fax: 0580 714994

A recently formed and constantly updated library holding 35mm and medium format colour transparencies catering for magazine and book publishing. Coverage includes most home interests and travel. Architectural details – both exteriors and interiors, antiques, children, garden features, flowers and arrangements, house interiors, furnishings. Countries include Sweden, France, USA, Hong Kong, Sri Lanka, Indonesia, Thailand. From landscapes, abstract textures and underwater photography to street markets and people. Commissions undertaken by professional photographers.
Quantity ** Format S/M Colour D

S & O Mathews Photography
Stitches Farm House, Eridge, East Sussex TN3 9JB
Tel: 089 285 2848
Contact: Oliver Mathews
Fax: 089 285 3314

Library of colour transparencies taken by Sheila and Oliver Mathews. Subjects include country life, country details, landscapes, seascapes, agriculture, natural habitats, wild flowers, gardens, garden details and garden flowers.
Quantity ** Format S/M Colour C-D

The Military Picture Library
TV House, 45a Whitemore Road, Guildford, Surrey GU1 1QU
Tel: 0483 573400
Contact: Peter Russell
Fax: 0483 573686, Newbury Office
Tel: 0635 36184
Contact: David Adshead

A specialist library covering in depth the Armed Forces of the UK and NATO. Extensive coverage of land, air and naval forces ranging from the recent Gulf War to routine exercises and training worldwide. Current stock includes uniforms and weaponry, support arms and logistics services needed by modern forces. Photographs of Soviet and Eastern Bloc equipment are also available. Our photographers' wide experience of military life gets them close to the action. Military photographic assignments are undertaken on location or in our fully-equipped studio using all formats and the latest specialist high-technology hardware.
Quantity ** Format S/M Colour B-C-D B/W

Millbrook House Picture Library
90 Hagley Road, Edgbaston, Birmingham B16 8YH
Tel: 021 454 1308
Contact: Patrick Whitehouse
Fax: 021 454 4224(Millbrook Ho)

One of the largest specialist libraries dealing comprehensively with railway subjects worldwide, in colour and B/W. Subjects date from the turn of the century to the present day. Up to date material of UK, South America and the Far East especially China, but not Japan. Cities, rivers, bridges and general travel scenes. Also, England in the 1950's and 60's and a collection of steam and sail shipping. Mainly 35mm but some medium format. Rapid reply on availability. Orders dispatched same day. Clients welcome by appointment. The collection is ideal for books, magazines, advertising and calendars.
Quantity * Format S/M Colour A-B-C-D B/W+ Illustration**

Lee Miller Archives
Burgh Hill House, Chiddingly, Nr Lewes, East Sussex BN8 6JF
Tel: 0825 872691
Contact: Carole Callow
Fax: 0825 872733

The collected work of Lee Miller (1907-1977). 40,000 B/W negatives, 500 original prints. Main subject areas are: Surrealist and contemporary artists, poets and writers from the late 20's to 1970 including Aragon, Braque, Chadwick, Craxton, Delvaux, Dubuffet, Eluard, Ernst, Lam, Magritte, Man Ray, Moore, Miro, Penrose, Picasso, Steinberg, Tapies. Extensive studies of Egypt, the Middle East and the Balkans in the 30's, London during the Blitz, celebrities and fashion, War in Europe, siege of St Malo, liberation of Paris, Russian/American link-up at Torgau, fighting in Alsace, liberation of Dachau.
Quantity * B/W**

Monitor Syndication
17 Old Street, London EC1V 9HL
Tel: 071 253 7071
Contact: David Willis, Picture Editor
Fax: 071 250 0966

This is an agency created by Monitor International and City Syndication merging. Monitor Syndication specialises in leading international personalities in colour and B/W. Politics, unions, business, stage and screen, pop, sports, law, the Royal Family – a large selection being added every day. Daily syndication to international, national and provincial media.
Quantity ** Format S/M Colour B-C-D B/W+**

Morocco Scapes
Seend Park, Seend, Wiltshire SN12 6NZ
Tel: 0380 828533
Contact: Chris Lawrence
Fax: 0380 828630
Telex: 444110

A comprehensive collection of over 10,000 35mm and medium format colour originals covering most aspects of scenery, characters, cities, shopping scenes, trekking and luxury hotels throughout Morocco. The library is being constantly updated and commissions can be arranged in conjunction with Chris Lawrence's frequent visits. We also have a wide selection of travel related pictures of Greece.
Quantity * Format S/M Colour D

The MovieStore Collection Ltd
56 Abbey Business Centre, Ingate Place, London SW8 3NS
Tel: 071 498 2555
Contact: Ysanne Slide or Daniel McCormack
Fax: 071 498 6413

A new source of motion picture material from a small but rapidly expanding library. A large part of our stock has been shipped over from America and much of it has never been used before having come from a private collection. We also hold a small selection of classic US TV material. Any special requests, ie obscure TV movies, may be obtained from our US sources if you have a few days. We are sure we can surprise you with the quality of our images and our quick personal service.
Quantity ** Format S/M/L Colour A-B-C-D B/W+

Moving Image Research and Library Services Ltd
21-25 Goldhawk Road, London W12 8QQ
Tel: 081 740 4606/4631
Contact: Michael Maloney
Fax: 081 749 6142

At Moving Image, thousands of images can be moving your way in a matter of minutes. The library, serviced by an expanding team of dedicated staff, is fully catalogued on a user friendly computer network. Each shot is carefully logged in great detail allowing instant access to the right material. For more information please call us. We look forward to your call.
Quantity * Format S/M/L Colour D

David Muscroft Picture Library
Vision House, 16 Broadfield Road, Heeley, Sheffield S8 0XJ
Tel: 0742 589299
Contact: David Muscroft
Fax: 0742 550113

The David Muscroft Picture Library is a specialist collection of images of snooker, dating from the 19th Century and covering all aspects of the game in high quality colour and B/W. The collection is constantly being updated and expanded. We specialise in supplying large numbers of images for book publishers and packagers. Specific requests can be shot on commission. Material normally dispatched same day. We also hold a small, unique collection of pictures showing all aspects of Falkland Islands life from 1880 to the present day. This includes contemporary colour of a fast expanding economy.
Quantity ** Format S Colour D B/W+

Museum of Antiquities
Department of Archaeology, The University, Newcastle upon Tyne, Tyne and Wear NE1 7RU
Tel: 091 222 7846/7844
Contact: Lindsay Allason-Jones
Fax: 091 261 1182
Telex: 53654 UNINEW G

The collection includes the Hadrian's Wall Archive: B/W photographs (scenic views, excavations, etc.) taken over the last 100 years, including some J P Gibson. Also the Gertrude Bell Archive taken throughout the Near East during her travels 1900-1926 and the Libyan Society Archive. British material includes aerial photographs of archaeological sites in Northumberland and Capability Brown landscapes. Prehistoric, Roman, Anglo Saxon and Medieval artifacts from the Museum of Antiquities, including famous items such as Rothbury Cross and South Shields Bear Cameo. Visitors welcome and enquiries cheerfully answered.
Quantity ** Format S/M Colour D B/W

Museum of London Picture Library
150 London Wall, London EC2Y 5HN
Tel: 071 600 3699
Contact: Gavin Morgan
Fax: 071 600 1058

The history of London and its people from pre-history to the present day. More than 500,000 photographs, mostly B/W covering the topography, social and industrial history of London from 1840, including rare collections such as the Port of London, Pavlova and Suffragette collections. 15,000 negatives record paintings, prints, drawings, costumes and other artifacts from the museum. The archaeology collection includes 90,000 transparencies and B/W negatives of excavations and associated finds from the London area during the last 15 years. The Lord Mayor's Show recorded in detail since 1982 is represented by more than 5,000 transparencies.
Quantity ** Format S/M/L Colour C-D B/W Illustration**

National Maritime Museum
Romney Road, Greenwich, London SE10 9NF
Tel: 081 312 6604
Contact: David Spence

The National Maritime Museum has over 3 million artifacts in the collection including more than 3,000 oil paintings from the 17th to 20th Century, over 50,000 prints and drawings, copies of plans of every ship built in the UK going back to the 17th Century, plus a huge collection of navigational instruments, rare maps and charts, manuscripts such as letters from Nelson and Pepys, ceramics, weapons, uniforms, etc. The museum also houses a collection of more than 300,000 historical photographs from 1840 to the present day. Every maritime related subject is covered in the world's most comprehensive Maritime Museum. As the Museum records these items on film, more and more images are becoming available to the general public and to commercial users.
Quantity ** Format L Colour B-C-D B/W Illustration**

National Medical Slide Bank
Graves Educational Resources, 220 New London Road, Chelmsford, Essex CM2 9BJ
Tel: 0245 283351
Contact: Julie Dorrington
Fax: 0245 354710

A specialist picture bank of over 12,000 transparencies of clinical and general medicine with associated pathology and medical imaging, drawn from collections of leading hospitals and medical schools in the UK. The only collection of its kind, this picture bank has been created specially to meet the needs of publishers, authors and educators in the medical, nursing and general healthcare fields. As an aid to searching, the bank has recently been recorded onto videodisc.
Quantity ** Format S/M Colour A-B-C-D

National Monuments Record RCHME
Fortress House, 23 Savile Row, London W1X 2JQ
Tel: 071 973 3086
Contact: Anne Woodward
Fax: 071 494 3998

The NMR, part of the Royal Commission on the Historical Monuments of England (RCHME), is the national collection of photographs, drawings and written records of archeological sites and historic buildings in England. The core of the collection is the RCHME's work of survey and record carried out since 1908, supplemented by the holdings of the original National Buildings Record, the Ordnance Survey Archeology Division and the Department of the Environment's library of air photographs. The archive is divided into three parts: the National Buildings Record and the National Archeological Record in London and the National Library of Air Photographs at Swindon.
Quantity ** Format S/M/L Colour A-B-C-D B/W+**

National Portrait Gallery
Picture Library, 2 St Martin's Place, London WC2H 0HE
Tel: 071 306 0055
Contact: Shruti Patel
Fax: 071 306 0056

The National Portrait Gallery holds the most comprehensive collection of portraits of famous British men and women in the world. Well over 700,000 images in various media dating from medieval times to the present day are available for editorial and commercial purposes from the picture library. Black and white prints can be purchased and colour transparencies hired for a monthly fee. New photography may be required for rarer items but can easily be undertaken and colour prints can be made to order for displays. Orders must be confirmed in writing and are always treated as urgent.
Quantity ****

National Railway Museum
Leeman Road, York, North Yorkshire YO2 4XJ
Tel: 0904 621261
Contact: The Librarian
Fax: 0904 611112

The Library of the National Railway Museum holds outstanding railway photography and railway poster collections. The photographs range from official railway company views of locomotives and carriages to amateur views of locomotives in action. The number of negatives held totals some 250,000 and includes views of railway air services, docks, ships and road vehicles as well as views of locomotives and carriages. The poster collection contains 6,000 railway advertising posters dating from the late 19th Century to the present day. Many of the images were commissioned from well-known artists such as Norman Wilkinson, Frank Newbould, Tom Purvis and Joan Hassall.
Quantity ** Format S/M Colour A-B-C B/W Illustration**

The National Trust Photographic Library
36 Queen Anne's Gate, London SW1H 9AS
Tel: 071 222 9251/7690
Contact: Patricia Eaton
Fax: 071 222 5097

A library of mixed-format transparencies by leading specialist photographers. Principally comprising landscape and coastline in England, Wales and Northern Ireland the collection also covers agriculture, architecture, interiors, gardens, paintings and works of art, as well as conservation and the environment. Visitors are welcome at our St James's Park office and can use our computer catalogue system which includes a keyboard search facility. The National Trust plays a vital rile in protecting much of Britain's landscape and historic buildings. All income from the photo library is re-invested in continuing the work of the Trust.
Quantity ** Format S/M/L Colour D B/W+

Natural Science Photos 33 Woodland Drive, Watford, Herts WD1 3BY
Tel: 0923 245265
Contact: Peter Ward
Fax: 0923 246067

A library of colour transparencies, mainly 35mm and some medium format, of a wide range of natural science subjects from many parts of the world, including animals, birds, reptiles, amphibia, fish, insects, terrestrial and aquatic invertebrates, habitats, plants and fungi. There is an extensive coverage of British botany and a growing collection of horticultural, ethnic and freshwater angling photographs. Associated photographers, UK and overseas, subject to availability, will undertake commissions and speculative work. Applications for photographs may be made by phone or in writing. Visitors are welcome by appointment.
Quantity * Format S/M Colour B-C-D**

Nature Photographers Ltd
Ashley, Orchard Road, Basingstoke, Hants RG22 6NU
Tel: 0256 479617
Contact: Dr Paul Sterry
Fax: 0256 810880

Colour and B/W photographs of worldwide natural history and environmental subjects. We specialise in all aspects of British wildlife including birds, mammals, reptiles, amphibians, insects, plants, fungi and the sea shore. Our large collection of scenic shots are carefully sub-divided into region and habitat. The library also contains an extensive collection of African mammals, birds and scenics but our foreign coverage extends worldwide to include shots taken from the polar ice caps to the Amazon rainforests.
Quantity * Format S/M Colour C-D B/W**

Network Photographers 3-4 Kirby Street, London EC1N 8TS
Tel: 071 831 3633
Contact: Steve Mayes
Fax: 071 831 4468
Telex: 263484 NETWK

Network was founded in 1981 by a group of dedicated photojournalists and remains distinguished amongst British agencies as an organisation owned and directed by photographers with a sustained commitment to reportage. The Network archive is an extensive collection of images in both colour and B/W, fed by the continuing work of the photographers with current affairs, portraits and features from Britain and around the world. The accumulation of more than ten years photojournalism provides a huge stock resource as well as intelligent coverage of many specialist interests. The Network library now includes Fay Godwin's extensive archive. All Network photographers are available for editorial and corporate assignments.
Quantity * Format S/M Colour C-D B/W+**

Newsfocus Press Photograph Agency Ltd
18 Rosebery Avenue, London EC1R 4TD
Tel: 071 833 8691
Contact: David Fowler
Fax: 071 278 9180

Specialists in portrait photographs of leading British and International personalities, which are syndicated to the press, television and magazines. Photographs are in both 35mm colour and B/W and subjects covered include politics, entertainment, sport, media and Royalty.
Quantity * Format S Colour D B/W+

The NHM Picture Library
Cromwell Road, South Kensington, London SW7 5BD
Tel: 071 938 9122/9035
Contact: Lodvina Mascarenhas or Martin Pulsford
Fax: 071 938 8709

The NHM Picture Library contains a wide range of subjects derived from the unique collections of The Natural History Museum including items on display and material held in the Museum's libraries and the research and reserve collections. Subject categories include animals, plants, flowers, fossils, dinosaurs, reconstructions of extinct animals and past environments, minerals, gems, rocks, portraits, historic artworks by such artists as Audubon, Bauer, Gould, RedoutÇ and Parkinson, Museum buildings and exhibitions etc. Commissions for new photography of Museum specimens, artwork and exhibits undertaken.
Quantity * Format L Colour D B/W+

NHPA
Little Tye, 57 High Street, Ardingly, Sussex RH17 6TB
Tel: 0444 892514
Contact: Tim Harris
Fax: 0444 892168

The Natural History Photographic Agency (NHPA for short!) is a comprehensive library of colour transparencies covering all aspects of the natural world. Active contributors from many countries provide a steady input of high quality pictures. As well as extensive files on mainstream flora and fauna, NHPA's archives contain much environmental, agricultural and scenic material. Specialisations include the unique high-speed photography of Stephen Dalton, excellent coverage on tropical rainforests and Antarctica, the World of Shooting collection and unrivalled coverage by Peter Johnson and Anthony Bannister on African wildlife and the Kalahari Bushmen. UK agent for Australasian Nature Transparencies. Large studio available for commissions.
Quantity * Format S/M/L Colour B-C-D B/W**

David Noble Photography
Longleigh, 28 Coolinge Lane, Folkestone, Kent CT20 3QT
Tel: 0303 254263
Contact: David or Jenny Noble
Fax: 0303 850714(Bureau)

Featuring exclusively the work of David Noble. Landscapes and cities of the UK and USA on medium and large format. Some Continental including France and a good range on Vienna. Areas of US covered include New York, Washington DC, Los Angeles, Las Vegas. San Francisco, New Orleans, Boston, Florida and some National Parks. In the UK, a good coverage of the South East, South, South West, Wales, London and Blackpool. Also a striking range of scenic impression images.
Quantity ** Format M/L Colour C-D

The Northern Picture Library
Unit 2, Bentinck Street Industrial Estate, Ellesmere Street, Manchester M15 4LN
Tel: 061 834 1255
Contact: Roy Conchie
Fax: 061 832 6270

Colour transparencies in all formats. Landscapes and topographical photographs of British and world views. Also, general subjects: trees, animals, industry, farming, winter sports, seasons, sport, flowers. Poster available on request. Photographers available for commissions, possibly on a cost share basis.
Quantity * Format S/M/L Colour B-C-D**

Observer Colour Library
PO Box 33, Edenbridge, Kent TN8 5PB
Tel: 0342 850313
Contact: Alan M Smith
Fax: 0342 850244
Telex: 95351 TOPHAM G

Weekly since 1964, the Observer Magazine has created a very individual picture library. This collection of more than half a million outstanding pictures is now available for all media users from Topham Picture Source qv.
Quantity ** Format S/M Colour B-C-D**

Christine Osborne Pictures/MEP
53a Crimsworth Road, Vauxhall, London SW8 4RJ
Tel: 071 720 6951
Contact: Christine Osborne or Diana Baudraz
Fax: 071 720 6951

Life in the Middle East and developing nations of SE Asia, the Indian sub-continent and Pacific basin forms the core of Australian writer and photographer Christine Osborne's stock. Main subjects are religion, especially Muslim, Sikh, Coptic and Christian, vanishing cultures, human settlement, natural resources, tourism and the environment, agriculture and food, crafts and minority groups including gays.
Quantity ** Format S Colour B-C-D B/W+

Only Horses Picture Agency
27 Greenway Gardens, Greenford, Middlesex UB6 9TU
Tel: 081 578 9047
Contact: Mike Roberts
Fax: 081 570 7595

A specialist library covering all aspects of the horse from foaling to retirement. Top action pictures taken at the Grand National, Derby, International Show Jumping and eventing here and abroad. Horse personalities, veterinary, breeds and polo. Photographs in colour and B/W available for editorial

George Outram Picture Library
195 Albion Street, Glasgow G1 1QP
Tel: 041 305 3209
Contact: David Ball
Fax: 041 553 1355
Telex: 94018916

A comprehensive picture library of over 6 million photographs dating from c1900, serving the Glasgow Herald and Evening Times. Particular strengths are news, current affairs, Scotland, Glasgow, Clydeside, shipbuilding and engineering, personalities, World Wars One and Two and sport.
Quantity ** Colour D B/W+**

Oxford Picture Library
1 North Hinksey Village, Oxford, Oxfordshire OX2 0NA
Tel: 0865 723404
Contact: Annabel Webb or Chris Andrews
Fax: 0865 725294

A wide choice of landscape, architecture and scenic views of Oxford, particularly strong on details in Oxford colleges, the results of many commissions, mostly on 35mm with some 6 x 6. Landscape and architecture from Romance of... series of atmospheric cards and calendars, notably the Cotswolds, Henley, Stratford-upon-Avon and the Channel Islands. Pictures of historic houses, wildlife, people, aerial views. Some travel abroad. Geographical coverage is expanding. Commissions undertaken.
Quantity * Format S/M Colour D

Oxford Scientific Films Ltd Photo Library
Lower Road, Long Hanborough, Witney, Oxfordshire OX8 8LL
Tel: 0993 881881
Contact: Sandra Berry
Fax: 0993 882808
Telex: 83147 VIAOR OSF

Over 250,000 colour transparencies covering all aspects of the natural world – mammals, birds, reptiles, fish, frogs, insects, plants, landscapes, habitats, pollution, conservation, plus files on industry and technology, some special effects, high-speed and time-lapse and some B/W prints and electron micrographs. UK agents for Animals Animals and Photo Researchers/Nature Source, New York and Okapia, Frankfurt. Photo features and illustrated articles supplied for UK and world markets. Fast, efficient service. Visitors welcome by appointment. Free colour catalogue available on request.
Quantity * Format S/M/L Colour C-D B/W+**

Hugh Palmer
Knapp House, Shenington, Nr Banbury, Oxon OX15 6NE
Tel: 0295 87433
Contact: Hugh Palmer
Fax: 0295 87709

Photographer's growing collection of medium format garden pictures, amassed during numerous specialist commissions for books and magazines. Extensive coverage of Britain and an increasing number of European gardens. Practical gardening techniques, design ideas and plant types are included. Also represented in the collection are interior and exterior architectural shots from all parts of Britain – stately homes, country houses, conservatories and garden buildings.
Quantity ** Format M Colour D

Panos Pictures
9 White Lion Street, London N1 9PD
Tel: 071 278 1111
Contact: Adrian Evans
Fax: 071 278 0345
Telex: 9419293 PANOS G

Documentary colour and B/W library specialising in Third World and Eastern European photography with an emphasis on environment and development. Important issues covered include: deforestation, desertification, erosion, pollution, agriculture, industry, ethnic, religion, housing, health and sanitation and all aspects of rural and urban life. Fast efficient service. Brochure available on request. All profits from the library are covenanted to the Panos Institute to further its international work in sustainable development.
Quantity ** Format S Colour D B/W

Papilio Natural History Library
44 Palestine Grove, Merton, London SW19 2QN
Tel: 081 687 2202
Contact: Robert Pickett or Justine Bowler

A world wide natural history library covering numerous biological, ecological and science related subjects; animals, birds, plants, fish, insects, reptiles as well as landscapes etc. Papilio is run by Robert Pickett and Justine Bowler, Robert has been taking pictures for many years, has travelled throughout the world and has extensive knowledge of natural history. All colour transparencies are either 35mm or medium format, all fully captioned. We are expanding rapidly, taking on new photographers work and currently hold more than 16,000 pictures, the library is fully computerised, leaving valuable time free to devote to each client personally, so pictures can be dispatched promptly after receiving a request.
Quantity ** Format S/M Colour D

David Paterson Library
88 Cavendish Road, London SW12 0DF
Tel: 081 673 2414
Contact: David Paterson
Fax: 081 675 9197

The David Paterson Library is a highly edited personal collection of photographs with a strong emphasis towards landscape and travel. The library has two specialities – Scotland and Nepal – with large collections of each in all formats. There are also selections on Donegal, the Falklands, France, Germany, Greece, Italy, Japan, London, the Malvern Hills, North West England, Oman and the Emirates, Portugal, Sicily, Shropshire and Herefordshire, Spain, Tenerife, Tunisia and Turkey. General subjects are also covered such as industry, nature and the environment, skies and weather effects.
Quantity ** Format S/M/L Colour C-D

The Performing Arts Library
52 Agate Road, London W6 0AH
Tel: 081 748 2002
Contact: Emma Gregg
Fax: 081 563 0538

An archive in colour, 35mm and medium format and B/W based on the work of Clive Barda, covering all aspects of classical music, opera, theatre, ballet and the performing arts. Conductors, orchestras, instrumentalists, recording studios, sections of the orchestra, concerts and a wide range of costume stage shots of operas

Photo Flora
46 Jacoby Place, Priory Road, Edgbaston, Birmingham B5 7UN
Tel: 021 471 3300
Contact: Andrew N Gagg

An extensive and rapidly expanding specialised collection of colour transparencies of British and European wild plants. Thousands of subjects including virtually all the British species, rare and common, flowering plants, wild herbs, trees, shrubs, water plants, grasses, sedges and ferns, all accurately named, using up-to-date scientific and English nomenclature. Attractive coverage of each subject with pictures suitable for both popular and scientific applications. Habitat pictures also available. Applications for photographs may be by post or telephone and are normally dealt with by return. Full list on request.
Quantity ** Format S Colour C-D

Photo Library International Ltd
PO Box 75, Leeds LS7 3NZ
Tel: 0532 623005
Contact: Kevin Horgan
Fax: 0532 625366
Telex: 55293 Chamcon G/PLI

Comprehensive modern colour library servicing advertising, publishers, travel industry, calendar and greeting card companies, etc. Specialist subjects include various aspects of industry and Yorkshire views. Large format dupes supplied.
Quantity ** Format L Colour A-B-C-D

Photo Press Defence
Gilder House, 14 Addison Road, Plymouth, Devon PL1 1AA
Tel: 0752 251271
Contact: David Reynolds
Fax: 0752 222482

A specialist library of military images covering all areas of UK armed forces on land, at sea and in the air. Our files also include campaigns in Cyprus, Aden, the Falklands, the streets of Ulster, the Gulf and the war in Yugoslavia. The majority of the library's pictures have been shot on 35mm and our innovative computer system can pinpoint the library's best picture to meet a client's requirements. Researchers can visit Monday to Friday, by arrangement.
Quantity * Format S/M Colour B-C-D B/W+**

Photo Resources
The Orchard, Marley Lane, Kingston, Canterbury, Kent CT4 6JH
Tel: 0227 830075
Contact: Michael Dixon
Fax: 0227 830075

Archaeology, art, ancient art, ethnology, history, mythology, world religion, museum objects, ancient warfare. Colour in 35mm and medium format and B/W.
Quantity ** Format S/M Colour C-D B/W

Photofusion
17A Electric Lane, Broxton, London SW9 8LA
Tel: 071 738 5774
Contact: Janis Austin
Fax: 071 738 5509

The Photofusion picture library, formerly the Photo Co-op picture library, is now based in our new Photography Centre. The collection represents over 70 photographers and covers all aspects of contemporary life in Britain, with an emphasis on social issues. We now have 40,000 B/W images and 10,000 colour transparencies and new images are coming in every day. Areas which are growing rapidly are babies and children, disability, education, the elderly, the family, health, housing and homelessness, people and work. Within easy access of Brixton British Rail and Underground stations. For more information or if you want to visit please call Janis or Emma.
Quantity ** Format S/M Colour D B/W+

Photographers International Ltd
Sandilands, Blackheath, Nr Guildford, Surrey GU4 8RB
Tel: 0483 898695
Contact: Terry or Jane Fincher
Fax: 0483 898695

This unique small family agency founded in 1971 is run by Terry and Jayne Fincher. The library covers assignments world-wide from Royal, wars, personalities, animals and travel material. The comprehensive Royal collection includes special sittings by Jayne. Terry's war coverage includes Vietnam and the Israeli Yom Kippur. We are contactable 24 hours a day usually 7 days a week for requests. We undertake commissions on 35mm to 5 x 4 format. Represented by Gamma overseas.
Quantity * Format S Colour C-D B/W+**

The Photographers' Library
81a Endell Street, London WC2H 9AJ
Tel: 071 836 5591/240 5554
Contact: Bill Holden
Fax: 071 379 4650

The library has a large, constantly updated coverage of the principal European, Eastern European, North American, African and Far Eastern centres and areas. Most other favourite subjects such as industry, transport, sport, skiing, families, girls, scenics, sunsets and seascapes are also covered comprehensively. Orders are despatched the day they are requested or clients are welcome to undertake their own research. Free brochure available.
Quantity * Format S/M/L Colour C-D**

Photos Horticultural
169 Valley Road, Ipswich, Suffolk IP1 4PJ
Tel: 0473 257329
Contact: Michael Warren
Fax: 0473 233974

Horticultural pictures covering all aspects of gardening, including practical, plants and places to visit in Britain and abroad. Also wild flowers and specialist collections of garden pests and diseases. Original colour transparencies in medium and large format.
Quantity ** Format M/L Colour B-C-D

PictureBank Photo Library Ltd
Parman House, 30/36 Fife Road, Kingston upon Thames, Surrey KT1 1SY
Tel: 081 547 2344
Contact: Martin Bagge
Fax: 081 974 5652
Telex: 8811940

Colour library with rapidly expanding stock. Major selection of girl photography of leading models, keep-fit beauty to nude, mostly medium or large format. Catering for magazine, calendar, travel, advertising, etc. Children, couples, families, for all requirements. European and world scenics, many on large format for jigsaws, the travel market, etc. Large London collection, extensive and mainly European hotel collection including people. Mood, animals, sport, technology and a growing collection of paintings. Library visits welcome. Photographers available for commission.
Quantity ** Format S/M/L Colour D**

Picturepoint Ltd
94b Dedworth Road, Windsor, Berkshire SL4 5AY
Tel: 0753 833680
Contact: Ken Gibson
Fax: 0753 833681

The Picturepoint collection has more than half a million high quality colour transparencies in all formats and of all subjects. Very strong on aviation, geographical, travel, Biblical, historical, fine art, food, antiques, people, sport, industry and agriculture. Also, a collection of early 20th Century advertising. The collection grows by more than 1000 per month from the world's best freelance photographers. We relentlessly remove all the ancient, pink grotties from our files so that all our bright and colourful transparencies are matched only by our bright and cheerful welcome.
Quantity ** Format S/M/L Colour B-C-D**

Pictures Colour Library Ltd
10a Neals Yard, Covent Garden, London WC2H 9DP
Tel: 071 497 2034
Contact: Michael Queree
Fax: 071 497 3070

Pictures is a leading London library, offering top quality images from photographers specialising in the following: landscapes, travel, people, children, food, interiors, architecture, glamour, industry and still life. We also have some computer graphics. Our transparencies are individually presented and are in all formats. The library is open for business from 9.30 to 5.30 and requests taken by phone are researched and dispatched the same day. Clients are most welcome to visit the library and carry out their own research. If you need more information, please ring us.
Quantity ** Format S/M/L Colour D

Planet Earth Pictures/Seaphot Ltd
4 Harcourt Street, London W1H 1DS
Tel: 071 262 4427
Contact: Jennifer Jeffrey
Fax: 071 706 4042

Worldwide marine and natural history photographs. All aspects of the sea and man's involvement with it and a comprehensive collection of underwater photographs. Marine photographs include seascapes, marine animals and plants, underwater technology, oil production and fishing. Wildlife from the poles to the tropics include mammals, insects, birds, fish, reptiles, amphibians etc. Flowering and non-flowering plants. Landscapes include mountains, deserts, icebergs, space, coastlines, forests and rivers. Farming, pollution, ecology. Watersports, scuba diving, canoeing, hang gliding and windsurfing. Commissioned photography and film production undertaken, particularly underwater.
Quantity * Format S/M/L Colour C-D**

Axel Poignant Archive
115 Bedford Court Mansions, Bedford Avenue, London WC1B 3AG
Tel: 071 636 2555
Contact: Roslyn Poignant
Fax: 071 636 2555

Emphasis on anthropological and ethnographic subjects and also natural history, landscape and aerial photography, particularly from Australia and the South Pacific. Some European material, mainly Sicily, England and the mythology and early history of Scandinavia.
Quantity ** Format S/M Colour A-B-C-D B/W Illustration

Popperfoto Paul Popper Ltd
The Old Mill, Overstone Farm, Overstone, Northampton NN6 0AB
Tel: 0604 670670
Fax: 0604 670635

Popperfoto, credit line for Reuter and UPI(UK) qv, Agence-France Presse and European Pressphoto Agency qv, Acme, INP, Planet, Paul Popper, Exclusive News Agency, Victory Archive qv, Odhams Periodicals Library, Illustrated, H G Ponting, Harris Picture Agency, etc. Colour from 1940 and B/W from 1870 to the present. Ponting's collection holds the Scott 1910-12 Antarctic expedition. Major subjects include events and personalities, war – particularly World War Two – Royalty, sport, politics, transport and crime, the history and social conditions of countries all over the world, mainly 1930 to '60s and '70s with updating where possible. The policy of Popperfoto is to make material readily available, usually the same day, to publishers and media throughout the world. Material is loaned and reproduction fees charged. Daily deliveries to London by in-house motorcycle courier.
Quantity ** Format S/M/L Colour A-B-C-D B/W+ Illustration**

Poseidon Pictures
38 Penn Road, London N7 9RE
Tel: 071 607 4810
Contact: Michael Nicholson
Fax: 071 700 6202

The collection of former TV researcher, author and investigative journalist Michael Nicholson. Colour transparencies of Greek and Roman civilisations, Mosaics and sculptures, Western, Central and Eastern Europe including St Petersburg, Warsaw, Cracow, Budapest, Stockholm, Helsinki, Milan, Rome, Grenada, Cordoba, the Middle East, India, Pakistan, Afghanistan and Central America. Also recent transparencies of British towns, monuments and statues, natural features, rivers and bridges. A substantial collection of eighteenth and nineteenth century prints, primarily architecture, portraits, British social and colonial history, trade union certificates. Some twentieth century history including Nazi Germany. Free research, visits by appointment, prints and copy transparencies normally available within 48 hours.
Quantity ** Format S Colour D B/W Illustration

Fiona Pragoff
Acorn Hall, East Row, London W10 5BX
Tel: 071 240 7361
Contact: Lucy
Fax: 071 831 1489

An extensive collection of 35mm, medium format and B/W of children from birth onwards. Both studio and location work are represented, covering a wide range of subjects and activities. The collection has expanded and developed over ten years work in advertising, editorial and publishing, and is now housed with Stockphotos qv 7 Langley Street, Covent Garden, London WC2H 9JA. Subjects not on file can be commissioned by contacting Peter Bailey on 071 935 2626.
Quantity ** Format S/M Colour D B/W

Premaphotos Wildlife
2 Willoughby Close, Kings Coughton, Alcester, Warks B49 5QJ
Tel: 0789 762938
Contact: Jean Preston-Mafham
Fax: 0789 762938

As the Wildlife part of our name implies, we specialise in natural history subjects taken in their true environments and illustrating natural behaviour. Though we have material from many parts of the world, our coverage of tropical rainforest is superb. In addition to supplying a wide range of flora and fauna, we can also provide specialist knowledge along with the pictures. Great care is taken with identification and we aim to provide as much information as possible on each caption. Our computer also holds details of all the pictures thus enabling us to do searches using specific criteria.
Quantity ** Format S Colour C-D

The Press Association
85 Fleet Street, London EC4P 4BE
Tel: 071 353 7440
Contact: Milica Timotic
Fax: 071 353 0784
Telex: 922330

The PA Photo Library holds in excess of two million news and feature photos from 1902 to the present day. The archives include material from Central News and London News Agency. Specialising in historical, and news related subjects the library catalogues all photos issued by the Press Association, the UK National News Agency. The stock is principally of UK origin but as UK agents for European picture agencies, notably EPA, DPA and AFP, the PA has unlimited access to international pictures. The library has exceptional black and white material and an expanding colour collection. Since July 1990 PA photographers have shot exclusively on colour film.
Quantity ** Format S/M/L Colour A-B-C-D B/W Illustration**

Professional Sport
8 Apollo Studios, Charlton Kings Mews, London NW5 2SA
Tel: 071 482 2311
Contact: Tommy Hindley
Fax: 071 482 2441
Telex: 265871 MONREF G

Professional Sport featuring the work of Tommy Hindley, Chris Cole and Tony Henshaw. The library covers all aspects of sporting events and includes a specialist collection on tennis, dating back to the 18th Century. All major sporting events worldwide are covered. 35mm and B/W prints are available for editorial, advertising and commercial use. Official photographers to the Lawn Tennis Association.
Quantity ** Format S/M Colour C-D B/W**

Punch Cartoon Library
Ludgate House, 245 Blackfriars Road, London SE1 9UZ
Tel: 071 921 5900
Contact: Amanda-Jane Doran
Fax: 071 928 5158

Cartoons, caricatures and illustrations on all subjects: personalities, politics, fashion, royalty, the arts, sport, animals, law, medicine, family life including thousands of victorian engravings. Sole copyright holders of punch cartoon material, the collection extends pre-Punch (1841) and to international cartoon material. Cartoons are subject indexed, same day print service available. Researchers welcome by appointment at our convenient South Bank offices, alternatively phone or fax your enquiries.
Quantity ** Illustration**

QA Photos Ltd
8 Stade Street, Hythe, Kent CT21 6BD
Tel: 0303 268233
Contact: Villy Pereboom
Fax: 0303 266273

QA Photos are the official photographers for Eurotunnel on the Channel Tunnel Project and have been involved since the early days. Thus the library has a large, increasing collection covering all facets of the tunnel works, including those in France, plus many other aspects of the project. The photographs are those which are valuable for technical reasons as well as many which are visually interesting. Due to the nature of the project, the stock is held principally on colour negative film which produces exceptionally high quality prints or transparencies. A significant stock of other material is available covering Dover Harbour, cross-channel ferries and other transport and maritime subjects.
Quantity * Colour D**

Quadrant Picture Library
Quadrant House, The Quadrant, Sutton, Surrey SM2 5AS
Tel: 081 661 8888
Contact: Kim Hearn
Fax: 081 661 8933
Telex: 892084 REEDBP G

A collection of colour on 35mm and medium format and B/W, covering all aspects of transport and motorsports from the early years of the century to the present day. Included are cars, commercial vehicles, bicycles, aeroplanes, motor boats, yachts and trains. Material is produced by the journals of Reed Business Publishing Ltd. Also included is a collection of motoring artwork from the 1920's and 30's, which is available on transparency.
Quantity ** Format S/M Colour C-D B/W Illustration**

Railways and Steam Locomotives of the World
Milepost 92 1/2, Newton Harcourt, Leicestershire LE8 0FH
Tel: 0533 592068
Contact: Maggie Grzyb
Fax: 0533 593001

Twenty years ago, Colin Garratt devoted his life to documenting professionally the last working steam locomotives of the world. His pictures are known internationally for their beauty and range of expressions – every mood, colour and location to provide the definitive source of images for every conceivable use. Already he has covered some fifty countries but his global quest proceeds apace providing a continuous source of exciting, fresh material of both steam and modern railways. The library also contains the work of other leading railway photographers including Dr Bill Sherman's celebrated collection of famous trains, tourist/preserved railways and modern traction. Brochure available.
Quantity ** Format S/M Colour A-B-C-D B/W Illustration

Raleigh International Picture Library
Raleigh House, 27 Parsons Green Lane, London SW6 4HS
Tel: 071 371 8585
Contact: Mark Bainbridge
Fax: 071 371 5116
Telex: 892781 RALLON G

A new source of colour images from locations around the world. The picture library provides striking new insights into all aspects of stock location photography by some of Britain's top professional photographers. We update our unique 50,000+ stock eight times each year. Alongside the location collection we offer a specialist photographic service: shooting to specific order on location at standard reproduction fee rates (portfolio reference available on request). We also produce a wide range of photo features from each expedition which can be tailored to specification by our writers, available as exclusives for national and international publication. Free search for first time users and open to researchers by appointment, 9.30 – 5.30 weekdays (weekends on request).
Quantity ** Format S/M Colour C-D B/W

Redferns
7 Bramley Road, London W10 6SZ
Tel: 071 792 9914
Contact: David Redfern
Fax: 071 792 0921

David Redfern's photo library covers every aspect of popular music from the 1920's to the present day. Rock & Pop, Jazz & Blues, Folk & Country, Cajun & Zydeco, Heavy Metal, Reggae and World music. With an ever increasing range of over 5,000 artists, the library also contains one of the largest Jazz and Blues collections in the world, incorporating a unique selection of black & whites from the 20's to the 50's jazz era. Other subjects include musical instruments, orchestras, recording studios and equipment, CD and record manufacturing, atmospherics, stage lighting and special effects, crowd scenes, festivals and dancers. Full library list and colour brochure available on request.
Quantity ** Format S/M Colour A-B-C-D B/W+**

Reed Consumer Books Picture Library
Michelin House, 81 Fulham Road, London SW3 6RB
Tel: 071 581 9393
Contact: Sally Claxton
Fax: 071 589 8421

The Reed Consumer Books Picture Library is an established source holding a wide range of subjects, in all formats, colour and B/W. We have an extensive selection of high quality cookery pictures, and other strong areas include gardening, natural history, health and fitness and history. The library was originally set up to serve the Octopus Publishing Group (Octopus, Hamlyn and Mitchell Beazley publishers) and to store pictures which were commissioned for our books over the years, but in recent times we have built up our service to include clients from outside the group. We do, however, reserve the right not to sell rights to competing book publishers.
Quantity * Format S/M/L Colour C-D B/W**

Reflections Photolibrary
The Bath Brewery, Toll Bridge Road, Bath, Avon BA1 7DE
Tel: 0225 852554
Contact: Colin Bowers or Jennie Woodcock
Fax: 0225 852528

A specialist library with a comprehensive stock of colour transparencies of people, world wildlife and landscapes. Jennie Woodcock has an established reputation for photographic quality and a sensitive approach in the areas of maternity, childhood, family life, health and education. Jennie is continuously adding new material to the library and is also available for commission. Martin Dohrn is a highly respected wildlife cameraman and whilst filming, has taken many stunning and rare transparencies of birds, animals, insects, tribes and landscapes in locations as varied as Papua New Guinea and Bolivia.
Quantity ** Format S Colour D B/W+

Relay Photos Ltd
10 Vale Royal, York Way, London N7 9AP
Tel: 071 700 0771
Contact: Andre Csillag
Fax: 071 700 6842

Comprehensive library of over 500,000 colour and B/W pictures covering popular music over the last twenty five years. Specialising in rock, pop, soul and heavy metal, the roster of over 1500 groups and artists is constantly being expanded and updated from work undertaken worldwide. Full list available on request. Researchers welcome by appointment. Requests by phone or fax dispatched same day.
Quantity ** Format S Colour B-C-D B/W**

Repfoto London
74 Creffield Road, Acton, London W3 9PS
Tel: 081 992 2936
Contact: Robert Ellis
Fax: 081 992 9641

Specialists in rock, pop, folk and jazz music and musicians. The library consists of colour on 35mm and medium format and B/W photographs of musicians performing, backstage, on the road and in the photo studio, on location, in the recording studio, at festivals. Particularly strong on rock and heavy metal subjects from the late '60s to date.
Quantity ** Format S Colour B-C-D B/W

Retna Pictures Ltd
1 Fitzroy Mews, (off Cleveland St), London W1P 5DQ
Tel: 071 388 3444
Contact: Anne Holley
Fax: 071 383 7151

An extensive library of colour transparencies in all formats and B/W prints, representing a large number of top class photographers. The library specialises in high quality portraits and performance shots of international rock and pop personalities, actors and actresses, entertainers and celebrities. We can also provide material from our general stock library which covers an increasing range of subjects including travel, flora and fauna, people, the environment, sport and leisure, etc. Offices in New York and Los Angeles and associated agencies worldwide. Colour brochure available. Personal callers welcome.
Quantity ** Format S/M/L Colour A-B-C-D B/W**

Retrograph Archive Ltd
164 Kensington Park Road, Notting Hill Gate, London W11 2ER
Tel: 071 727 9378/9426/6422(24hr)
Contact: Jilliana Ranicar-Breese
Fax: 071 229 3395

A vast archive of commercial and decorative art (1860-1960). Worldwide labels and packaging for food, wine, chocolate, soap, perfume, cigars and cigarettes. Fine art and commercial art journals, fashion magazines, posters, Victorian greeting cards, wallpaper and gift wrap sample books, music sheets, folios of decorative design and ornament – Art Nouveau and Deco – hotel, shipping and airline labels, memorabilia, tourism, leisure, poster art, postcards, food and drink, transport and entertainment. Suitable for books, cards, calendars, gift and social stationery, compact discs. Originals viewed then photographed to order. Lasers for book dummies, packaging mock-ups, film and TV action props. Brochure on request.
Quantity ** Format M Colour D B/W Illustration**

Reuter and UPI
Available from Popperfoto, The Old Mill, Overstone Farm, Overstone, Northampton NN6 0AB
Tel: 0604 670670
Fax: 0604 670635

Daily news coverage on international events, taking in around 90-150 B/W pictures daily. Subjects include international politics, wars, disasters, Royalty, personalities and worldwide news events. Photos are transmitted from the ends of the Earth, so there is no waiting for planes to arrive. Popperfoto qv have been the UK agents for UPI for many years and Reuters since the photo service started in 1985. The UPI collection includes Planet News and commences mid 1920's continuing, largely complete, through to today's news photos.
Quantity ** B/W+**

Rex Features Ltd
18 Vine Hill, London EC1R 5DX
Tel: 071 278 7294/3362(Library)
Contact: Paul Brown
Fax: 071 837 4812
Telex: 25491 REXPHO G

Comprehensive colour – 35mm and some medium format – and B/W library established in the early 1950s. Constantly expanded stock includes national and international news, politics, personalities, show business, rock and pop, glamour, animals both humorous and scientific, art, medicine, science, situations and landscapes. Specialities include current affairs, off-beat and amusing pictures, candid and studio celebrities and British and foreign Royalty. Many renowned photographers are represented. Pictures readily available both individually and as features with quick access via a fully computerised system. Rex also has access to the Russian historical and space archives,
Quantity ** Format S/M/L Colour A-B-C-D B/W+ Illustration**

Rida Photo Library
21 Victoria Road, Surbiton, Surrey KT6 4JZ
Tel: 081 399 0810
Contact: David Bayliss
Fax: 081 390 5400
Telex: 291561 VASOS G

An established library specialising in geological and geographical subjects, urban and rural life, scenery, architecture and places of general interest. Fossils – collection and preservation, dinosaurs and other reptiles, mammals, birds, invertebrates, plants, trace fossils, early man etc. Minerals and rocks – most common types and many rare varieties. Field geology/geography – mountains and volcanoes, rock outcrops and structures, coastal features, rivers, glaciers, deserts, habitats, soils, weather etc. Economic geology/geography – oil, mining and quarrying, industry, farming, fishing, power generation, dams, reservoirs, transport and communications etc. Also regional collections especially of the British Isles, Western Europe, Africa and the USA.
Quantity * Format S/M/L Colour B-C-D B/W

Ann Ronan at Image Select
Premier House, 2 Gayton Road, Harrow, Middlesex HA1 2XU
Tel: 081 863 9001
Contact: Alexander Goldberg
Fax: 081 861 4755

History of science and technology: illustrations, mainly from printed sources from AD1500 to early twentieth century, including personalities, scientific experiments, manufacturing processes, mining, agricultural practices, transport, working and living conditions, child labour, cookery, communications, recreations, medicine, etc. Approximately 7% in colour. Original material not loaned but supplied as B/W prints or colour transparencies.
Quantity * Illustration**

Royal Air Force Museum
Grahame Park Way, Hendon, London NW9 5LL
Tel: 081 205 2266 ext 208
Contact: Christine Gregory
Fax: 081 200 1751

The photographic collection records the history of military aviation from its earliest days to the present. The development of aircraft is covered both at home and overseas, from balloons to space flight. The majority of the collection is black and white. Some colour photographs are available from World War Two to the present. All formats are available and copies can be supplied. The museum also owns the Charles E Brown Collection. The Reading Room can be used by prior appointment Monday – Friday, 10 – 4.30. Limited research will be carried out and search fees will be charged.
Quantity * Format S/M/L Colour A-B-C-D B/W**

Royal Geographical Society Picture Library
1 Kensington Gore, London SW7 2AR
Tel: 071 589 5466
Contact: Nicky Sherriff
Fax: 071 584 4447

The bulk of the collection consists of some 200,000 monochrome prints of geographical exploration, travel and environment dating from the 1870's to the middle of this century. In 1990, Remote Source Photographic Library was amalgamated with our collection which brings this global coverage up to date as photographers on directory bring back images from all parts of the world. Thus the collection constitutes a unique record of the world, its landscapes and its peoples over the past century. Notable collections include the expeditions of Scott and Shackleton to Antarctica, and the successful 1953 British ascent of Everest. This tradition is continued today to cover recent RGS expeditions to remoter regions of the world.
Quantity * Format S/L Colour A-B-C-D B/W+ Illustration**

The Royal Opera House Archives
The Royal Opera House, Covent Garden, London WC2E 9DD
Tel: 071 240 1200
Contact: Francesca Franchi
Fax: 071 836 1762

The Royal Opera House Archives were formally established in 1969 with the aim of recording the history of the Royal Opera House since the first theatre opened on the site in 1732. Visual material includes some 18th and 19th century prints and song sheets and an ever increasing collection of photographs, principally of the three ROH companies and the building. The Archives also contain costume and set designs, programmes, posters, press cuttings, correspondence and administrative records. Open by appointment, weekdays except Wednesday. Hire fee for duplicate B/W and colour transparencies of non-copyright material. Copyright clearance, where applicable, responsibility of the user.
Quantity * Format S/M Colour B-C-D B/W+ Illustration**

Royal Photographic Society
The Octagon, Milsom Street, Bath, Avon BA1 1DN
Tel: 0225 462841
Contact: Deborah Ireland
Fax: 0225 488688

This collection of over 80,000 images covers the history and progress of photography. The subject emphasis is pictorial and photography as an art rather than documentary record, though there are exceptions. Dating from 1827 with heliogravures by NiÇpce, the collection is represented by all legendary photographers from both sides of the Atlantic, is largely donated and represents the photographer rather than the subject. There are substantial holdings on portraiture, 19th Century landscapes, architecture, India, Victorian rural life, etc. Staff are happy to help with queries about more esoteric subject matter. 15,000 B/W images arranged in an alphabetical index make subject searching relatively easy. Prints are available and other material can be copied on request. Visits by appointment only, Monday to Friday, 10-5. Charges depend on degree of staff involvement. Express Service.
Quantity * Format S/M/L Colour A-B-C-D B/W**

RSPB Photolibrary
The Lodge, Sandy, Bedfordshire SG19 2DL
Tel: 0767 680551
Contact: Chris Sargeant
Fax: 0767 692365

The RSPB is Europe's largest voluntary conservation organisation and the Society's photo library reflects the scope of our conservation effort. 50,000 colour transparencies in all formats and 15,000 B/W prints – and expanding, representing various photographers. Subjects include British birds, butterflies, mammals and reptiles. RSPB nature reserves, habitats and land management, environmental threats, practical conservation work, birdtables and feeders, birdwatching activities and oil pollution. All profits directed to RSPB's conservation work. Visitors by appointment please.
Quantity ** Format S/M/L Colour D B/W+

The Russia and Republics Photo Library
Conifers House, Cheapside Lane, Denham, Uxbridge, Middlesex UB9 5AE
Tel: 0895 834814
Contact: Mark Wadlow
Fax: 0895 834028

A growing colour library on 35mm and 6 x 6 formats covering the former Soviet Union. We have over 60 locations on file including a recently improved section on the Baltic republics. The library covers cityscapes, street scenes, famous landmarks, landscapes, festivals, the colourful markets and the different people and nationalities of Russia and the Republics.
Quantity * Format S/M Colour D

S & G Press Agency Ltd
68 Exmouth Market, Clerkenwell, London EC1R 4RA
Tel: 071 278 1223
Contact: Paul Kurton
Fax: 071 278 8480

Sport and General is one of the oldest press photo libraries in Britain. The library has more than 300,000 colour transparencies and over 1,000,000 B/W negatives reflecting each decade of this century. As the name suggests, we are a specialist sports library but we also have a vast collection of news, personality and Royalty photographs. Opening hours are 9 to 6. Requests can be made by phone or letter and the library is open for clients who would like to do their own research.
Quantity ** Format S/M Colour A-B-C-D B/W+**

Peter Sanders Photography
Shura Studios, 9 Meades Lane, Chesham, Buckinghamshire HP5 1ND
Tel: 0494 773674
Contact: Peter or Hafsa
Fax: 0494 722626
Telex: 838791/JMC G (Attn Shura)

Peter Sanders photographic library specialises in the Islamic World in all its aspects. This covers the modern, traditional and cultural, its people, cities, religious practices and beliefs. Countries included are Saudi Arabia, India, Egypt, Morocco, Sudan, Mali, Mauritania, Senegal, USA and of course the UK. We provide an insight into a once closed society. The library has now begun to expand and to explore other world religions and faiths. Regular travel updates the library with new material and this year we hope to be adding several exciting collections.
Quantity ** Format S/M Colour B-C-D B/W+

Science Photo Library Ltd
112 Westbourne Grove, London W2 5RU
Tel: 071 727 4712
Contact: Michael Marten
Fax: 071 727 6041

The world's leading source of imagery on all aspects of science, technology and medicine. Top quality colour and B/W pictures on 35mm and medium format. Spectacular abstract, specialist and false-colour images. Fast, expert service, detailed captions. Laboratories, hospitals, industry, technical and medical pictures. Astronomy, biology and biotechnology, botany, chemistry, computers and computer graphics, earth sciences and terrestrial phenomena, genetics, landscapes, medicine and physiology, physics, satellite imagery, scientific illustrations and artworks, spaceflight, technology and zoology. Free 48pp colour brochure available.
Quantity * Format S/M Colour C-D B/W+ Illustration**

Scottish Highland Photo Library
Croft Roy, Crammond Brae, Tain, Ross-shire IV19 1JG
Tel: 0862 892298
Contact: Hugh Webster

The Scottish Highland Photo Library is a contemporary photo resource specialising in subjects from the Highlands and Islands of Scotland. We are attempting to cover the whole spectrum of life, leisure, landscape, and work in the Highlands and Islands. From beautiful landscapes of all seasons to castles and Highland games, from crofting life in remote areas to modern agriculture, from traditional industries like whisky to computers, from skiing to gold panning, from salmon fishing to golf. The material is of high quality and available for most forms of usage, a proportion of the material would also be suitable for stock illustration. This Library now manages much of the Scottish material belonging to Alba Pictures. Commissions very welcome.
Quantity ** Format S/M Colour D B/W

Screen Ventures Ltd
49 Goodge St, London W1P 1FB
Tel: 071 580 7448
Contact: Michael Evans
Fax: 071 631 1265
Telex: 8951182 GECOMS

Extensive collection in colour and B/W of Asia, the Middle East and Northern Africa. Coverage includes every aspect of life in these areas: cultural, everyday scenes, landmarks, customs, the arts, technology, education, leisure, industry, agriculture, politics, religion and religious activities and personalities. Specialised knowledge and latest back-up information may be provided when requested. Commissions undertaken in the areas covered.
Quantity ** Format S Colour C-D B/W

Sealand Aerial Photography
Goodwood Airfield, Chichester, West Sussex PO18 0PH
Tel: 0243 781025
Contact: Malcolm Knight
Fax: 0243 531422

Comprehensive colour aerial photographic coverage of subjects throughout the UK. We operate all through the year, utilising our own aircraft. The library contains over 400,000 negatives and transparencies on medium format. All applications of aerial photography are covered and rapid searches can be made through our computer data-base system.
Quantity ** Format M Colour D**

Sefton Photo Library
30 Mason Street, Manchester M4 5EY
Tel: 061 832 7670/834 9423
Contact: Sefton Samuels
Fax: 061 834 9423

Wide selection of general subjects from the obvious to the obscure – Sewage works to the Seychelles, via the Bacup Coconutters. Industry, oil rigs and refineries, space photos, pictorials both UK and abroad, Northern speciality. The environment, farming, sunsets, family scenes, business situations, sport, animals, tropical beaches, Victorian/Edwardian collection, historic transport, personalities of the area and now Sefton's own atmospheric jazz pictures, shown at the Barbican recently. We cater for advertising and publishing outlets. Down to earth Northern prices too! Colour on 35mm and medium format and B/W.
Quantity * Format S/M Colour C-D B/W+**

Select Photo Agency & Picture Library
N5 Studio, Metropolitan Wharf, Wapping Wall, London E1 9SS
Tel: 071 265 1422
Contact: Shirley Berry
Fax: 071 265 1421
Telex: 8591182 GECOMS G

Select specialises in news and current affairs, as well as the economy, the environment and Europe. The library expands weekly as the 14 photographers add fresh material from all over the world. Our photographers include Dario Mitidieri, Steve Connors, Simon Norfolk and TJ Lemon (South Africa). We also represent OROP, Paris, Cover, Madrid, Granata, Milan, Zenit, Berlin, Eastern Network, Vienna and JB, New York. Commissions undertaken. Researchers welcome.
Quantity * Format S/M Colour D B/W+**

Phil Sheldon Golf Picture Library
3 Grimsdyke Crescent, Arkley, Barnet, Herts EN5 4AH
Tel: 081 440 1986
Contact: Gill Moyes
Fax: 081 440 9348

The Golf Picture Library comprises over 200,000 colour and B/W photographs dating from 1976, including detailed coverage of over 40 major championships, several Ryder Cup matches and over 300 other golf tournaments. This expanding collection also includes player action, portraits, instruction material, trophys and over 150 golf courses from around the world. A new addition to the collection is the work from the 60's and early 70's of photographer Sidney Harris – mostly in B/W but includes some colour.
Quantity * Format S Colour C-D B/W+**

Brian Shuel
13 Woodberry Crescent, London N10 1PJ
Tel: 081 883 0083
Contact: Brian Shuel
Fax: 081 883 9215

The founding part of Collections qv, consisting of British traditional customs, British bridges, a sizable file on London and a miscellany of black and white fun. The custom files, covering over 200 subjects and including old illustrations, developed from a B/W project on the 'folk revival' in the sixties, with the earliest pictures of some now famous performers. The 350 bridges include every type from the pre-historic 'clam' bridges to the latest in pre-stressed concrete. The black and white is the result of 30 years of professional work as well as 30 years of sheer pleasure in photography.
Quantity * Format S/M Colour B-C-D B/W+ Illustration**

Anthea Sieveking
13 Woodberry Crescent, London N10 1PJ
Tel: 081 883 0083
Contact: Laura Boswell
Fax: 081 883 9215

A major part of Collections qv, consisting of over 24,000 transparencies on 35mm and medium format, specialising in human relationships from pregnancy, through birth, babies, child development, education, health and family life to old age. The collection was re-edited in 1990 but continues to grow. Commissions are welcomed – many have been carried out for the World Health Organisation and for a number of books, notably Dr Miriam Stoppard's definitive New Baby Care Book published in 1990. An interesting B/W collection of sixties portraits includes famous actors and authors and Sir Winston Churchill.
Quantity ** Format S/M Colour B-C-D B/W

Skishoot – Offshoot
28 Dalebury Road, London SW17 7HH
Tel: 081 767 0059
Contact: Jo Hiles or John Packington
Fax: 081 767 6680

Skishoot is Britain's specialist ski picture library specialising in high quality original transparencies. More than 50,000 colour transparencies feature every aspect of the sport including action shots, snowboarding, parapente, children, fashion, snowscapes and all major resorts in the Alps, USA, and Japan. Most of our pictures are taken by our own staff photographers, and we will also shoot for you on location or in a studio. Offshoot is a travel picture library specialising in high quality originals of all the major countries of the world.
Quantity ** Format S/M Colour D B/W

Skyscan Balloon Photography
Oak House, Toddington, Cheltenham, Gloucestershire GL54 5BY
Tel: 0242 621357 (24hrs)
Contact: Brenda Marks
Fax: 0242 621343

A unique collection of aerial views of Britain taken from a camera platform suspended beneath a tethered balloon. Cameras are remotely controlled by a ground operator and flown at heights of 60' to 600' – lower and closer to the subject than aircraft. A TV link allows precise composition and the vibration free system results in high quality images. The collection ranges from industrial and city scenes to open countryside and coastal views with an emphasis on landscape, stately homes and heritage sites and a large collection of the Thames, the Cotswolds and London. Transparencies, colour negative and B/W on medium format. Commissions undertaken, also infra-red and thermographic aerial surveys.
Quantity ** Format M Colour D B/W+

South American Pictures
48 Station Road, Woodbridge, Suffolk IP12 4AT
Tel: 0394 383963/383279
Contact: Marion Morrison
Fax: 0394 380176

Marion and Tony Morrison offer 100,000 colour and 25,000 B/W images of South America, Central America and Mexico. The collection is backed by 25 years' experience of film-making, travel and writing about South America. Almost every topic is covered and some – Amazonia, archaeology and environment – are extensively represented. Associates based in Latin America constantly send new pictures and information. Complementing the photographs our extensive library offers an archive of historical pictures and documents from most countries.
Quantity * Format S/M Colour B-C-D B/W+**

Space Frontiers Ltd
The Telegraph Colour Library, Visual House, 1 Mastmaker Rd, London E14 9WT
Tel: 071 987 1212
Contact: Julie Potter
Fax: 071 538 3309
Telex: 888258

Specialist library of still and movie images derived from the US manned and unmanned space programme – rocket launches, deep space and orbital views of the Earth and its regions, including the UK, men and machines in 'free' space and on the moon, spacecraft images of sun and planets, computer enhancements, images of spacecraft and a large selection of space shuttle material. Images of Earth from British, European and Japanese resource centres and space agencies. Pictures of constellations and telescope views of comets, planets, galaxies and nebulae. Space art. Earth surface/weather pictures of natural phenomena. Technical consultancy and editorial service on these subjects from H J P Arnold on 0705 475313.
Quantity ** Format S/M/L Colour A-B-C-D B/W

Spectrum Colour Library
41-42 Berners Street, London W1P 3AA
Tel: 071 637 1587
Contact: Keith Jones
Fax: 071 637 3681
Unit 13 Holly Park Mills, Woodhall Road, Calverley, Pudsey, West Yorkshire LS28 5QS
Tel: 0532 394020
Contact: Peter Dransfield
Fax: 0532 361506

A large and extensive general library of modern, selectively edited, high-quality transparencies with superb up to date travel coverage suitable for advertising, brochure and editorial use etc. We handle the work of over 600 international photographers and more than 30 corresponding worldwide photo libraries. We also handle the material from the ILG, Intasun, Global, Lancaster, Select, NAT travel libraries. The north of England is serviced by our Leeds office. Our colour catalogues are free to professional photography buyers. We offer fast, friendly and efficient service. 'Phone us first on 071 637 1587 in London or 0532 394020 in Leeds.
Quantity ** Format S/M/L Colour C-D B/W+**

Split Second
1a Doughty Street, Grays Inn Road, London WC1N 2PH
Tel: 071 831 4316
Contact: Leo Mason
Fax: 071 831 4322

Leo Mason specialises in sports and live action with a very high creative bias and is available for directly commissioned work. In addition, Split Second has a very comprehensive selection of original colour transparencies on 35mm and medium format, all of which can be viewed at the office or sent upon request.
Quantity ** Format S Colour C-D**

Frank Spooner Pictures Ltd
Room B7, Hatton Square, 16-16a Baldwins Gardens, London EC1N 7US
Tel: 071 405 9943
Contact: Mike Soulsby
Fax: 071 831 2483

In addition to British news coverage, this agency handles the distribution in the UK of pictures from Gamma Presse Images of Paris and Gamma Liaison in New York, whose photographers cover the world. Most subjects including war, fashion, politics, travel, adventure, tennis, yachting, glamour, animals, personalities, films and a host of others, can be found in our extensive libraries in London, Paris and New York. Contained in these three libraries there are 8,000,000 photographs, the work of 1,700 photographers. The libraries are computerised and an expert staff can handle requests quickly. Colour and B/W.
Quantity ** Format S Colour B-C-D B/W+**

Sporting Pictures (UK) Ltd
7a Lambs Conduit Passage, Holborn, London WC1R 4RG
Tel: 071 405 4500
Contact: Steve Brown
Fax: 071 831 7991
Telex: 27924

Professional, amateur and leisure sports covered by our specialist photographers result in a comprehensive library of over 3 million colour and B/W pictures of major sporting names and events throughout the world over the last fifteen years. Researchers are always welcome in the library, as are requests for pictures by phone. All assignments undertaken on request.
Quantity ** Format S Colour C-D B/W+**

The Still Moving Picture Company
67a Logie Green Road, Edinburgh EH7 4HF
Tel: 031 557 9697
Contact: John Hutchinson/Sue Hall
Fax: 031 557 9699

The unique collection of 150,000 colour transparencies (mostly 35mm) and 30,000 black and white prints (1940's to date) from the Scottish Tourist Board's library. Subjects include Scottish scenics, industry, travel, gardens, wildlife, sports, food and culture. We are sole agents for Allsport qv in Scotland and we have the AEA Technology portfolio of industrial shots. The library also holds extensive up-to-date 16mm movie film footage of Scotland – hence Still and Moving.Other photographers work includes North, South and Central America, Japan and the Far East, the Pacific and Africa. We guarantee a friendly and efficient service. Visitors are welcome.
Quantity * Format S/M Colour B-C-D B/W**

Still Pictures Environmental Agency
199a Shooters Hill Road, Blackheath, London SE3 8UL
Tel: 081 858 8307
Contact: Mark Edwards or Christine Suckling
Fax: 081 858 2049

Still Pictures Environmental Agency was founded by Mark Edwards who has photographed environment and Third World development issues for over 20 years. The library has grown substantially in the last year and now includes the work of a number of highly acclaimed specialist environmental photographers and the award winning under-water pictures by Norbert Wu. The photographs from over fifty countries illustrate the planets environmental crisis, but they also portray the many positive things which are being done in response to that crisis. Main subjects covered are agriculture, AIDS, animals, children, communication, cities, deforestation, development issues, drugs, economics, energy, forests, global warming, industry, landscape, rivers, tourism, transport, water, waste, youth culture.
Quantity ** Format S/M Colour B-C-D B/W+

Stockfile
PO Box 605, Virginia Water, Surrey GU25 4SS
Tel: 0344 844395
Contact: Steven Behr or Jill Behr
Fax: 0344 843513

Specialist mountain biking and skiing library. Comprehensive skiing section includes high energy action skiing, snowboarding and snow based activities as well as apres ski, families and resort shots. All aspects of mountain biking are covered including action, leisure, families and children, touring and racing and technical aspects. General cycling is also included. Other leisure/action pursuits such as paragliding, ballooning, inline skating and various watersports are represented. A selection of travel images are filed including UK/Europe, USA, Australia, New Zealand, Seychelles and Bali. The computerised collection consists largely of 35mm colour transparencies, with some medium format. Commissions undertaken. Callers welcome by appointment.
Quantity * Format S/M Colour D

Stock Shot
Mirefoot, Burneside, Kendal, Cumbria LA8 9AB
Tel: 0539 740770
Contact: Jess Stock
Fax: 0539 731546

The Stock Shot library contains solely the work of Jess Stock, ex-British ski champion, ex-mountaineer and ex Yeti-hunter with Chris Bonington qv and BBC2. Primarily skiing shots, mountaineering, mountain biking and expeditions, the latter in Pakistan, Nepal, Tibet and New Zealand. Office and library are based in Cumbria but the winter months are spent in the French Alps, producing action ski photography with the latest equipment and fashions, tourist shots and plenty with children. Many images feature the British Ski Team since Jess is their official photographer.
Quantity ** Format S Colour D

Stockphotos Inc.
3rd Floor, 7 Langley Street, London WC2H 9JA
Tel: 071 240 7361
Contact: Neil Andrews
Fax: 071 831 1489
Telex: 894839 TIB G
55 Spring Gardens, Manchester M2 2BX
Tel: 061 236 9226
Contact: Rowan
Fax: 061 236 8723

Call for our latest catalogue which features the work of leading international and UK photographers, covering a broad range of subjects including people, families, couples, executives, scenics, industry, sport and leisure, travel, medical, food and drink and special effects. The Manchester branch of Stockphotos has recently opened, offering a dedicated service to our clients in the North. Visit either this office, or our London office in Covent Garden, receive prompt, efficient attention from our team of experienced researchers and see why Stockphotos is one of the fastest growing libraries in the UK.
Quantity * Format S/M/L Colour D**

Tony Stone Worldwide Photolibrary
Worldwide House, 116 Bayham Street, London NW1 0BA
Tel: 071 267 8988
Contact: Jackie Lancaster
Fax: 071 722 9305

A free catalogue – available on request – provides an introduction to an exclusive file of colour photography by leading professionals, taken specially for books, magazines, partworks, AV, advertising, corporate promotions, record sleeves, etc. This is a large general library of international interest which includes specialist collections of travel, wildlife, industry, sports, people and human relationships and historic transport. TSW provides access to major editorial collections of Americana and French life and culture in its subsidiaries in the USA and France and provides access as well to miscellaneous collections housed in its other offices.
Quantity ** Format S/M/L Colour D**

Jessica Strang
86 Cambridge Gardens, London W10 6HS
Tel: 081 969 7292
Contact: Jessica Strang

The photographs cover a wide range of subjects but have a special interest in design, so countries tend to feature architectural detail, sculpture, markets and local colour rather than tourism. Countries include Bali, Malaysia, Singapore, Burma, Australia, America, Kenya, Sicily, Corsica, Spain, Holland and France. The bulk of the collection however is on current architecture and interior design, mainly domestic. Also designers', architects' and artists' homes together with their idiosyncratic collections and work. Special collections: greening the cities and minimal gardens, domestic recycling, working men and women as objects and the vanishing architectural detail of London.
Quantity ** Format S Colour C-D

Survival Anglia Photo Library
48 Leicester Square, London WC2H 7FB
Tel: 071 321 0101
Contact: Kathryn Shreeve
Fax: 071 493 2598

The library has grown up over the many years that the award-winning Survival programme has been on the ITV network. It is now an outstanding collection of natural history photographs by some of the world's top wildlife photographers. From pole to pole, on land, underwater and in the air, all aspects of natural history are covered, mostly on 35mm and some medium format colour transparencies plus B/W prints. Free subject catalogue on request.
Quantity * Format S/M Colour B-C-D B/W**

Sygma Ltd
The Paddock Suite, The Courtyard, 55 Charterhouse Street, London EC1M 6HA
Tel: 071 608 3690/353 4551
Contact: Helen Finney
Fax: 071 608 3757

On April 1st 1990, Sygma opened its own London office to provide a comprehensive stock library to its customers, as well as its specialist collections. Sygma's strength is in showbiz material by top-name photographers such as Douglas Kirkland, Helmut Newton, Eddie Adams and Bettina Rheims; first-class news coverage from around the world; in-depth features which stand independent of copy; personalities from all walks of life and extensive historical material from the archives of L'Illustration and Keystone. Sygma's aim is to provide you with what you need as quickly as possible from the London library or the extensive resources in the Paris-based head office.
Quantity ** Format S Colour A-B-C-D B/W**

Syndication International Ltd
Unique House, 21-31 Woodfield Road, London W9 2BA
Tel: 071 266 1133/1199
Contact: Joe Leahy
Fax: 071 266 2563

Picture agents for Mirror Group Newspapers, BBC News and Current Affairs, The Financial Times (photos and computer-generated graphics), Berlitz Guides, The British Tourist Authority/English Tourist Board and freelance photographers worldwide. Specialities in personalities, Royalty, cinema, crime, travel worldwide, gardening and horticulture. Special collections are the Alfieri (horticulture), the Picturegoer (movies)

Swift Picture Library
Claremont, Redwood Close, Ringwood, Hants BH24 1PR
Tel: 0425 478333
Contact: Mike Read
Fax: 0425 473160

Specialists in wildlife, scenic and travel photography. Also environmental subjects, conservation, gardens, country houses etc. Original colour transparencies on 35mm and medium format. Extensive coverage of Britain, as well as Africa, Europe, Greenland, USA, Canada and more. Scenics include wild landscapes, country and urban scenes, aerial views, and atmospheric compositions. Natural history subjects are available as portraits, close-ups, action and behavioural shots of birds, mammals, reptiles, amphibians, insects, plants and fungi, etc. Friendly and prompt service with accurate picture sourcing. Visitors by appointment. Commissions undertaken.
Quantity * Format S/M Colour B-C-D**

The Telegraph Colour Library Ltd
Visual House, 1 Mastmaker Road, London E14 9WT
Tel: 071 987 1212
Contact: Julie Potter
Fax: 071 538 3309

One of the UK's leading stock photography agencies covering a wide range of subjects including business, sport, people, industry, ecology, animals, medical, nature, space, travel and graphics. The Stock Directory Volume 2 is the latest publication to be presented by The Telegraph Colour Library. Inside its 208 pages there are over 1,167 specially edited colour stock photos with a comprehensive index. We operate a fast sameday service for all our UK clients. Free catalogues are available upon request. Call Julie Potter now for further information.
Quantity ** Format S/M/L Colour D B/W+ Illustration**

Topham Picture Source
PO Box 33, Edenbridge, Kent TN8 5PB
Tel: 0342 850313
Contact: Alan Smith
Fax: 0342 850244
Telex: 95351 TOPHAM G
5.31, 76 Shoe Lane, London EC4R 3JB
Tel: 071 583 5900
Contact: Alan M Smith
Fax: 071 583 5901

One of the largest general agencies with colour and B/W pictures. Historic and up to date files. Convenient for Gatwick Airport and London. Our file of 5 million pictures includes personalities, pop, warfare, Royalty, sport, topography, France, natural history, plus a day by day world news file from original sources: UPI (1932-70) qv, INP, Press Association (1946-60), Central News (1903-36), Planet News (1932-), Alfieri (1914-40), Pictorial Press (1936-60). Agents for Associated Press Photos (APP) London, Observer Colour Library qv and Press Association Photos. Daily news update.
Quantity ** Format S Colour A-B-C-D B/W+ Illustration**

B M Totterdell Photography
Constable Cottage, Burlings Lane, Knockholt, Kent TN14 7PE
Tel: 0959 532001
Contact: B M Totterdell

Specialist volleyball library covering all aspects of the sport – international, national, seniors, juniors, technical, coaching, referees, personalities, tournaments, beach and recreational. A growing collection in a growing sport.
Quantity ** Format S/M Colour D B/W+

Tessa Traeger
7 Rossetti Studios, 72 Flood Street, London SW3 5TF
Tel: 071 352 3641
Contact: Michelle Ingram
Fax: 071 352 4846

Food photographs in colour, 35mm and medium format including many of a highly inventive nature. Gardens in England and France. UK and foreign travel in colour on 35mm and general editorial subjects including a selection of artists in colour and B/W. Visitors welcome by appointment.
Quantity ** Format S/M Colour D B/W+

Travel Ink Photo & Feature Library
The Old Coach House, 14 High Street, Goring-on-Thames, Nr Reading, Berkshire RG8 9AR
Tel: 0491 873011
Contact: Abbie Enock
Fax: 0491 875558

Travel Ink Photo & Feature Library is an expanding colour and B/W library specialising in travel, tourism and lifestyle matters in a range of countries and destinations worldwide, including the UK. Article-and-picture packages can also be supplied. Aspects covered include business and industry, hotels, photo-essays, landmark establishments, sights, landscapes, cityscapes, culture, nightlife, tourist facilities, remote tribes, adventure holidays, cameo shots and portraits. Although new contributors are now being sought, the library is based on the material of international photographer and journalist Abbie Enock, who has worked on picture and editorial assignments all over the world. Open round-the-clock 7-days-a-week: if we haven't got what's wanted, we'll try and suggest someone who has.
Quantity ** Format S Colour D B/W+

The Travel Library
29 Swan Way, Church Crookham, Fleet, Hampshire GU13 0TU
Tel: 0252 627233
Contact: Philip Enticknap or Val Crisp
Fax: 0252 812399

The Travel Library is a new library established to market the work of travel photographer Philip Enticknap. Although not a general library covering every country, it holds approximately 5000 images of specialised areas on 6 x 7 format. For example, Malta and Northern Spain feature predominantly. Also, through regular assignments it may be possible to shoot material to a specific brief. Picture researchers are advised to register for a regular updated list of areas covered rather than be inconvenienced by requesting unavailable material whilst the library is developing. Contact us for further information.
Quantity * Format M Colour D

TRIP
4 Meadway, Epsom, Surrey KT19 8JR
Tel: 0372 729884
Contact: Helene Rogers
Fax: 0372 740785

Worldwide travel, leisure, people, business and customs. Specialist library on India, UAE, Yemen, Far East, Iceland, Morocco and Taiwan. Other subjects include the UK and people of all ages, also illustration. Most pictures can be photographed on spec by our worldwide network of contributors.
Quantity ** Format S/M Colour B-C-D B/W+**

Tropix Photographic Library
156 Meols Parade, Meols, Wirral, Merseyside L47 6AN
Tel: 051 632 1698
Contact: Veronica Birley
Fax: 051 632 1698

The developing world in all its aspects: environment and humankind. Extensive files from Africa, the Indian sub-continent, South East Asia, Papua New Guinea, Central and South America, and growing collections from the Middle and Far East. Specialist and well informed pictures on the following subjects. Environment: conservation, desertification, alternative energy, erosion, landscapes, land use, nature, pollution, recycling, salination and many aspects of forests. Economy: agriculture, aid, commerce, communications, industry, irrigation, mining, refugees, technologies, trade, work. Daily life: adults, children, crafts, culture, health care and medicine, housing, religions, training and education. Fast, efficient, fully computerised library.
Quantity ** Format S/M Colour C-D B/W+

United Press International
UPI 1932 to 1970, PO Box 33, Edenbridge, Kent TN8 5PB
Tel: 0342 850313
Contact: Alan M Smith
Fax: 0342 850244
Telex: 95351 TOPHAM G

A major international newsfile commencing with Planet News in 1932 and incorporating International News Photos (INP). Approximately one million negatives are filed with Topham Picture Source qv, affording an unrivalled window on the past.
Quantity ** B/W**

Universal Pictorial Press and Agency Ltd
30/34 New Bridge Street, London EC4V 6BN
Tel: 071 248 6730 (6 lines)
Contact: Terry Smith
Fax: 071 489 8982
Telex: 8952718 UNIPIX G

Syndication of a daily press and library service to national and provincial press, periodicals, book publishers and TV. Over 1.25 million colour and black and white images of international leaders and personalities. Royalty, politics, civil service, trade unions, diplomats, law and order, military, education, church, medical, business, literary, ballet, opera, orchestral, associations, arts, stage, TV, films, pop, football, rugby, cricket, tennis, golf, motor sports, equestrianism, boxing, wrestling, athletics, swimming and skating

Victory Archive
Available from Popperfoto, The Old Mill, Overstone Farm, Overstone, Northampton NN6 0AB
Tel: 0604 670670
Fax: 0604 670635

Victory, based on the Odhams Periodical Library, includes the magazine photo collections of Illustrated, Today, Woman, Woman's Own and other women's journals until the late 1960's. There is some smashing early colour from the 1940's and a vast collection of B/W. Subjects include personalities, fashion and other feature material from 1940's to 1960's. Victory also includes a transport section with a particularly fine collection of all types of naval shipping from late 19th Century onwards and any sea transport.
Quantity ** Format M/L Colour A-B-C-D B/W**

V & A Picture Library
Victoria and Albert Museum, Cromwell Road, South Kensington, London SW7 2RL
Tel: 071 938 8352/4
Contact: Isobel Sinden
Fax: 071 938 8353/8477
Telex: 268831 VICART G

A rapidly expanding, established picture library of 20,000 colour transparencies, mostly medium format and quarter of a million B/W images in the decorative and applied arts field. Wide range of subjects with emphasis on ceramics, furniture, gold and silver, oriental art, glass, jewellery, costume, textiles including carpets and tapestries, ivories, enamels, stage and ballet, metalwork, prints and drawings, Indian, Far Eastern and Islamic objects, musical instruments, manuscripts, photographs, bookplates, sculpture, miniatures, toys and dolls. B/W prints to order. Colour available immediately. Express service.
Quantity ** Format S/M/L Colour A-B-C-D B/W**

The Venice Picture Library
Please refer to BAPLA, 13 Woodberry Crescent, London N10 1PJ
Tel: 081 444 7913
Fax: 071 883 9215

A specialist collection in colour and B/W covering most aspects of the city of Venice, the islands and lagoon. Captions are accompanied by additional historical research if required. Commissions are undertaken.
Quantity * Format S Colour C-D B/W

Viewfinder Colour Photo Library
90 Whiteladies Road, Bristol BS8 2NT
Tel: 0272 237268/239449
Contact: Sarah Boait
Fax: 0272 239198

Viewfinder is one of the fastest growing colour libraries in the UK. We are a general library and our continuously expanding files cover a wide range of subjects. We pride ourselves in our fast, efficient and friendly service. If you need pictures same day, we will get them to you by courier or Red Star – generally we dispatch by First Class Registered Mail. Call us today and find out how you can avoid search fees. Colour folder available.
Quantity * Format S/M/L Colour D**

Visionbank Library Ltd
Suite 212, Business Design Centre, Islington Green, London N1 0QH
Tel: 071 288 6080
Contact: Ray Daffurn
Fax: 071 288 6094

Visionbank offers some of the best international pictures on CD-ROM and provide a new direct on-line service via high speed ISDN telephone lines. A traditional service is, of course, maintained, although digital images can be provided on disk if required. We hope this will assist many of our clients who use DTP extensively. Images are updated on a constant basis on-line. Our subsidiary library England Scene qv houses the world's largest – and, we like to think, best – collection of pictures of England. Please telephone for details and speak to Ray Daffurn.
Quantity ** Format S/M/L Colour D Illustration**

Visnews Stills Library
Cumberland Avenue, Park Royal, London NW10 7EH
Tel: 081 453 4233/4227
Contact: Hanna Davies
Fax: 081 965 0620
Telex: 22678

A library of 35mm colour transparencies of international political leaders, personalities and locations. Video stills service available from Visnews' exclusive international coverage, BBC news material, client's own video cassette or Aston caption generator.
Quantity * Format S Colour C-D**

The Charles Walker Collection
Kingswood House, 180 Hunslet Road, Leeds, West Yorkshire LS10 1AF
Tel: 0532 433389
Contact: Jo Robinson
Fax: 0532 425605

This is one of the foremost collections in the world of subjects listed under the popular title of Mystery, Myth and Magic. The library consists of over 12,000 colour transparencies and 5,000 B/W prints relating to arcane, esoteric, hermetic and occult subjects and is divided into eleven main sections. Alchemy, astral, astrology, demons, divination, herbal/medical, magical symbols, mystical sites, myths, practical occultism and witchcraft. Colour catalogue available on request.
Quantity ** Format M Colour D B/W Illustration

John Walmsley Photo-Library
April Cottage, Warners Lane, Albury Heath, Guildford, Surrey GU5 9DE
Tel: 0486 413846
Contact: John Walmsley
Fax: 0486 413846

Specialist collection of learning, training and working subjects. Schools, colleges, universities, adult education, skills centres, City Technology College, apprenticeship, etc. School section is catalogued by age and subject, including field trips, hobbies and sports. A growing collection of occupations. Also, an extensive series on complementary or alternative medicine. The collection reflects a multi-racial Britain. All material is recent, 35mm, in candid style with very natural interior lighting. Commissions undertaken. Most happy to discuss shooting on spec.
Quantity * Format S Colour D

WaterAid
1 Queen Anne's Gate, London SW1H 9BT
Tel: 071 233 4800
Contact: Gerry Mitchinson
Fax: 071 233 3161
Telex: 918518

WaterAid is a charity financing and providing engineering expertise to Third World countries in the fields of water supply and sanitation. The photograph collection reflects the charity's interest in East and West Africa, the Indian sub-continent and Nepal. Problems of water shortage and collection, health education and water and sanitation schemes are the main subjects. Colour transparencies are the main format but colour and B/W prints are also held, also videos and slide sets on specific countries and subjects.
Quantity ** Format S Colour D B/W

Waterways Photo Library
39 Manor Court Road, Hanwell, London W7 3EJ
Tel: 081 840 1659
Contact: Derek Pratt
Fax: 081 567 0605

A specialist photo library on all aspect of Britain's inland waterways. Top quality 35mm and medium format colour transparencies, plus a large collection of B/W. Rivers and canals, bridges, locks, aqueducts, tunnels and waterside buildings, town and countryside scenes, waterway holidays, traditional canal art, boating, fishing and wildlife. Also a growing collection of recent non-waterway material from Britain, much of it 'off the beaten track'.
Quantity ** Format S/M Colour B-C-D B/W+

Weimar Archive
8-9 The Incline, Coalport,
Telford, Shropshire TF8 7HR
Tel: 0952 680050
Contact: Dr Simon Taylor
Fax: 0952 587184

Picture library specialising in German and Central European history, politics and culture from the Middle Ages until 1945. Searches are computerised. Major categories include European Royalty; landscapes, architecture, people and culture in Europe pre-1914; illustrations of the First World War – photographs and paintings of all the major campaigns and the war at sea; an extensive collection of German painting, sculpture, literature, music, film and theatre, especially during the Weimar period and the Third Reich. Specialist material on anti-Semitism and the rise of Nazism. We cover science and technology, sport, travel, fashion and advertising and have recently added a collection on the German Democratic Republic, plus a comprehensive collection on modern Czech literature. We also speak English!

Elizabeth Whiting & Associates
21 Albert St, London NW1 7LU
Tel: 071 388 2828
Contact: Liz Whiting
Fax: 071 387 1615

Specialist library of colour transparencies covering all aspects of contemporary interior decoration, gardening and architecture. A group of 30 photographers, based at home and abroad ensure new material is added on a regular basis. The library of individual images is classified by room, type of garden and cross-referenced by subject. Clients are welcome to search for themselves or we offer an intelligent and fast research service. There is always a selection of new features showing different types of homes and gardens – London family house, NY loft, Dockland conversion, Scandinavian garden, Californian beach house etc. An A-Z of garden plants has been commenced recently.
Quantity * Format S/M/L Colour C-D**

Janine Wiedel Photo Library
6 Stirling Rd, Stockwell, London SW9 9EE
Tel: 071 737 0007
Contact: Janine Wiedel

A wide and continually expanding collection of social concern built up during twenty years of documentary reportage. An in-depth coverage of education, contemporary society, industry, women's issues including childbirth, ethnic groups, including Eskimos, Gypsies, Asian and Black communities in the UK and USA. Overseas coverage includes the Arctic, Iceland, Galapagos Islands, Iran, Europe and USA. Commissions undertaken. Clients welcome by appointment. Leaflet available.
Quantity * Format S Colour C-D B/W+**

Wiener Library Ltd
4 Devonshire Street, London W1N 2BH
Tel: 071 636 7247
Fax: 071 436 6428

This is a private library funded by charitable donations. The collection includes material on the Holocaust, Germany before, during and after World War Two, Jewish history and life, refugees and migration, war activities and war crimes and trials and all allied subjects. The collection also includes cartoons, posters and leaflets, photo albums and many identity cards, certificates and examples of forms and questionnaires.
Quantity ** B/W Illustration

Wilderness Photographic Library
Mill Barn, Broad Raine, Sedbergh, Cumbria LA10 5ED
Tel: 05396 20196
Contact: John Noble
Fax: 05396 21293

An expanding 35mm colour library specialising in mountain and wilderness regions worldwide, including associated aspects of people, places, natural history, geographical features, exploration, mountaineering and adventure sports. Material is suitable for advertising, publishing, postcards, calendars, TV and film location. Assignments undertaken.
Quantity * Format S Colour B-C-D

Andy Williams Photo-Library
3 Levylsdene, Merrow, Guildford, Surrey GU1 2RS
Tel: 0483 572778
Contact: Andy Williams
Fax: 0483 304829

A comprehensive coverage on medium and large format of the British Isles and near continent. Specialist landscape and architectural collection includes London, castles, historic houses, great gardens, cottages, old inns, golfing scenes, country scenes, moods of nature, waterfalls, windmills, lighthouses, etc. Library visits welcome and commissions readily undertaken.
Quantity ** Format M/L Colour C-D

David Williams Picture Library
50 Burlington Avenue, Kelvindale, Glasgow G12 0LH
Tel: 041 339 7823
Contact: David Williams
Fax: 041 337 3031

A personal collection of 35mm and medium format colour transparencies of Scotland and of Iceland. The main topics covered are landscapes, countryside scenes, historic sites, geology and geomorphology.
Quantity ** Format S/M Colour D

S & I Williams Power Pix International Picture Library
Castle Lodge, Wenvoe, Cardiff CF5 6AD
Tel: 0222 595163
Contact: Steven Williams
Fax: 0222 593905

Comprehensive and expanding colour library on all formats. A wide range of subjects includes abstracts, agriculture, aviation, ballooning, birds, boats, butterflies, castles, children, churches, clouds, couples, diving, fish and fishing, flowers, fungi, gardens, girls and glamour, industry, landscapes, lightning, mountaineering, natural history, people worldwide, sunsets, sport, sub-aqua, transport, trees, watersports and yachting. Countries covered include especially America, Australia, Canada, Europe, India, Japan and Britain. Commissions undertaken. Colour posters and catalogue available on request.
Quantity * Format S/M/L Colour A-B-C-D**

The Wingfield Sporting Art Library
35 Sibella Road, London SW4 6JA
Tel: 071 622 6301
Contact: Mary Ann Wingfield
Fax: 071 622 6301

The Wingfield Sporting Library is a unique colour and B/W library specialising in sporting works of art, both historical and contemporary. The library was formed to reproduce high quality, large format colour transparencies of paintings and some prints, covering 50 different sports. It was originally inspired by Mary Ann Wingfield's Sport and the Artist series of books published by the Antique Collectors Club which trace the history and the art of each sport. Research commissions welcome. Clients by appointment.
Quantity * Format S/M Colour D B/W Illustration

Roger Wood
45 Victoria Road, Deal, Kent CT14 7AY
Tel: 0304 372786
Contact: Roger Wood
Fax: 0304 368910 att R WOOD

A specialist library concentrating mainly on countries in the Middle East, with particular reference to tourism and antiquities. Includes Egypt, all the North African countries, Iran, some Gulf states, Greece, Turkey and Ethiopia. Also Pakistan and Bangladesh. Colour is mostly medium format. Many items available in B/W.
Quantity ** Format M Colour B-C-D B/W

Woodmansterne Picture Library
2 Greenhill Crescent, Watford Business Park, Watford, Hertfordshire WD1 8RD
Tel: 0923 228236
Contact: Johanna
Fax: 0923 245788

Britain, Europe and the Holy Land. Architecture, especially cathedrals and stately home interiors, painting, sculpture, decorative arts, interior design, natural history, butterflies, geography, volcanos, transport, space exploration, opera and ballet, seasonal and sunset views, major state occasions. All in colour.
Quantity ** Format S/M/L Colour A-B-C-D

Michael Woodward Licensing
Parlington Hall, Parlington, Aberford, West Yorkshire LS25 3EG
Tel: 0532 813913
Contact: Michael Woodward
Fax: 0532 813911
Telex: 55293 CHACOM G

International art licencing agents for art and photography, representing over 100 illustrators, artists and photographers. Specialists in design for greeting cards, stationery, calendars, fine art prints, posters and jigsaws. Besides producing commissioned artwork, we have extensive files on most subjects available on large format transparencies through our art library. Brochure available on request. Offices in Antwerp and New York.
Quantity ** Format L Colour D Illustration

World Pictures
1st Floor, 85a Great Portland Street, London W1N 5RA
Tel: 071 437 2121/436 0440
Contact: Gerry Brenes
Fax: 071 439 1307

Over 600,000 medium and large format colour transparencies aimed at travel and travel related markets. Extensive coverage of cities, countries and specific resort areas, together with material of an emotive nature, ie children, couples, families on holiday, all types of winter and summer sporting activities, motoring abroad etc. Catalogue and leaflets available.
Quantity ** Format M/L Colour D**

George Wright
Mountover Farm, Rampisham, Dorchester, Dorset DT2 0PL
Tel: 0935 83333
Contact: George Wright
Fax: 0935 83326

Photographer's own collection including English and European gardens, landscape, people, events and cookery as featured in the pages of the Observer and Independent magazines as well as travel stories from European Travel & Life. Some coverage of India, Nepal and the Middle East. Large collection on Barcelona.
Quantity ** Format S/M Colour C-D B/W+

York Archaeological Trust for Excavation and Research Ltd
1 Pavement, York, North Yorkshire YO1 2NA
Tel: 0904 643211 ext 223
Contact: Katie Jones
Fax: 0904 640029

The authoritative archive of the antiquities, archaeology and architecture of the City of York and surrounding areas. The library holds in excess of 40,000 colour transparencies and as many B/W negatives, illustrating the heritage of this ancient and attractive city. Original photography of the city and surrounding areas, archaeological excavations, archaeologists and their techniques, and superlative images of their finds, with magnificent details of many artifacts, all represent the finest aspects of modern archaeological science. The presentation of archaeology, architecture and the city's heritage to the public is also extensively covered, including photographs of the world famous Jorvik Viking Centre.
Quantity * Format S/M/L Colour C-D B/W+**

The John Robert Young Collection
61 De Montfort Road, Lewes, East Sussex BN7 1SS
Tel: 0273 475216
Contact: Jennifer Barrett

This is a distinctive picture collection of fine images, including historical material, on the French Foreign Legion, the People's Liberation Army (China), the Spanish Legion and the Royal Marines. Also a multitude of transparencies from all parts of the globe on varying subjects – water pollution in Colombia, natural childbirth (Dr Michael Odent), Texas Rangers, Britain's choir schools and an ever increasing collection on women priests and other religious subjects. The library also contains scenic material from Britain, France, Djibouti, Corsica, Hong Kong, Malta, Morocco, French Guiana including Devil's Island, etc. A small B/W collection includes 'Swinging 60's', Thames lightermen, premature childbirth, rodeo's, Hong Kong boat people and Brighton. All material is of the highest quality being shot with Leitz lenses.
Quantity ** Format S Colour C-D B/W

FOREIGN MEMBERS

Irish Picture Library
4 Clanwilliam Terrace, Grand Canal Quay, Dublin 2
Tel: 0103531 611038
Contact: David or Edwin Davison
Fax: 0103531 761456

A brand new member from whom we have not yet received a proper biography. Irish heritage and Irish landscape and the Fr. Browne Collection.
Quantity ** Format S/M Colour A-B-C-D B/W+ Illustration

Maxwell's Photo Library
Dargle House, 98 Lower Drumcondra Road, Dublin 9
Tel: 0103531 308072
Contact: Marie Maxwell
Fax: 0103531 307237

Our agency has been in business in Dublin since 1955. We have a large range of pictures covering Irish life style, political happenings and personalities who made the news from this period up to the present time. Irish literary Greats and artists are on file including a unique collection of Brendan Behan. Irish working life such as basket making, cheese making, harps and many other subjects are available in B/W and colour along with all the news-making pictures taken since we started. Wire photo transmitting machines, B/W and colour in use.
Quantity * Format S/M Colour B-C-D B/W**

The Slide File
79 Merrion Square, Dublin 2
Tel: 0103531 766850
Contact: George Munday
Fax: 0103531 608332

Just 100 yards from the Dail – the Irish Parliament – The Slide File is situated in the finest Georgian square in the British Isles. The company was set up in 1979 by two professional photographers and has since become the authoritative source for Irish pictures. The images have been widely used by publishers of books and magazines and for advertising campaigns in the UK, the USA and Europe. Fifty photographers regularly supplement the 40,000 carefully edited transparencies which, apart from a small international section, illustrate most aspects of Irish Life.
Quantity ** Format S/M/L Colour C-D

The Stock House Ltd
Room 1202 On Hong Commercial Bldg, 141-147 Hennessy Road, Wanchai
Tel: 0108525 8660887
Contact: Ivy Davis
Fax: 0108525 8662212

A general library containing over 350,000 colour transparencies on all formats, covering all parts of the globe, with a major collection of Asian material. Affiliated to libraries in London, New York and Tokyo. Stock pictures for advertising and editorial from around the world.
Quantity ** Format S/M/L Colour C-D**

Don Sutton International Photo Library
11 Eglinton Court, Eglinton Road, Donnybrook, Dublin 4
Tel: 0103531 269 6684
Contact: Don Sutton
Fax: 0103531 269 6684

Colour transparencies of Ireland on 35mm to 5 x 4. Most aspects of Ireland are covered, especially those which are tourism related. Several travel desinations outside Ireland are also available.
Quantity ** Format S/M/L Colour D

'GIVE US A BREAK'

THE COLLEGES FEATURED ON THE FOLLOWING PAGES ARE ALL AFFILIATED TO THE ASSOCIATION OF PHOTOGRAPHERS. MANY OF THE STUDENTS WHOSE NAMES APPEAR IN THE CREDITS WILL SHORTLY BE ENTERING THE HIGHLY CROWDED AND COMPETITIVE WORLD OF PROFESSIONAL PHOTOGRAPHY. KODAK LIMITED IS PROUD TO HAVE HELPED BRING THESE PAGES INTO BEING, AND THE WORK OF THESE STUDENTS TO YOUR NOTICE.

PHOTOGRAPHIC COLLEGES

Barking College

Contact: Ed Kinge

Dagenham Road
Romford
Essex RM7 0XU

Tel: 0708 766841

The photograph shown is by a student on the BTEC National Diploma course in Photography, which offers a broad based education in the application of creative professional photography. Many students progress to HND or Degree courses.
The College also offers City & Guilds 747, which allows students to study professional photography competences.

JOHN KNOCK

Berkshire College of Art & Design

Department of Graphic Communication
Kings Road
Reading RG1 4HJ

Tel: 0734 583501

The College offers a F.T. BTEC National Diploma in Photography which, while being broad based, offers students the opportunity to study at greater depth either commercial and advertising or industrial and technical photography during the second year of the course.

Students also undertake a range of supporting studies which include: business and communication studies, computing and D.T.P., Video, design and image analysis.

Day Release courses: C.G.L.I. 7470 and a BTEC HNC in Medical and Technical Photography are also offered.

MARCUS WOODS

DEBBIE STRUTT

DEBBIE STRUTT

FIDELLE RINALDI

Blackpool & Fylde College

Contact: Geoff Clark

Palatine Road
Blackpool
Lancashire FY1 4DW

Tel: 0253 52352 ext. 3254
Fax: 0253 752209

We know it's tough but
we still believe in magic.

I hope it shows.

CHRIS AIREY

GLEN GARNER

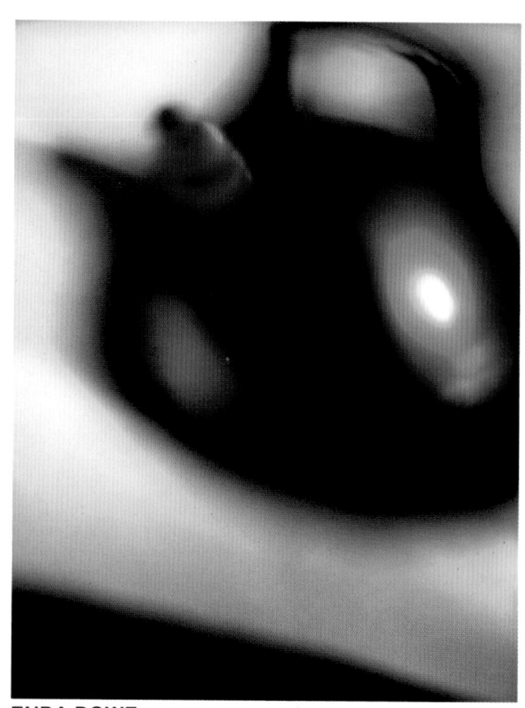

ENDA BOWE

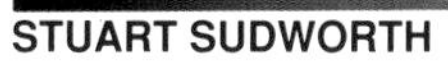

STUART SUDWORTH

AWN JOHNSON

SIMON STOCK

MAT WRIGHT

ROB QUICK

DAVE EVANS

ANDY THOMPSON

STEVE HARDMAN

CAROLINE DITCHFIELD

MORGAN SILK

BOB WILSON

CATH ROWLANDS

400 **Bournemouth & Poole College of Art & Design**

Contact: Sylvia Barnes

Head of School: Photography
Wallisdown
Poole
Dorest BH12 5HH

Tel: 0202 533011 ext. 246
Fax: 0202 537729

If you are: a talented, creative, self motivated individual who is: excited by change! motivated by challenge! not intimidated by the future!
If you want the opportunity: to be on the leading edge of image making and technology, to aspire to the top echelons of the photographic industry, to work in a national and international context, to work with professionals, to launch yourself into the professional arena then join an award winning team in the "School of Photography!"

SPIROS POLITIS

Cheltenham & Gloucester College

Photography
Pittville Campus
Albert Road
Pittville
Cheltenham GL52 3JG

Tel: 0242 532210

The college proposes to offer a three year vocational BA Honours degree from 1993 (subject to validation).
Students are offered professional modules selected from Photography, Graphics or Video. The aim is to provide maximum opportunity to utilise resources and expertise available in these key media subjects.
Students can follow a professional specialism or mix subjects to broaden career prospects.

New purpose built studios, computer suites, audio and video facilities provide the degree students with state of the art accommodation.

NIGEL STEAD

ANGUS CUNNINGHAM

SARAH EVANS

LEE MART

Cleveland College of Art & Design

Green Lane
Linthorpe
Middlesbrough
Cleveland TS5 7RJ

Tel: 0642 821441
Fax: 0642 823467

The Department of Design offers two courses:
BTEC Higher National Diploma in Photography (Advertising, Fashion & Editorial).
BTEC Higher National Diploma in Photography (Documentary).
The HND Courses has a national reputation and is attracting students from Europe and the UK. Our level of success in national awards and competitions speaks for itself.

EMMA AMSDEN

SIMON GREGORY

IAN CUMMINGS

NEIL CASH

Glasgow College of Building and Printing

Department of Design and Photography
Glasgow College of Building and Printing
60 North Hanover Street
Glasgow G1 2BP

Tel: 041 332 9969
Fax: 041 332 5170

Contact: Ian Campbell

The College offers full and part time courses in Photography and Audio Visual Production, at Certificate and Higher National Diploma Level (SCOTVEC). Specialist options are available in Advertising and Commercial, Applied Photography and Audio Visual Production.

JOHN CARBERRY

CHARLES D. GILMOUR

CHARLES D. GILMOUR

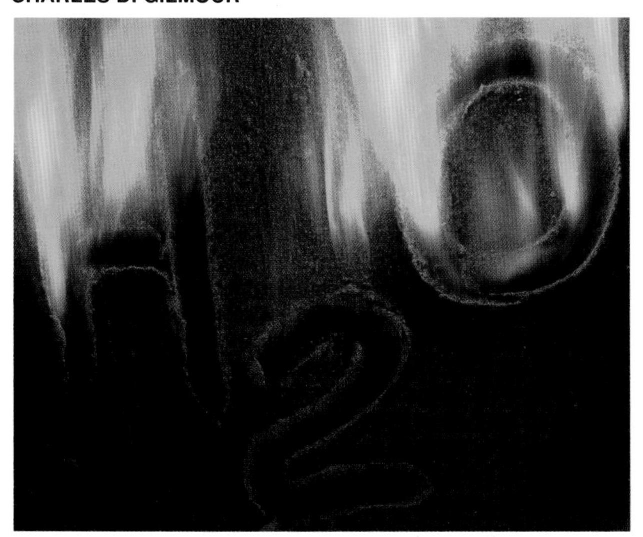

GERRY FOX

Dewsbury College

Halifax Road
Dewsbury
West Yorkshire WF13 2AS

Tel: 0924 465916
Fax: 0924 457047

The photography department at Dewsbury College operates from purpose-built, well equipped accommodation within a large and long established School of Art.
Courses are offered at both National and Higher National Diploma level and aim to provide an environment in which the student is able to develop a portfolio to the highest professional standards in advertising/commercial photography.

Within this framework, students are encouraged to develop their individual direction through a programme of negotiated projects.
For further information and course details, please contact Keith Orange or Ian Ingram.

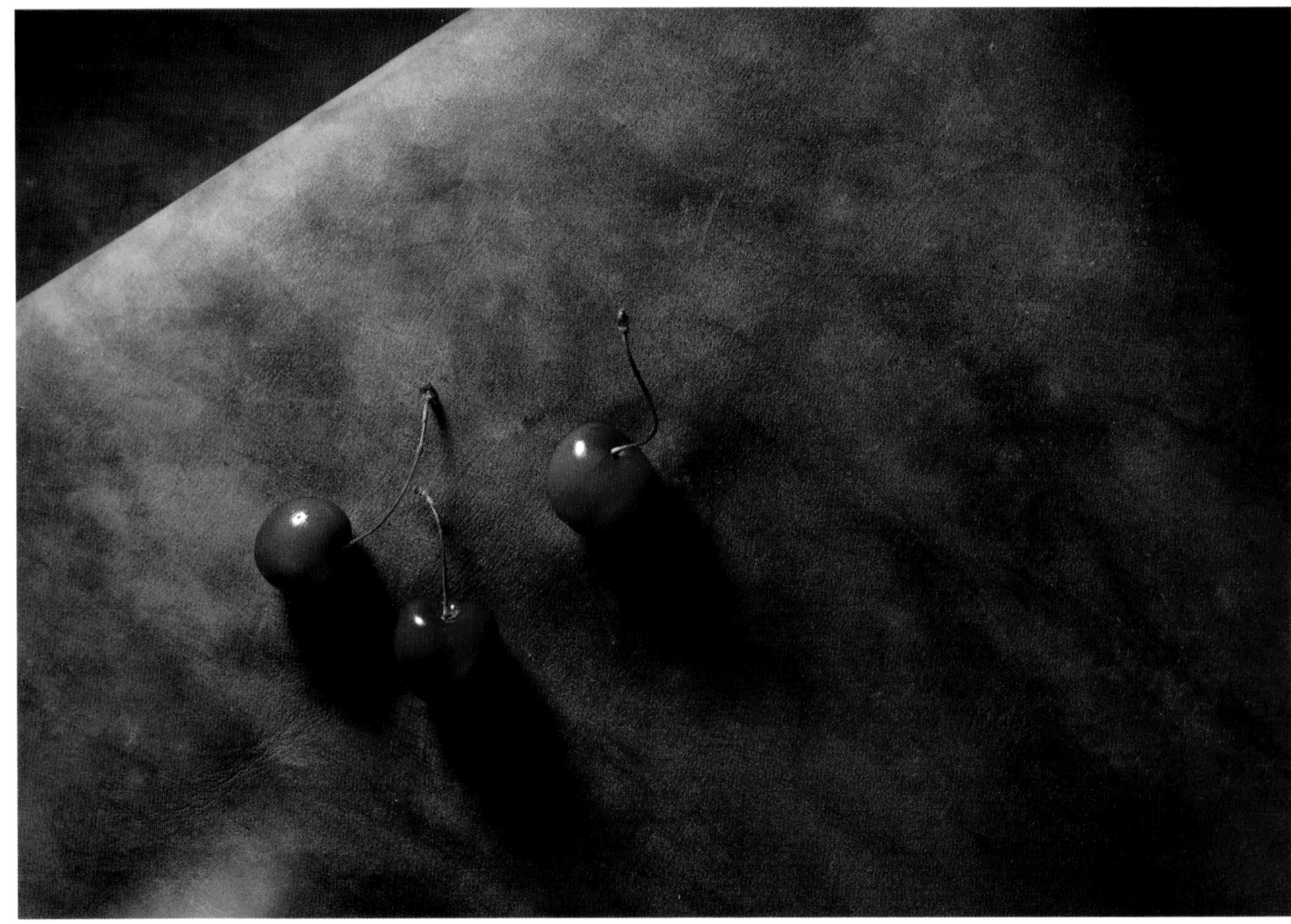

AMANDA DODD

DONNA TAYLOR

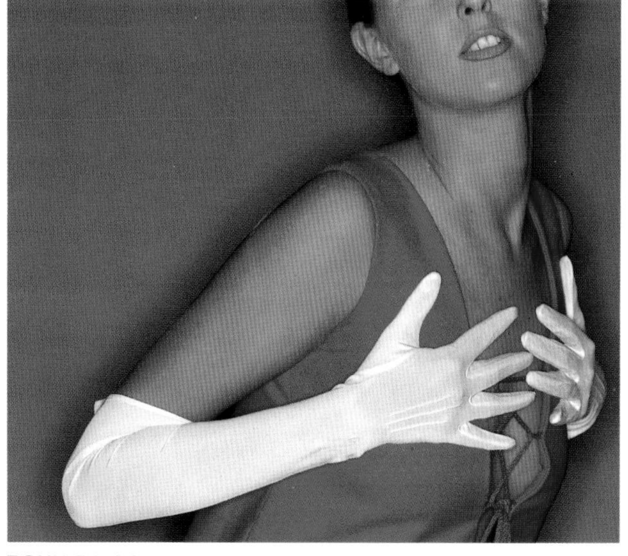

RONNIE MOORE

YASMIN HUSSAIN

SHAUN FORSTER

Kent Institute of Art & Design

Contact: George Wattson

Rochester-upon-Medway College
Fort Pitt
Rochester
Kent ME1 1DZ

Tel: 0634 830022 ext: 273

The Photographic Department at Rochester-upon-Medway offer a two year full-time course leading to the Higher National Diploma in Advertising & Editorial Photography.
Each year 'Medways' reputation attracts a substantial number of mature students from the UK, together with applicants from Europe and overseas. The close proximity to London and well established contacts with Advertising and Editorial Photographers, is reflected in both students' Industrial Release and their immediate post college professional career.
The photograph below by Adam Law, was the winning submission for the letter 'r' in the 1992 Metro Photographic Student Awards. Adam, who is currently assisting on a freelance basis can be contacted on Maidstone 0622 39755.

Kingston University

Photography Department
Knights Park
Kingston-upon-Thames
Surrey KT1 2QJ

Tel: 081 547 2000 ext. 4144
Fax: 081 547 7011

This is an intensive one year course which is a unique opportunity in photographic education.
The programme is designed for students who wish to pursue a course of study in the interest of preparing or upgrading a personal portfolio suitable for entry into professional practice or photographic higher education.
The course is based on a series of lectures, workshops, project briefings, group criticism sessions, and individual tutorials.

EMMA PEIOS

JOE FARRINGTON

BEN WOOD

OSMO PATANA

Napier University

61 Marchmont Road
Edinburgh EH9 1HU

Tel: 031 455 2604
Fax: 031 228 3828

The Department of Photography, Film and Television offers courses in a variety of audio and visual media at both undergraduate and postgraduate level. The newly approved BA/BA Honours Degree has a common first year then options in Stills Photography or Film and Television production and also covers other visual media including electronic imaging.

The course remains one of the few Degree programmes where photography is studied within a professional context.

ROB SMITH

Newcastle College
School of Art & Design

Contact: Allan Hamer or Bill Jenkins

Rye Hill
Newcastle-upon-Tyne NE4 7SA

Tel: 091 273 8866
Fax: 091 272 4297

Newcastle College offer a BTEC Higher National Diploma in Photography.
The photography option is centred on the development of skills, creativity and the use of experimental work, every opportunity for self expression being encouraged.
The School of Art and Design lies close to the city centre which hosts many attractions for young people. Students are encouraged to take an active interest in national competitions in which they have gained considerable success.

DEBBIE KIMMINS

STEPHEN FINCH

ALAN SCRYMGEOUR

JULIE FORTUNE

Plymouth College of Art and Design

Plymouth College of Art and Design
in Partnership with
The University of Plymouth
Plymouth College of Art and Design
Tavistock Place
Plymouth PL4 8AT

Tel: 0752 385959
Fax: 0752 385977
Contacts: Bryan Preston, Roger Swingler

Our courses in Photography, Film and Television produce the talented practitioners of the future. They are creative and dynamic, responsive and professional, but still have time to enjoy themselves. Photography, Video, Multi-Image, Computer Animation, Film, Computer Graphics and Sound are all available, so if you would like to contact us we would love to hear from you. What makes us extra special is that we also have students with expertise in Underwater Photography, Film and Video.

KRISTINA DOGGE

DAN BURTON

SIAN HEMMINGS

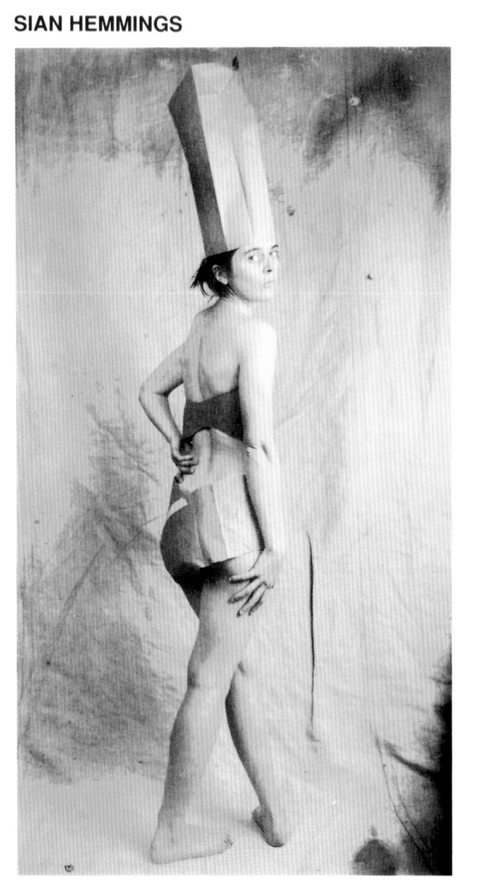

PAUL SLATER

CAROLINE GARSIDE

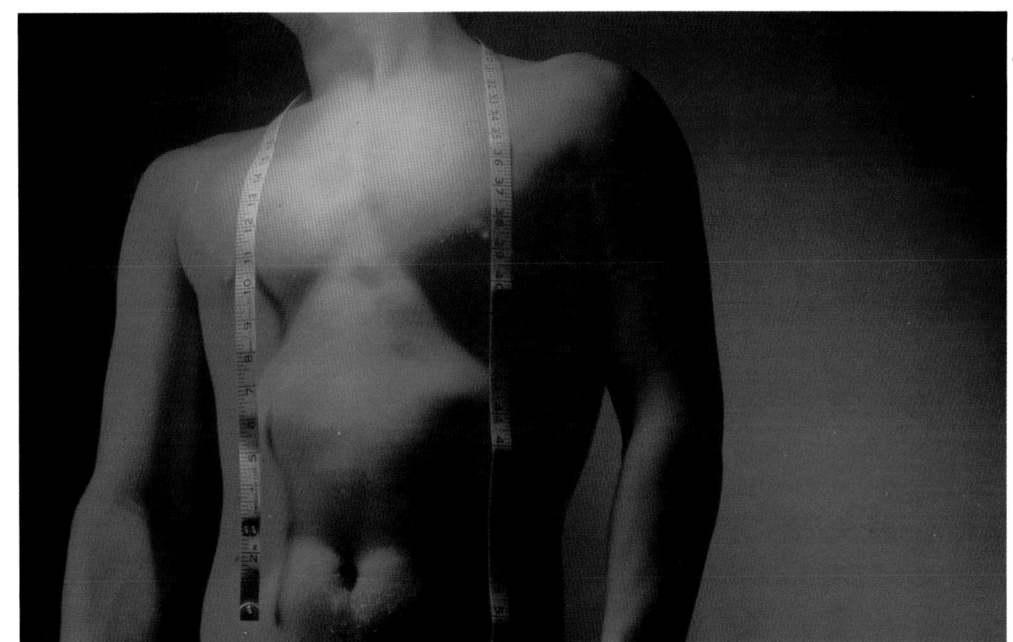

JASON HINDLEY

MICHELLE WILLETS

JULIA PORTER

Pimlico Arts & Media Scheme

St. James The Less School
Moreton Street
London SW1V 2PT

Tel: 071 976 6133
Tel: 071 630 6409
Fax: 071 630 9517

Photography Foundation (Portfolio)
The centre offers an intensive one year course in Photography Foundation Studies, aimed at students at the beginning of their careers.
The four-term course comprises:
A beginners intensive block
An introduction to four major areas of photography
A Portfolio building block in one specialist area
A work-experience orientated final block
Technical instruction is progressive, culminating in an exhibition of students' work.
Students are encouraged to apply for further studies at BA or HND level, or to seek employment on completion.

JACKIE STEFANO

LESLEY SHEARER

ANNE PRICE

ALBERTO ARZOZ

Southampton Institute of Higher Education

Contact: Stephen Woods

Design Division
East Park Terrace
Southampton
Hampshire SO9 4WW

Tel: 0703 229381
Fax: 0703 222259

The Design Division offers courses in Communications, Fashion, Graphics, Industrial Design and Fine Art, at Degree and Higher National Diploma levels. All students study photography, using their creative skills as designers to attain a high degree of expertise and professional ability. The Divisions accommodation looks out on pleasant parkland in the very heart of the city with easy access via the M3 and M27 motorways, intercity rail links and into Europe by air from Eastleigh Airport and Continental Ferry ports.

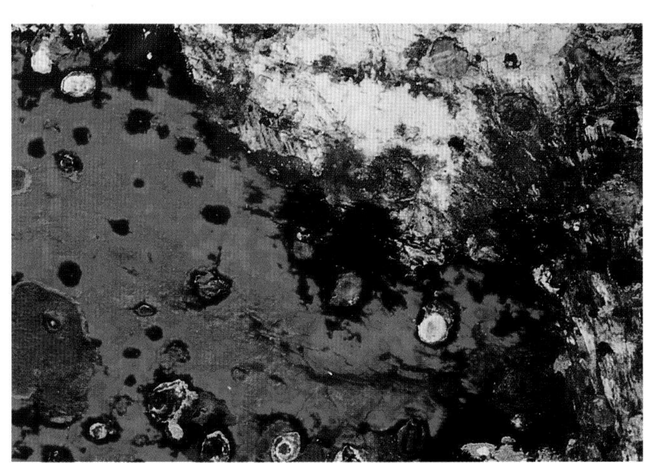

ROSY MAGUIRE

MIRANDA ROCK

TREVOR HALTON

BECKY BATTERSON

Salisbury College

Southampton Road
Salisbury
Wiltshire SP1 2LW

Tel: 0722 323711
Fax: 0722 326006

Salisbury College's reputation in photographic education is well known through its performance in national photographic competitions.
The success of its graduates in their chosen profession is less well publicised but equally impressive.
The College now offers two major options in its courses, Stills Photography and Broadcasting & Video Production.

Both seek to educate multi-skilled, motivated and professionally aware graduates – tomorrow's image makers.

ADRIAN THORNTON
Aerial/Advertising/Still-life Contact 0404 44801

ALAN MARTIN
Landscape/Travel Contact College

KAY LOWRIE
Fashion/People Contact College

ROB WATKINS
Advertising Still-life Contact College

VANESSA DAVIES
Fashion/People Contact College

DAVID CURTIS
Advertising Still-life Contact College

KAM MAN YEUNG
Fashion/People Contact College

MATTHEW WAIN
Advertising Still-life
Contact College

Staffordshire University

Contact: Mike Berry
School of Design and Ceramics

College Road
Stoke-on-Trent ST4 2DE

Tel: 0782 744531
Direct Line: 0782 573303
Fax: 0782 745637

Photography is one of the areas of specialisation within the BA(Hons) design course, one of the largest in Britain. We aim to educate and encourage students to communicate imaginatively and with effect, using photography, in its broadest applications. Students also have the opportunity to extend their experience and abilities into additional design disciplines offered on the course, involving graphics, audio visual and computer aided design. Graduates enter a wide range of employment, from film production, art direction, to the whole spectrum of photographic practice.

LYNN-MICHELLE MOLYNEUX

MATT FORMAN

Stockport College of Further & Higher Education

Faculty of Design
Wellington Road South
Stockport
Cheshire SK1 3UQ

Tel: 061 474 3711

Course Tutor Barry Ainsworth

BTEC HND Design – Documentary Photography Option
Documentary photography is defined as visual evidence, dealing with real issues, happenings or circumstances. It is with this definition in mind that this course was formulated, to cater for a growing group of photographers with a passion to communicate ideas and events important to them.
Our aim is to produce well informed, creative and honest photographers capable of working at the highest possible level within their chosen field. This is achieved through a two year intensive course which essentially adopts a 'hands on' practical approach to the medium. Students are encouraged to make the most of the facilities offered by the department, and to explore their motivations for taking photographs. They should work in a disciplined, organised and considered manner, and be prepared to put an awful lot of film through their cameras!

MAURIZIO ANTONUCCI

PETER FLEMMICH

ANDY THORNE

West Herts College

Faculty of Visual Communications
School of Media
Photography Section
Water Lane
Watford
Herts WD1 2NN

Tel: 0923 257508
Fax: 0923 212087

This full-time National Diploma comprises a three-phased practical programme of studies, promoting Visual awareness, effective and creative skills in Advertising, Editorial and Commercial photography and an opportunity for researching and realising specialised project work.
The provision of Complementary studies across a multi-disciplined curriculum provides an appropriate framework for both life skills and academic development.

CHRIS DYER – TEL: 081 954 4857

LUCY DIGBY – TEL: 0296 661256

JEM PEARCE – TEL: 081 207 1182

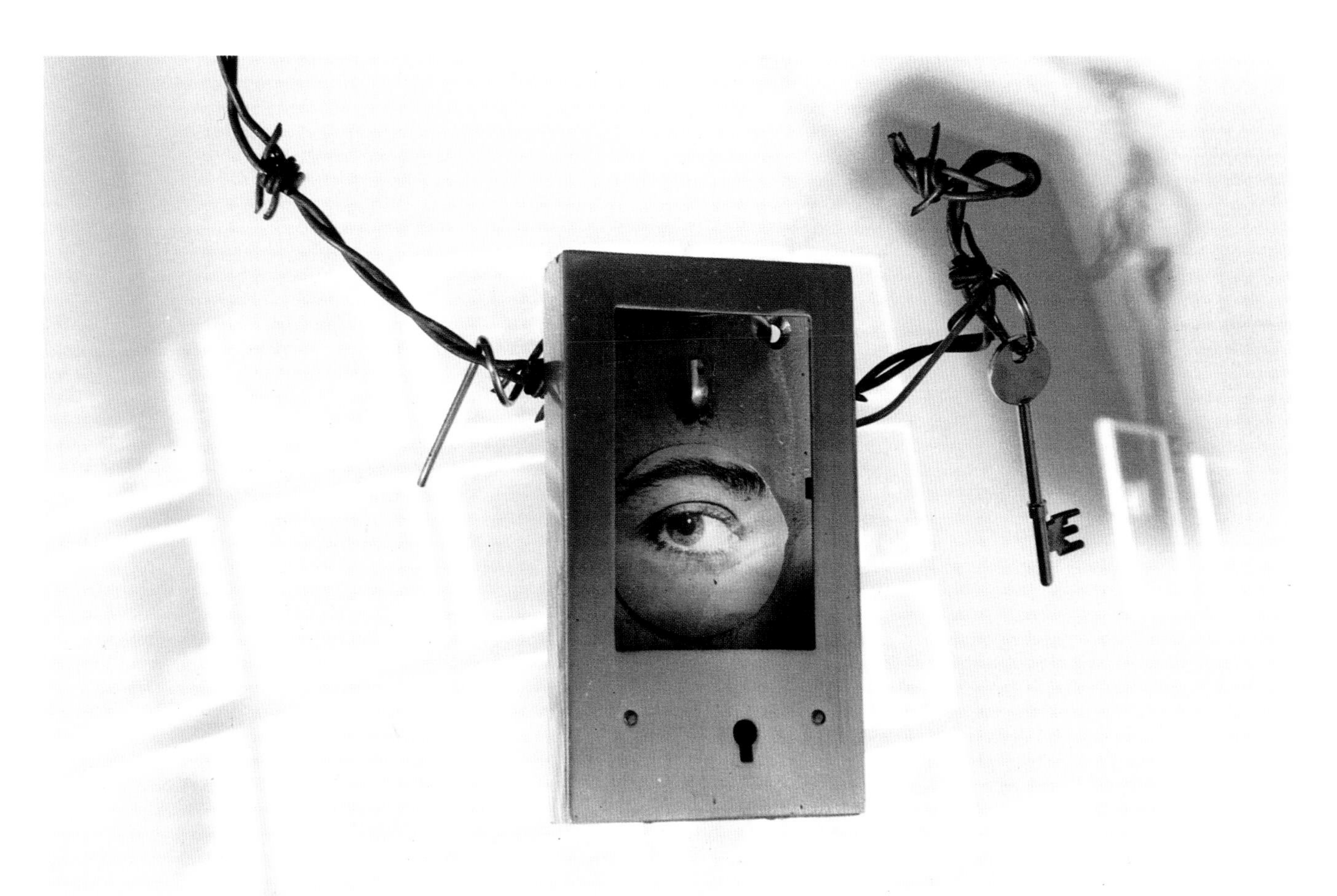

PAUL GRIFFITHS – TEL: 0908 377679

VISUAL & CREATIVE PUBLICATIONS FROM ELFANDE

THE LEADER OF THE PACK
How to design successful packaging

The full packaging design story
of Minale Tattersfield

BINDING – HARDBACK + LAMINATED JACKET
PRINTED FULL COLOUR THROUGHOUT
No. OF PAGES – 224
SIZE 260 x 210mm

INTRODUCED BY
JEREMY MYERSON

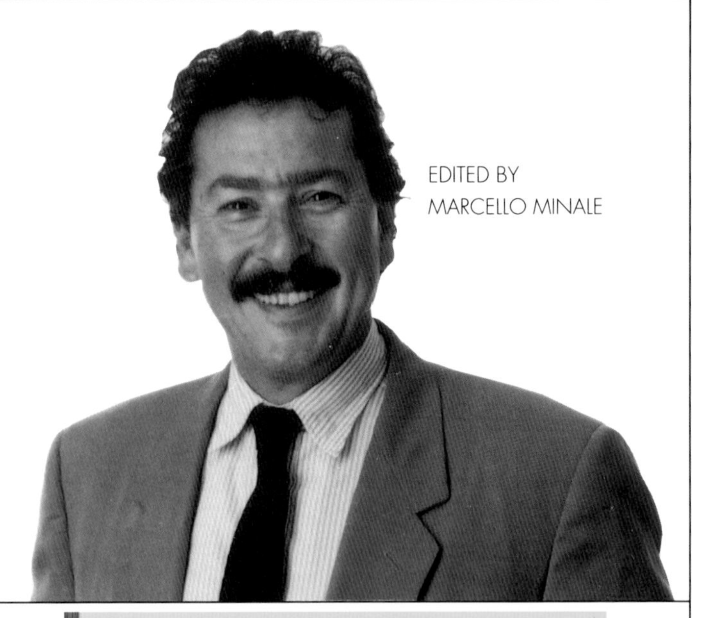

EDITED BY
MARCELLO MINALE

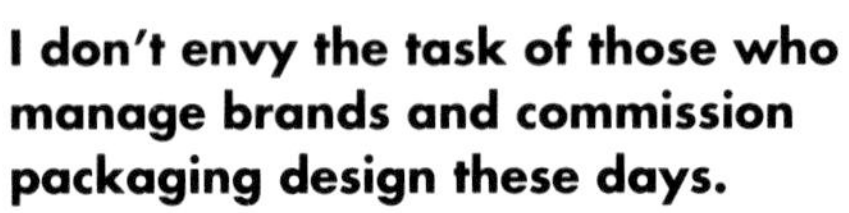

I don't envy the task of those who manage brands and commission packaging design these days.
There has been a proliferation of competing products in every market sector you can think of. Patterns of distribution and marketing have become more complex. The behaviour of consumers has become more unpredictable and difficult to interpret.
Add to that the growing need to create packaging in a pan-European context and you have the potential to turn even the most basic packaging exercise into a logistical and cultural nightmare.
Finding the right visual and verbal language to cross national frontiers and attract the Euro-consumer in large numbers is no easy task. This Esperanto of design has become the Holy Grail of marketing.
In the combination of colour, structural form, typography, photography and illustration (the cocktail which creates the world's best known packs), a vast potential minefield of linguistic and aesthetic confusion opens up before the new product development team on every project.
Brand managers need to base their design decisions on knowledge and experience of what is likely to work and what will fail to inspire and engage. Which is where this new Minale Tattersfield Design Strategy book comes into the frame.
The international design group founded by the Anglo-Italian partnership of Marcello Minale and Brian Tattersfield has been producing successful packaging for clients since the early 1960s.
Simple case studies of the firm's projects

shown here take the marketing team through a wide range of problems, products and markets. There is much to admire in solutions for a diverse range of companies and brands. Designers don't always make the best commentators on their own work. But Minale Tattersfield has an unusually strong track record in producing books which show the design process at its most active, creative and analytical.
This is the latest in a series of successful titles which takes the client behind the scenes to see how it was done. It provides such a rich seam of talent and wisdom in packaging design that no marketing manager today can afford to pass it by.
Jeremy Myerson

£38.00

ISBN No. 1 870458 50 8

VISUAL & CREATIVE PUBLICATIONS FROM ELFANDE

'BEWARE WET PAINT'
100 DESIGNS BY ALAN FLETCHER

Written by Jeremy Myerson

BINDING – SOFTBACK LAMINATED GATEFOLD
PRINTED FULL COLOUR THROUGHOUT
No. OF PAGES – 152
SIZE 230 x 230mm

A major new book on the work of one of the world's most influential personalities in graphic design and communication.
Beware wet Paint: 100 Designs by Alan Fletcher explores the creative thinking of a leading figure in the success of Pentagram through the medium of 100 of Fletcher's designs – many of which have never been published before.
The new biography is timely in that Alan Fletcher is now entering a new phase in his career as an individual artist-designer. He left Pentagram last year after 20 years with the famous consultancy.
Author of the book is Jeremy Myerson, the well-known design writer whose previous titles include a biography of Gordon Russell, a monograph about Minale Tattersfield and the Twentieth Century Conran Design Guides.

£19.50

ISBN No. 1 870458 60 5

HOW TO RUN A SUCCESSFUL MULTI-DISCIPLINARY DESIGN COMPANY

By Marcello Minale/Minale Tattersfield

BINDING – SOFTBACK LAMINATED GATEFOLD
No. OF PAGES – 203
SIZE 210 x 150mm
FULLY ILLUSTRATED B/W & COLOUR

Marcello Minale, colourful and controversial chairman of world-renowned design consultants Minale Tattersfield, provides a practical guide to running your own multi-disciplinary design company – based on 25 years of his own experiences as a designer.
The triumphs and the disasters. The clients who said yes and the solutions which went wrong. The power of publicity and the dangers of diversification. It is all here in *How To Run A Successful Multi-Disciplinary Design Company*, a book rich in useful information and entertaining anecdote written by one of the most engaging and enduring personalities on the contemporary design scene.

£16.50

ISBN No. 1 870458 27 3

PROFILE EUROPEAN DESIGNERS

Foreword Jeremy Myerson

BINDING – HARDBACK + LAMINATED JACKET
PRINTED FULL COLOUR THROUGHOUT
No. OF PAGES – 144
SIZE 280 x 280mm
OVER 500 COLOUR IMAGES

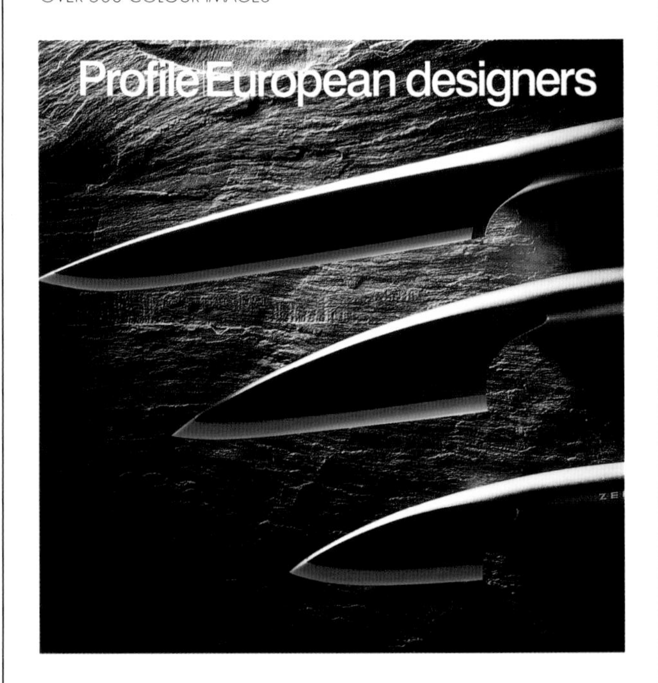

The large format book celebrates some of the best known design talent currently at work on the European stage. A double page spread in colour is devoted to both company information together with examples of client work. The categories of design include:

Corporate identity
Business interiors
Exhibition design
Packaging
Design for public use
Product design
Business Graphics
Retail design

£19.50

ISBN No. 1 870458 23 0

GRIMWOODS TAILS
illustrated by Brian Grimwood
Verses by Nick Would

BINDING – HARDBACK PLUS JACKET
PRINTED FULL COLOUR THROUGHOUT
No. OF PAGES – 32
SIZE 260 x 210mm

Brian Grimwood and Nick Would first met each other in 1975, since then they have remained close friends. They have worked on a number of projects together, both visual and musical, the latest of which is a book entitled "Grimwoods Tails."
The illustrations for the book are drawn from the very successful 1980 Grimwood exhibition, "Behind The Screens" in which, with his unique style, Grimwood portrayed animals as they had never been seen or imagined before.
The freshness of these images, their wit and appeal have been perfectly echoed and complimented in verse by Nick Would, a modern day Lewis Carroll crossed with Edward Lear.
The result is a book of great originality and humour.

£7.50

ISBN No. 1 870458 70 2

VISUAL & CREATIVE PUBLICATIONS FROM ELFANDE

CONTACT ILLUSTRATORS 9TH EDITION

BINDING – HARDBACK / LAMINATED
PRINTED FULL COLOUR THROUGHOUT
No. OF PAGES – 304
SIZE 280 x 210mm
APPROX. No. OF IMAGES 900

CONTACT 9 ILLUSTRATORS

Think of a style of illustration, then the medium, be it coloured pencil, pen and ink, Air-brush, Wood-Cut, etc, and you'll find it here within the 900 images featured in this latest Contact Annual. There can't be much going on in the illustration scene that's not shown within the covers of this comprehensive source book. Every year this book is eagerly awaited for, by those interested in commissioning work ranging from advertising campaigns, Book and magazines covers, packaging, CD Covers and a vast variety of work too long to list here. It will come as no surprise to hear that Contact is probably the largest independent collection of illustrators produced in a single book anywhere in the world!

£30.00

ALL PREVIOUS EDITIONS OF CONTACT ILLUSTRATORS SOLD OUT

ISBN No. 1 870458 40 0

CONTACT ILLUSTRATORS' AGENTS 9TH EDITION

BINDING – HARDBACK / LAMINATED
PRINTED FULL COLOUR THROUGHOUT
No. OF PAGES – 218
SIZE 280 x 210mm
APPROX. No. OF IMAGES 700

The wide range of different styles depicted makes this edition an amazing source of reference featuring more artists agents than any other publication in Europe. Examples shown, cover commissions for advertising campaigns, design projects, fashion, childrens books, giftware, corporate literature, posters, bookjackets and many more where a brief has been passed to an illustrator for their own unique style of interpretation. All of those whose work is shown may be contacted through their agents, with the relevant details to be found at the top of each page.

£30.00

ISBN No. 1 870458 45 1

VISUAL & CREATIVE PUBLICATIONS FROM ELFANDE

CONTACT PHOTOGRAPHERS 9TH EDITION

BINDING – HARDBACK / LAMINATED
PRINTED FULL COLOUR THROUGHOUT
No. OF PAGES – 432
SIZE 280 x 210mm
APPROX. No. OF IMAGES 760

Shows the commercial work currently being done for ad. agencies, design groups, publishers and corporate business.This very varied collection of over 700 images comprises; Still-life, food & drink, Interiors, exteriors, location work, architectural, abstract industrial and corporate photography with some personal work.
The best and largest visual source book of its type in Europe.

£30.00

ALL PREVIOUS EDITIONS OF CONTACT PHOTOGRAPHERS SOLD OUT

ISBN No. 1 870458 35 4

EUROPEAN CONTACT PHOTOGRAPHERS & ILLUSTRATORS – 5TH EDITION

BINDING – HARDBACK / LAMINATED
PRINTED FULL COLOUR THROUGHOUT
No. OF PAGES – 444
SIZE 280 x 210mm
APPROX. No. OF IMAGES 1,100

Now in its fifth year, artbuyers around europe are slowly looking at the work of creative skills beyond their own national boundaries. Thanks to the fax machine where both brief and ideas can be instantly seen and discussed, it is now becoming more usual to consider the work of someone whose studio is several hundreds of miles away. The book features projects by creative individuals who wish to work beyond their own domain and for that reason examples are shown by those based in Holland, Spain, Germany, Ireland, Denmark and the UK.

£30.00

SMALL QUANTITY OF FOURTH EDITION AVAILABLE

ISBN No. 1 870458 55 9

INDEX

BAPLA PICTURE LIBRARY ADVERTISERS (ILLUSTRATED)

COLLEGES

ELFANDE

PUBLISHERS & PROMOTERS OF
CREATIVE PEOPLE AROUND
THE GLOBE!